Biologically Active Substances
—Exploration and Exploitation

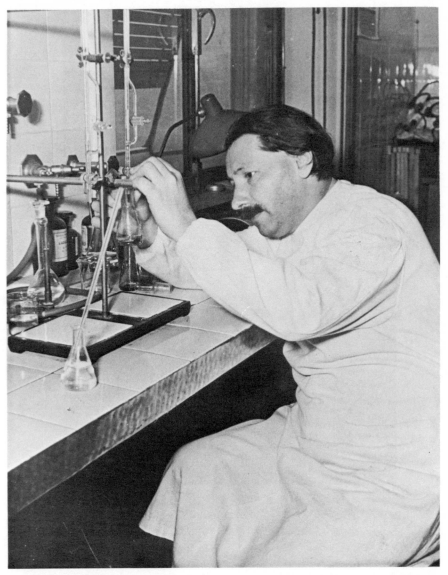

Sir Ernst Chain at work in the Sir William Dunn School of Pathology, Oxford, 1939

Biologically Active Substances
—Exploration and Exploitation

Edited by

D. A. Hems

Department of Biochemistry,
St. George's Hospital Medical School,
London

JOHN WILEY & SONS

Chichester · New York · Brisbane · Toronto

Library of Congress Cataloging in Publication Data:

Main entry under title:

Biologically active substances—exploration and exploitation.

   Papers presented at a symposium held at the Royal Society, London, in June, 1976, to honor Sir Ernst Chain.
   Includes bibliographical references and index.
   CONTENTS: Abraham, E. P. Biosynthesis of B-lactam antibiotics.—Rolinson, G. N. Biological properties of B-lactam antibiotics. [etc.]
   1. Antibiotics—Congresses. 2. Mircobial metabolites—Congresses. 3. Chain, Ernst, Sir, 1906–   I. Hems, D. A. II. Chain, Ernst, Sir,

1906–
QP981.A56B56   574.1'92   76-58496
ISBN 0 471 99489 8

Printed in Great Britain by J. W. Arrowsmith Ltd, Bristol BS3 2NT

Acknowledgements

This book is the record of the Symposium held in June, 1976 to celebrate the career and the 70th birthday of Sir Ernst Chain. A major debt is owed to all those at the Royal Society, who kindly acted as host for the Symposium, to Sir Derek Barton and the organizers of the meeting, to Drs. Ralph Kohn and Keith Mansford in particular, and to Miss J. Heiden, who gave superhuman assistance during the meeting. To the many distinguished scientists who served as Chairmen at the sessions, we also express our thanks. We were helped by many members of the Biochemistry Department at Imperial College including Elizabeth Rath, Janet Hawthorn, Chris Boles, Terry Verrinder, Elizabeth Sneiman, and Linda Archard. The symposium was the brainchild of Dr. Anne Beloff-Chain, the real instigator of this book.

All our efforts since the meeting, to turn 15 disparate manuscripts into a book, have been guided by Dr. Howard A. Jones, Molecular Sciences Editor at John Wiley and Sons. To him and his colleagues and to the contributors, I wish to pay special tribute.

In a different sense, I and all the contributors to this volume owe a debt to Sir Ernst Chain for combining our interests in one unifying theme, and to the scientists whose experiments are cited in the articles.

The Organizing Committee of the Symposium wish to acknowledge the generous financial support from the following

Advisory Services
   Clinical & General) Ltd.
Astra Läkemedel AB
BASF A. G.
Beecham Group
Bristol–Myers Company
Ciba–Geigy.
Eli Lilly and Company Ltd.
Farmitalia Gruppo Montedison
Mr. H. Gestetner
Hoechst, A.G.
Imperial Chemical Industries
Mr. Derrick Kleeman
Marks and Spencer Ltd.

May and Baker Ltd.
Merck, Sharp, and Dohme
Nestle S.A.
Rank, Hovis, McDougal Foods Ltd.
Rhône–Poulenc
A. H. Robins Company
Roche Products Ltd.
Sandoz Ltd.
Schering–Plough Corporation
Smith Kline and French Laboratories
E. R. Squibb and Sons.
The Upjohn Co.
Wellcome Trust

Contributors

ABRAHAM,   *Sir William Dunn School of Pathology, Oxford, U.K.*
Professor E. P.

ARCAMONE, Dr. F.   *Farmitalia Gruppo Montedison, Milan, Italy.*

BANKS, Mr. G. T.   *Dept. of Biochemistry, Imperial College of Science and Technology, London, U.K.*

BARROW, Dr. K. D.   *Department of Chemistry, Australian National University, Canberra, Australia.*

BARTON, Professor   *Department of Chemistry, Imperial College of Science and Technology, London, U.K.*
Sir Derek

BELOFF-CHAIN,   *Department of Biochemistry, Imperial College of Science and Technology, London, U.K.*
Dr. A.

BENNETT,   *Department of Physiology, St. George's Hospital Medical School, London, U.K.*
Dr. G. W.

BRADFORD,   *Department of Biochemistry, Imperial College of Science and Technology, London, U.K.*
Dr. H. F.

BUCK, Dr. K. W.   *Department of Biochemistry, Imperial College of Science and Technology, London, U.K.*

D'AGNOLO, Dr. G.   *Istituto Superiore di Sanità, Rome, Italy.*

DEWDNEY, Dr. J. M.   *Beecham Pharmaceuticals Research Division, Betchworth, Surrey, U.K.*

EDWARDSON,   *Department of Physiology, St. George's Hospital Medical School, London, U.K.*
Dr. J. A.

FALINI, Dr. R.   *Sterile Equipment Company, Milan, Italy.*

HASTINGS,   *Department of Neurosciences, University of California, San Diego, California, U.S.A.*
Professor
A. BAIRD

HEARSE, Dr. D. J.   *Myocardial Metabolism Laboratory, St. Thomas' Hospital, London, U.K.*

HEMS, Dr. D. A.   *Department of Biochemistry, St. George's Hospital Medical School, London, U.K.*

KITS VAN   *Fysiologisch Laboratorium, Jan Swammerdam Instituut, Universiteit van Amsterdam, Holland.*
HEIJNINGEN
Dr. A. J. M.

x

KREBS, Professor   *Metabolic Research Laboratory, Nuffield Department of*
Sir HANS   *Medicine, Radcliffe Infirmary, Oxford, U.K.*

MANSFORD,   *Beecham Pharmaceuticals Research Division, Betch-*
Dr. K. R. L.   *worth, Surrey, U.K.*

MELLOWS, Dr. G.   *Department of Biochemistry, Imperial College of Science and Technology, London, U.K.*

POCCHIARI,   *Istituto Superiore di Sanità, Rome, Italy.*
Professor F.

ROLINSON,   *Beecham Pharmaceuticals Research Division, Betch-*
Dr. G. N.   *worth, Surrey, U.K.*

Contents

4. The *Claviceps* Fermentation and the Development of New Ergoline Drugs

F. ARCAMONE

5. Fusicoccin Phytotoxins

K. D. BARROW *and* G. MELLOWS

6. Mycoviruses: The Quest for Components in Filamentous Fungi with Antiviral Activity in Animals

G. T. BANKS

7. Biochemical and Biological Implications of Double-stranded RNA Mycoviruses

K. W. BUCK

8. Clinical and Veterinary Application of Double-stranded RNA from Fungal Viruses

J. M. DEWDNEY

9. Pathways of Glucose Absorption and Metabolism

F. POCCHIARI *and* G. D'AGNOLO

10. Mechanism of Insulin Action

A. BELOFF-CHAIN *and* A. J. M. KITS VAN HEIJNINGEN

11. Liver Metabolism in Diabetes

D. A. HEMS

12. Metabolic Approaches to Myocardial Infarction

K. R. L. MANSFORD *and* D. J. HEARSE

13. Metabolism and Transmitter Function of Amino Acids in the Nervous System

H. F. BRADFORD

14. Hypothalamic Hormones and Mechanism of Neuroendocrine Integration

J. A. EDWARDSON *and* G. W. BENNETT

Preface

This volume has a simple origin. It is an embodiment of the career of Sir Ernst Chain. The towering achievement of Sir Ernst was, of course, to engage in experiments in collaboration with Professor Howard Florey and others at Oxford which resulted in the purification and therapeutic application of penicillin.

This triumph is merely the most visible sign of Sir Ernst's interest in a wide range of biological compounds, the truest form of biochemistry. According to this approach these substances must first be detected in organisms, then characterized, and synthesized. In parallel, biological properties of these molecules require to be elucidated. If and when living organisms are identified on Mars, Sir Ernst will wish to be the first to hear the results of any biological–chemical investigations.

Sir Ernst Chain has been interested in all aspects of the biology of chemicals, from the quest for new ones through to their chemistry, with the determination of structure, and their synthesis. This breadth of commitment is encapsulated in this volume, which has been written by scientists who have worked within his orbit. The contributors' interests in biological substances were revealed at the Symposium in Sir Ernst's honour held at the Royal Society, London, U.K. in June, 1976.

The Symposium was attended by many distinguished scientists who have been Sir Ernst's closest colleagues and friends over many years, including President Ephraim Katzir of Israel, himself a distinguished biochemist. Dr. M. Tishler, Professor S. J. Pirt, Dr. C. B. Anfinsen, Dr. M. Carlile, Professor S. Ochoa, Professor M. Sela, Professor Sir Rudolph Peters, Dr. A. B. Hastings, Professor R. H. S. Thompson, Professor H. Theorell and Professor D. Nachmansohn, kindly served as Chairmen at the sessions. Sadly, these scientists have not all left a written record in this volume, but their contribution to the Symposium will be remembered by all who were there.

Finally, several extra items are included in the book which speak for themselves.

Profile of Sir Ernst Chain

K. R. L. Mansford

Beecham Pharmaceuticals Research Division, Betchworth, Surrey

On the 30th January, 1933, Ernst Boris Chain left his native city of Berlin to escape from the mounting evils of Nazi Germany. He arrived in London with little but hope and a determination to follow one or other of his great passions—music or science. After a short interlude at University College, London, Chain had the good fortune to be recommended by J. B. S. Haldane to the great Sir Frederick Gowland Hopkins, then Head of the Sir William Dunn School of Biochemistry at Cambridge—perhaps the leading centre for biochemical research in the world at that time. Chain was overjoyed with this unexpected opportunity which he seized eagerly—the die was cast on the side of science rather than music. The concert hall had lost a talented pianist, but the emerging science of biochemistry had gained a powerful ally. The topic which engaged Chain's interest was the biochemical basis of the neurotoxic effects of snake venoms. At Cambridge, Chain found that some of the most potent venoms were able to inhibit alcoholic fermentation and glycolysis when added in very small amounts to cell-free extracts. Further studies showed that this was due to destruction of an essential coenzyme by simple hydrolysis. This approach of 'biological observation followed by biochemical explanation' is symptomatic of Chain's scientific philosopy which can be traced consistently through 40 years of amazingly diverse achievements.

After two years of working with 'Hoppy', Chain was approached by Professor Howard Florey with an invitation to join Florey's staff at the Sir William Dunn School of Pathology at Oxford. Florey had no biochemical training but he did have an awareness of the importance of biochemistry in the understanding of all biological sciences and in particular of his own field of experimental pathology. Florey drew Chain's attention to an observation by Fleming in 1924 concerning the lytic properties of tears, nasal secretions, and egg white on bacteria. Such a problem—to study the biochemical mode of action of a powerful bacteriolytic agent—was typical of the Chain approach. He was able to show that the lytic properties were due to lysozyme which acted upon a bacterial polysccharide. This investigation gave Chain his first taste of the problems of bacterial fermentation and, moreover, laid the foundation for a chapter of biochemical research which is still of central interest—the chemical nature of the cell wall and its enzymic hydrolysis and synthesis.

While preparing this work for publication in 1937–38, and arising from discussions with Florey, Chain stumbled upon the concept of growth inhibition by bacteria, fungi, and yeasts acting on one another. The progression from this field of research into the well-known era of Chain's work on pencillin at Oxford owes as much, perhaps, to Chain's pragmatism as it does to scientific logic.

Upon starting their systematic investigation of the antibacterial substances produced by micro-organisms, Florey and Chain were immediately embarrassed by a severe shortage of funds. One day in the autumn of 1937, Chain received a message from Florey stating that in view of the fact that the department had an overdraft of £500 no further equipment of any kind was to be ordered—not even a glass rod! This experience had a profound effect on the young, enthusiastic Chain who was impatiently waiting to unleash his energies on the new problem of explaining in chemical terms how bacterial growth was inhibited. An unsuccessful approach to the Medical Research Council reinforced his suspicions about University and Government financial support. Since that day, he has never allowed himself to become wholly dependent on political largesse, however respectable its facade, for research funds. Undeterred by this initial set-back, Chain discussed with Florey a grant application to the Rockefeller Foundation to cover the costs of the proposed programme for a number of years, so that financial stability could be ensured. To Chain's great delight, the Rockefeller Foundation were sympathetic towards biochemical research and granted him $5000 for five years.

Spurred on by this, Chain turned his attention to the famous observation by Fleming in 1928 of the growth-inhibiting properties of the contaminating spore of *Penicillium notatum*. This observation has been hallowed by time and repetition to the point that the element of serendipity has centred quite misleadingly on the spore floating in through the open windows of St. Mary's Hospital. As Chain pointed out (*Proc. Roy. Soc. Series B* (1971), **179**, 298), the happy coincidence was that Fleming had left a contaminated agar plate—a very common occurrence—on his laboratory bench for six weeks, instead of it being sterilized and washed up! Furthermore, the lytic effects of 'penicillin' on staphylococcal suspensions which Fleming observed, only occur under very special conditions and are quite difficult to reproduce unless the colonies are at just the right age and physiological state. Chain thought that Fleming had discovered a sort of mould lysozyme, while others thought it was a bacteriophage. Raistrick's group reported on the instability of penicillin to acid extraction thus strengthening Chain's views on the enzymic nature of penicillin. The advent of Heatley to the Oxford team, with his flair for devising and using micro-methods of analysis, soon enabled Chain to demonstrate that the active antibacterial principle was not a protein but a low molecular weight compound which could diffuse readily through cellophane membranes. The rest of the story of the extraction, purification, and structural characterization of penicillin is well-known as it culminated in a Nobel Prize for Chain and Florey in 1945.

Chain was not the type to rest on his laurels. He became increasingly frustrated by the problems of obtaining adequate facilities for the fermentation of micro-organisms on a semi-industrial scale. The methods used initially to provide impure penicillin for laboratory studies and even clinical trials were crude. Chain was very outspoken about the amateurish approach in Britain which he contrasted with the facilities available in the USA. He campaigned vigorously, at all levels, for fermentation pilot-plant facilities, but he was met by the implacable inertia of the Establishment who made it very clear that such facilities were a matter for industry and had no place in an academic ivory tower. Chain poured scorn on the view that the size of the reaction vessels should determine whether the biochemical problem to be investigated was 'pure' or 'applied'. In the true British spirit of compromise, Chain was finally offered a single fermenter of moderate dimensions. Chain's reply was to ask if an organic chemist would be prepared to limit himself to the use of one Erlenmeyer flask!

More in sorrow than in anger, Chain accepted in 1948 an invitation to organize a Department of Biochemistry at the Italian State Institute of Health in Rome. The temptation was made irresistable by the promise that in Rome an International Centre for Chemical Microbiology containing the controversial fermentation pilot plant with extraction and purification facilities would be made available. The period spent in Rome was both successful and frustrating for Chain. The magnificent facilities and the collaborations with Ballio, Dentice, Marotta (the Director of the Institute), and Pocchiari produced a rich harvet of publications in the new science of chemical microbiology and on the biochemical mechanisms of hormonal control. A constant stream of scientific visitors passed through Chain's laboratories in Rome, so that at any one time at least half-a-dozen different nationalities were represented.

Another important event occurred during this period. Chain married Anne Beloff in 1948 at the start of his Italian era and was devoted to his young family which thrived in the Mediterranean sunshine. His wife, who had trained under Sir Rudolf Peters and Baird Hastings, had an active team of collaborators in Rome investigating the mode of action of insulin.

Frustrations came from the highly political environment surrounding all academic institutions in Italy and, in particular, the Italian State Institute of Health. Bureaucracy was rampant, with promotions, at that time, being heavily dependent on political influence. A requisition for ethanol required the personal signature of the Director who had to spend much of his time placating his political masters. Chain developed a formidable reputation, and quite deservedly so, for jumping on bureaucrats, irrespective of political hue. This reaped benefits in the short term in that the work of Chain's laboratories proceeded at a pace well above the Roman norm, but in the long term united his political enemies against both Chain and the unfortunate Director Marotta. During the 1950s, however, the politics in the Institute were not so pressing as to divert Chain from his ideas on outwitting bacterial resistant to penicillin.

In 1940 Abraham and Chain had identified the enzyme penicillinase, which is capable of splitting and inactivating penicillin and which is produced, with great foresight, by numerous bacteria. Chain felt that the affinity of the pencillin molecule for this bacterial enzyme could be altered if the molecule could be chemically modified. Enormous effort had already been expended in the pharmaceutical industry in the search for chemical precursors acceptable to the *Penicillium* mould in the hope that novel penicillins with useful properties would be biosynthesized. Eli Lilly and Company Ltd. had shown that several derivatives of acetic acid could be incorporated to give different penicillins. Of these, phenoxymethylpenicillin (penicillin V) had turned out to be acid stable and useful clinically because of its ability to be successfully administered orally. Apart from this limited success, some disillusionment had set in regarding the prospects of obtaining novel penicillins, and many laboratories had turned their attentions to more promising areas of antibiotic research. Chain's idea was to improve upon nature by persuading the mould to grow *p*-aminobenzylpenicillin and then using the reactive amino group for further man-made chemical modifications.

Chain was approached in 1954 by the then Chairman of the Beecham Group, Henry Lazell, on the advice of the late Sir Charles Dodds, with a view to advising on the possibilities of Beechams entering the antibiotics field. Chain's enthusiasm and drive so impressed Lazell that Beechams soon found themselves with a fermentation pilot plant looking remarkably like the one in Rome, and a research programme aimed at modifying *p*-aminobenzyl-penicillin. A small team of scientists was sent to Rome by Beechams while the fermentation plant was being erected. During their stay in Rome in 1956, they and Chain noticed an interesting difference in the results of two assays of the crude microbial culture fluids. The chemical assay based on the behaviour of the thiazolidine-β-lactam ring consistently gave higher results than the bioassay which required the full penicillin molecule for biological activity. An explanation of this finding followed when the team returned to Beecham Research Laboratories in 1957 when they demonstrated that the discrepancy was due to the presence of the penicillin nucleus (6-aminopenicillanic acid) in the culture fluid. Chain was intimately involved in the subsequent work which succeeded in isolating and characterizing this compound. The gateway was now open to an enormous variety of chemically modified derivatives beyond all original expectations based on the limited synthetic variations possible with *p*-aminobenzylpenicillin. Beechams quickly exploited this major breakthrough in antibiotic research by synthesizing penicillins with very good intestinal absorption, with activity against Gram-negative micro-organisms previously not susceptible, and to Chain's delight, with outstanding activity against micro-organisms which had become resistant to natural penicillins by virtue of their producing penicillinase—Chain's original objective.

The focal point of antibiotic research had moved back to England, and this coincided with a worsening of the political situation in Rome. In the course of a visit to Rome in 1958, Professor P. M. S. Blackett discussed with Chain the possibility of setting up at Imperial College a comprehensively equipped Biochemistry Department modelled along the lines of the facilities available at the Institute. A further visit by the then Rector, Sir Patrick Linstead, led to a tentative proposal that Chain returned to England to re-establish biochemistry at Imperial College where the chair had been vacant since Chibnall left for Cambridge in 1943. The cost of all the fermentation equipment, instrumentation, electrical and mechanical workshops, and so on required to support and service the complex chemical microbiological research and metabolic biochemical investigations to be undertaken by Chain, was formidable and unheard of academically outside the realms of nuclear physics. The scheme was shelved. However, Chain accepted the challenge of an apparently insoluble difficulty and campagined vigorously to find independent funds for this imaginative project which complemented the already very strong chemical and chemical engineering interests of the College. As a result of Chain's efforts and Linstead's encouragement, the Wolfson Foundation provided £350,000 to establish the new Wolfson Laboratories, the Science Research Council granted £110,000 in support of fermentation research, and the Fleming Memorial Fund granted Chain £50,000 for basic medical research. Chain had not forgotten the lesson of the forbidden glass rod at Oxford!

Chain returned to take up his new appointment in October 1964 and the new laboratories were completed in the summer of 1965. Also, the Medical Research Council buried the hatchet by establishing a Metabolic Reactions Research Unit under Chain within the Department. Chain had insisted in his negotiations regarding the new laboratories that biochemistry was best taught by postgraduation grafting onto chemical or biological stock. Consequently, the new department was almost unique in having no undergraduates. This meant that postgraduate workers had to be attracted from other universities which induced envy in other, less fortunate, academic colleagues with heavy undergraduate teaching loads. The financial independence which Chain secured from the very conception of the new department also did nothing to endear him to the administrative Establishment which found him unimpressed by exhortations to economize in lean years. Minor officials in the Science Research Council and University Grants Committee secretariat found their cautious criticisms of Chain's eminently unreasonable demands quoted or even possibly misquoted by Chain in direct conversation with the Treasury or the Prime Minister (according to availability). In matters affecting his work plans, Chain was openly ruthless towards what he considered uninformed criticism. Staff in the Department learned to adjust to Chain's style of 'management by persuasion', or moved on to more tranquil waters. Apart from a handful of individualists, who had difficulty in agreeing with Chain even about the state of the weather, the majority of staff revelled in the magnificent facilities provided. The combination of lavish standard instrumentation together with fully equipped mechanical and electrical workshops, capable of developing special equipment, was unique for a biochemistry department. The analytical techniques developed enabled problems in the control of intermediary metabolism in complex systems, such as brain, heart, and liver, to be tackled whereas previously much of the work of this nature had centred around isolated cellular components. Chain decried the loud trumpetings of the disciples of 'molecular biology' which he felt to have little relevance to the problems associated with the metabolic balance and integrated control within functional intact organs and tissues. This was hardly a popular view at a time when the molecular biology lobby was suggesting that teaching of the genetic code should be tried out in the kindergarten.

Chain's special relationship with industry was often a cause of irritation to ultra-academic colleagues. He never missed an opportunity of drawing attention to the tremendous achievements of the pharmaceutical industry in medical and therapeutic innovation. His much publicized lecture on this subject to the Royal Society of Arts was taken as near treachery in some academic quarters which considered industry only worthy of fund-milking as opposed to true collaboration. Chain insisted that the postgraduate courses in his Department, while not being in any way intended as vocational training, should help participants intending to pursue careers in either medical research or in chemical microbiology (including fermentation technology). This outlook appeared, at the time, to complement the overall technological bias of Imperial College but engendered mutterings of 'applied' science in more conventional biochemical circles.

The premature death of Sir Patrick Linstead was a sad personal loss to Chain and a watershed in the fortunes of the Department. The sympathetic understanding which Chain had enjoyed with Linstead was irreplaceable and the special relationship of the Department, because of its high level of collaboration with industry and funding by charitable institutions, became almost an embarrassment in inter-College negotiations.

Chain's knighthood came as something of a surprise in 1969—not, of course, because of any doubts about his quite exceptional personal achievements over 35 years, but because his deliberate policy of Establishment boat-rocking had made a deep impression in what are termed darkly 'influential quarters'. It says something for the British political system that his scientific genius triumphed over his political reputation.

Although now officially retired from his Chair, his energy shows no signs of diminution and his enthusiasm can still be communicated to a faltering postgraduate student who is made to feel that a Nobel Prize is in the post. The ideas still come tumbling out so fast that five-year prospective programmes of work are handed out in five minutes. If some of the views are unconventional and go against the accepted dogma of the day, beware—for Sir Ernst suffers from the unforgivable sin of being right with a frequency of undoubted statistical significance.

Introductory Remarks

Sir Derek Barton, F.R.S.

Department of Chemistry, Imperial College of Science and Technology, London, U.K.

There are few scientists who, by the application of their science, have made a greater contribution to human welfare than Sir Ernst Chain. It is very fitting, therefore, that his friends and colleagues should organize this Symposium on Biologically Active Substances—Exploration and Exploitation, to celebrate Sir Ernst's 70th birthday.

In this book, it is perhaps not necessary to discuss in detail Sir Ernst's manifold contributions to biochemistry. I will, however, attempt a brief biographical survey of his life.

Sir Ernst Chain was born in Berlin on 19th June, 1906. He graduated in chemistry and physiology at the Fredrich–Wilhelm University, Berlin, some 24 years later. His first scientific work, which was carried out in Berlin, was on the optical specificity of esterases. But, in the early 1930s, political life in Germany took a tragic, and ultimately fatal, direction. Sir Ernst was wise enough to foresee what was to come and, in 1933, he moved to Cambridge, after a brief period in London, to work in the famous Biochemistry Department then headed by the father of British biochemistry, Sir Frederick Gowland Hopkins. For the next two years, Sir Ernst worked on the acid–base properties of phospholipids and on the inhibitory effect of snake venoms on glycolysis.

In 1935 there came the move to Oxford to a lectureship in the School of Pathology and the long collaboration with Lord Florey. The ensuing 13 years were most productive. Initially, Sir Ernst continued his studies on enzymes and it was in the belief that penicillin was an enzyme that the work on the antibiotic began. The story of penicillin, which culminated in the award of a Nobel Prize in 1945, has been told many times and there is no need to repeat it again here. The discovery of penicillin naturally stimulated a search for other antibiotics in which Sir Ernst played a leading role. It is well-known that, at that time (1946–48), the authorities in the UK were not prepared to provide an adequate pilot plant for use in the search for new antibiotics. Consequently Sir Ernst was obliged to move in 1949 to the Istituto Superiore di Sanità in Rome. There he was Head of the Biochemistry Department and of the International Centre for Chemical Microbiology.

The period in Rome showed the breadth of Sir Ernst's genius. He and his colleagues worked in two broad fields—microbiology and physiological biochemistry—both of which were to be pursued further at Imperial College. The former field of investigation again proved to be most fruitful. In collaboration with scientists working with the Beecham Group, 6-aminopenicillanic acid was isolated and its importance in the synthesis of semisynthetic penicillins adumbrated. Furthermore, a novel method for the preparation of lysergic acid was developed using deep fermentation. Interestingly, other workers on lysergic acid had always considered its production by deep fermentation to be impossible.

In 1964, Sir Ernst returned to the UK to become Head of the Department of Biochemistry at Imperial College, London, in a splendid new building which, this time, housed adequate pilot plant facilities for fermentation research. Here again the work in the area of microbiology proved to be of outstanding importance. Among the fields investigated, collaborative studies were carried out with scientists working at the Lord Rank Research Centre on single-cell protein from bacteria and moulds which hold increasing importance for a world requiring large supplies of protein. Also the isolation, and chemical and biological studies of RNAs from fungal viruses are again proving to be of exceptional promise for the treatment of disease.

From this brief account, it will be realized that throughout his long scientific career Sir Ernst has shown a genius for selecting topics which have not only been of scientific interest but also of great practical value for the welfare of mankind. In his accomplishments he is unique.

It would not be proper to conclude this brief biographical account without mentioning that Sir Ernst has been blessed with a very happy family life. He owes a great debt to his wife Anne (Dr. Beloff-Chain) for understanding him so well and also for her own contributions to the scientific work in Rome and at Imperial College.

1
Biosynthesis of
β-Lactam Antibiotics

E. P. Abraham

Sir William Dunn School of Pathology, University of Oxford, U.K.

INTRODUCTION

When I was asked to speak at this Symposium in honour of Sir Ernst Chain on his 70th birthday, it suddenly occurred to me that I had known him for more than 36 years and that there must now be few of his collaborators whose memories reach back much further. These years seem to have gone in a flash and to have occasioned remarkably little change in Sir Ernst's vivid personality. His ability to expound a constant flow of ideas in any one of several languages, his gift as a pianist, and his smile of welcome for time-consuming visitors are among the qualities which many of us must envy. However, it is his role in the introduction of penicillins into medicine which stands out above all. Not only was he responsible, with Florey, for initiating the work which transformed Fleming's penicillin from a bacteriological curiosity into a remarkable chemotherapeutic agent, but he was also a persuasive force behind decisions taken by the Beecham Group which led to the isolation of 6-aminopenicillanic acid in quantity and the discovery of a series of new penicillins of clinical importance.

In 1950, it did not seem that any exciting additions to the application of penicillin in chemotherapy were likely to be made, but things have turned out very differently. Throughout much of his working life Sir Ernst has witnessed a flood of publications, which still shows no sign of abating, on the scientific and medical aspects of β-lactam antibiotics. It therefore seems appropriate that consideration should be given to features of these microbial metabolites.

Among the seminal contributions to this subject are certainly descriptions of the isolation of new and active members of the β-lactam group of compounds obtained from culture filtrates. Such compounds have extended our knowledge of the effects of changes in the penicillin ring system and its substituents on biological activity and have provided starting points which have led to remarkable achievements by organic chemists. What I propose to do here is to mention the different types of β-lactam antibiotics and related compounds which are now known to be produced by micro-organisms and to consider some of the available information about the biosynthetic pathways leading to these compounds and the relationships between them.

β-LACTAM ANTIBIOTICS PRODUCED BY FERMENTATION

a. Penicillium chrysogenum

Studies of penicillin biosynthesis by *P. chrysogenum* began with the finding that the side chain of the penicillin produced by this micro-organism could be varied, within certain limits, by the addition of precursors to the culture medium (Behrens *et al.*, 1948). The different penicillins obtainable in this way appeared to be restricted to those with side chains (R.CO−) derived from relatively non-polar monosubstituted acetic acids (I). Nevertheless, two other

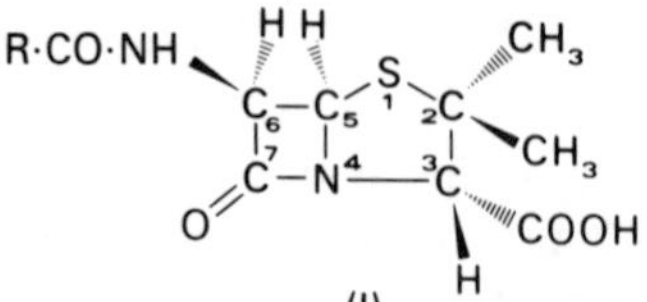

(I)

compounds with the penicillin ring system were subsequently found in these culture filtrates. The first was 6-aminopenicillanic acid (II) (Sakaguchi and Murao, 1950; Kato, 1953; Batchelor *et al.*, 1959, 1961) and the second was isopenicillin N, a penicillin with a δ-linked L-α-aminoadipyl side chain (III) (Flynn *et al.*, 1962; Cole and Batchelor, 1963).

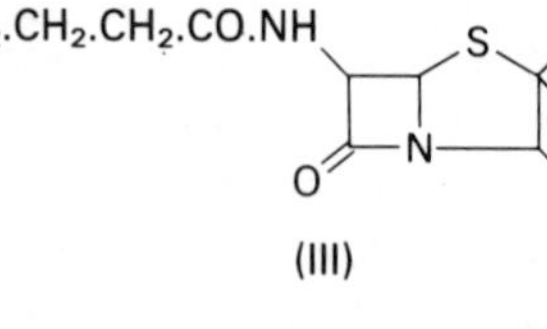

(II)

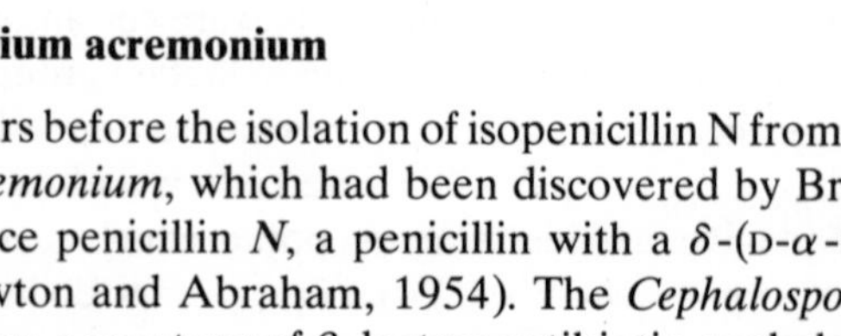

(III)

b. Cephalosporium acremonium

Nearly 10 years before the isolation of isopenicillin N from *P. chrysogenum*, a strain of *C. acremonium*, which had been discovered by Brotzu in 1948, was found to produce penicillin *N*, a penicillin with a δ-(D-α-aminoadipyl) side chain (IV) (Newton and Abraham, 1954). The *Cephalosporium* species produced, in addition, a new type of β-lactam antibiotic, cephalosporin C (Newton and Abraham, 1955) which was subsequently shown to have the structure V

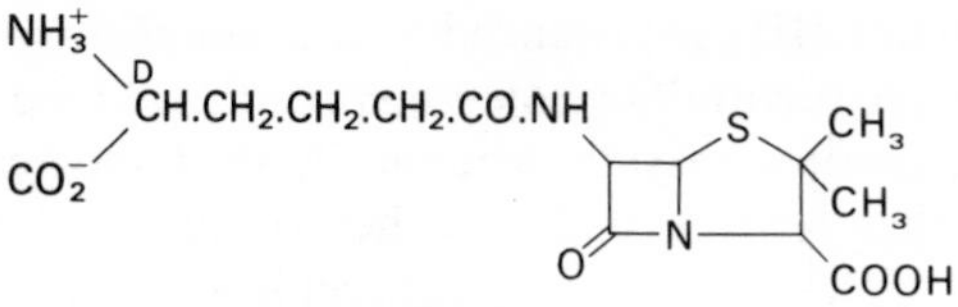

(IV)

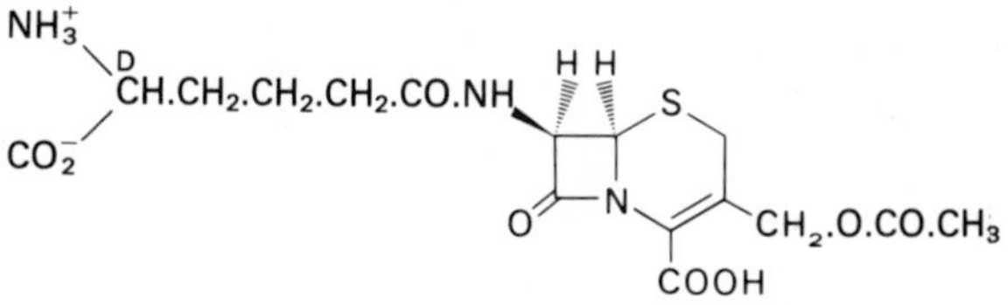

(V)

(Abraham and Newton, 1961; Hodgkin and Maslen, 1961). This compound also has a D-α-aminoadipyl side chain, but differs from the penicillins in its ring system. However, the culture fluid of the *Cephalosporium* species appeared to contain neither the nucleus of cephalosporin C, 7-aminocephalosporanic acid, nor any β-lactam antibiotics except those with side chains derived from D-α-aminoadipic acid.

c. Actinomycetes

The discovery of these two types of fermentation by eukaryotes was followed by the finding in the laboratories of Eli Lilly and Company and of Merck, Sharp and Dohme that the prokaryotic *Streptomyces* could produce penicillin N and 7-methoxycephalosporins (VI), again with a δ-(D-α-aminoadipyl) side chain but with groups other than acetoxy at C17 (Nagarajan *et al.*, 1971; Stapley *et*

(VI)

al., 1972). Recent work by the Beecham Group (1975) has shown that *S. clavuligerus* produces, in addition, clavulanic acid (VII), a powerful β-lactamase inhibitor (Howath *et al.*, 1976). Members of the Fujisawa Pharmaceutical Company Limited have reported that a monocyclic β-lactam

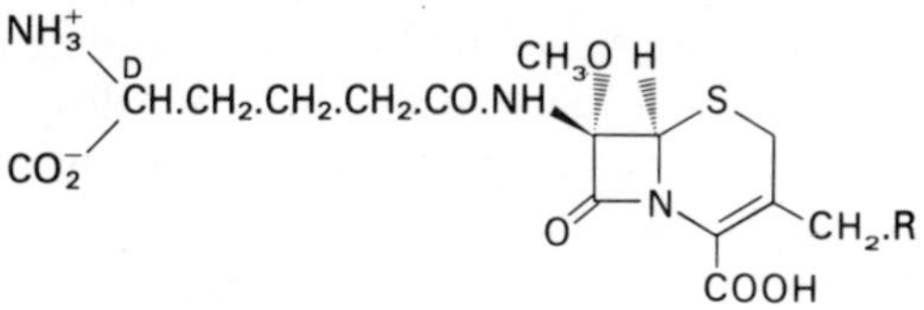

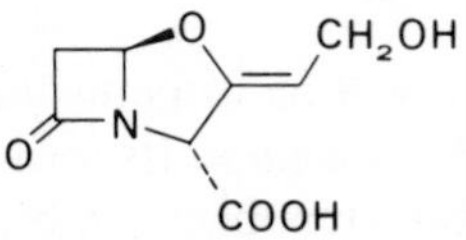

(VII)

4

antibiotic, nocardicin (VIII), is produced by a strain of *Nocardia* (Aoki *et al.*, 1976) together with structurally related compounds. These new compounds are of interest because they are stereochemically and biologically related to the penicillins and cephalosporins, and also they contain no sulphur. The total synthesis of 1-oxacephalothin and 1-carbacephalothin has shown that the

(VIII)

sulphur in cephalothin may be replaced by oxygen and $-CH_2-$ respectively without any great change in antibacterial activity (Cama and Christensen 1974; Guthikonda *et al.*, 1974). If β-lactam antibiotics have evolved because their antimicrobial activity has at some time endowed the micro-organisms producing them with a selective advantage, other compounds of this type may well be found which have no sulphur-containing fused ring system. However, it could be that the biosynthetic process is facilitated by the introduction of sulphur, rather than other atoms, into the ring system.

AMINO ACID PRECURSORS AND PEPTIDE INTERMEDIATES

A number of findings indicate that there is a close relationship between the biosynthetic pathways to the penicillins produced by *P. chrysogenum* and to both penicillin N and cephalosporins produced by other organisms.

Firstly, all these compounds have common amino acid precursors. It has been relatively simple, by the addition of isotopically labelled amino acids to mycelial cultures or suspensions, to establish that L-cysteine and L-valine are biogenic units from which both the penicillin and cephalosporin ring systems are synthesized, although L-valine provides the carbon skeleton of a D-penicillamine residue in the penicillins. L-α-Aminoadipic acid is the precursor not only of the L-α-aminoadipyl side chain of isopenicillin N but also of the D-α-aminoadipyl side chain of penicillin N and the cephalosporins.

Secondly, penicillin N appears to be produced in all fermentations which yield cephalosporins, although not *vice versa*, and the relative yields of penicillin N and cephalosporin C from *C. acremonium* may be changed inversely by variations in the degree of aeration of cultures, or by the addition of methionine, or carboxymethyl-L-cysteine, to a suspension of washed mycelium (Fawcett *et al.*, 1976).

Thirdly, benzylpenicillin, as well as isopenicillin N, needs α-aminoadipic acid for its production by *P. chrysogenum*. Its formation may be depressed by the addition of lysine, which exerts feedback inhibition of the biosynthesis of L-α-aminoadipic acid (Masurekar and Demain, 1974); in mutants in which the biosynthesis of α-aminoadipic acid is blocked, penicillin is not produced unless exogenous α-aminoadipic acid is available (Goulden and Chattaway 1968). Thus, it appears that α-aminoadipic acid has a central role in penicillin–cephalosporin biosynthesis by both fungi and *Streptomyces* species.

After the discovery of penicillin N, δ-(α-aminoadipyl)cysteinylvaline, a tripeptide containing residues of the amino acid precursors of this penicillin, was found in very small amounts in the mycelium of *P. chrysogenum* (Arnstein and Morris, 1960), but the configurations at the asymmetric centres in the peptide were not determined. Later, δ-(α-aminoadipyl)cysteinylvaline was isolated in small amounts from the mycelium of *C. acremonium* and shown to be the LLD isomer (IX) (Loder and Abraham, 1971*a*). Recently, we have shown that the LLD and LLL forms of this tripeptide can be separated as their sulphonic acids by electrophoresis at pH 1·8, and that the tripeptide from *P. chrysogenum*, like that from *C. acremonium*, is the LLD isomer. The same conclusion has been reached by Adriaens *et al.*, (1975) who used ion exchange chromatography to resolve the tripeptides in the –SH form. In addition, an apparently identical tripeptide has been detected in a strain of *S. clavuligerus* which produces penicillin N and a 7-methoxycephalosporin (Fawcett *et al.*, 1975*a*).

(IX)

The mycelial LLD tripeptide was found to be present in larger amounts in several high-yielding strains of the *Cephalosporium* species than in low-yielding strains and in some cases to be excreted into the culture fluid (Fawcett *et al.*, 1975*a*). The significance of these findings is not yet clear. To have determined whether the tripeptide was a precursor of some or all of the β-lactam antibiotics might appear to have been a simple matter. This has not in fact been so, because the peptide is not taken up by intact mycelial cells and the preparation of a cell-free extract in which the biosynthesis of the fused ring systems can be demonstrated has proved to be difficult. Labelled tripeptide can be synthesized from δ-(L-α-aminoadipyl)-L-cysteine and [^{14}C]valine in a broken-cell system obtained by ultrasonic treatment of the *Cephalosporium* species (Loder and Abraham 1971*b*). However when δ-(DL-α-amino[6-^{14}C]adipyl)-L-cysteine was added to suspensions of mycelium, the ^{14}C which entered the cells was almost entirely in α-amino[^{14}C]adipic acid which had been produced by enzymic hydrolysis of the dipeptide (Loder *et al.*, 1969).

Some progress has been made by use of a cell-free system from protoplasts of *C. acremonium*. The protoplasts were prepared by removal of the mycelial cell wall using a mixture of lytic enzymes from *Cytophaga* in a stabilizing concentration of sodium chloride (Fawcett *et al.*, 1973). A protoplast pellet was subjected to osmotic lysis by the addition of the minimum amount of dilute tris–HCl buffer, and the resulting preparation was used immediately in biosynthetic experiments after the addition of an energy-generating system composed of ATP, phosphoenolpyruvate, and pyruvate kinase (Fawcett *et al.*, 1976).

In this system, the ability of $[^3H]$-δ-(L-α-aminoadipyl)-L-cysteinyl-D-valine and related peptides to yield labelled penicillin N was tested (Fawcett *et al.*, 1976). In some experiments, the labelling was assessed by oxidation of the product with performic acid and determination of the radioactivity in the resulting penicillaminic acid after isolation of the latter by paper electrophoresis and chromatography. In others, the radioactivity was measured in a compound which was sensitive to penicillinase and which was not distinguishable by separation techniques from penicillin N itself. It was assumed, but has not yet been proved, that penicillin N rather than isopenicillin N would be produced in the cell-free system from the *Cephalosporium* species, as it is in intact mycelium.

Table 1.1 Incorporation of ^3H from valine-labelled compounds into penicillin N (penicillaminic acid) in a lysate of protoplasts of *C. acremonium*

Peptide	Incorporation of ^3H
LLD (γ)	+
LLD (α)	+
LLL (γ)	−
DLD (γ)	−
6-APA (γ)*	−
L-val (γ)	−

*6-APA = 6-aminopenicillanic acid.

The reults of these experiments are briefly summarized in Table 1.1. In the crude system from lysed protoplasts, ^3H was incorporated into penicillin N from the LLD tripeptide labelled in either the methyl groups (γ) or the α-position of its valine residue. No incorporation was observed from the corresponding labelled LLL or DLD tripeptide, although the presence of the unlabelled LLL isomer appeared to diminish the incorporation of ^3H from the LLD (Figure 1.1). Furthermore, no incorporation was observed from L-cysteinyl-D-$[4,4-^3H]$valine, from L-$[4,4-^3H]$valine, or apparently, from 6-aminopenicillanic acid labelled with ^3H in its 2-β-methyl group (Usher *et al.*, 1975). Incorporation from the LLD tripeptide was observed in supernatants obtained by centrifugation of the crude system at 20 000 *g* or 50 000 *g*, but not in suspensions of the corresponding sediments.

If these results with a cell-free system reflect what happens in intact mycelium it can be concluded that the LLD tripeptide is a precursor of penicillin

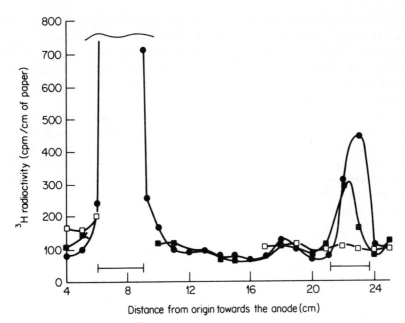

Figure 1.1 Incorporation of ^{3}H from δ-(L-α-aminoadipyl)-L-cysteinyl-D-[4,4-^{3}H]valine into material yielding penicillaminic acid on oxidation. Electrophoresis was carried out at pH 1·8. The bars show the positions of added markers of penicillaminic acid (right) and the tripeptide sulphonic acid (left): ●, labelled LLD tripeptide; ■, labelled LLD tripeptide plus unlabelled LLL tripeptide (20:1 mol/mol); □, control. From Fawcett *et al.* (1976), with permission.

N, but that the free LLL tripeptide is unlikely to be a precursor of the LLD peptide. The mechanism by which the epimerization of L-valine occurs remains to be determined. It does not involve the formation of a free intermediate containing an $\alpha\beta$-dehydrovaline residue, or the migration of hydrogen from C3 to C2, because the LLD tripeptide synthesized by *C. acremonium* in the presence of L-[2,3-^{3}H]valine contained ^{3}H at C3, but not at C2, of its valine residue (Huang *et al.*, 1975). It may take place on the enzyme concerned with the coupling of valine to δ-(L-α-aminoadipyl)-L-cysteine.

For nearly 20 years it has been an attractive hypothesis that the D-centre at C3 of the penicillins arises from an $\alpha\beta$-dehydrovalinyl derivative, such as that shown in structure X, during closure of the thiozolidine ring (Arnstein and Crawhall, 1957). However, the behaviour of the LLD tripeptide as a precursor makes an inversion at the stage of ring closure unnecessary, while the incorporation of ^{3}H into penicillin N from the LLD tripeptide labelled in the α-position of its valine residue indicates that an $\alpha\beta$-dehydrovaline residue is not present in any free intermediate and could only occur in an enzyme-bound form if the proton removed from the α-position by the enzyme was returned to this position on ring closure.

The small amount of the LLD tripeptide in *C. acremonium* is accompanied by even smaller amounts of related tetrapeptides. The latter may well be δ-(α-aminoadipyl)-cysteinylvalylglycine (XI) and δ-(α-aminoadipyl)-cysteinyl-β-hydroxyvalylglycine (XII) since they behave like the corresponding synthetic tetrapeptides on paper chromatography and electrophoresis (Usher, 1974). Whether the hydroxylation of a valine residue is involved in the formation of the thiazolidine ring has not yet been determined.

$$\overset{+}{N}H_3 \diagdown \qquad\qquad CH_2SH \qquad CH(CH_3)_2$$
$$\qquad\quad CH(CH_2)_3.CO.NH.CH.CO.NH.CH.CO.NH.CH_2COOH$$
$$CO_2^- \diagup \qquad\qquad\qquad\qquad\qquad\qquad\qquad\qquad\qquad (XI)$$

$$\overset{+}{N}H_3 \diagdown \qquad\qquad SHCH_2 \qquad HO.C(CH_3)_2$$
$$\qquad\quad CH(CH_2)_3CO.NH.CH.CO.NH.CH.CO.NH.CH_2COOH \qquad (XII)$$
$$CO_2^- \diagup$$

For the LLD tripeptide to be a precursor of penicillin N its L-α-aminoadipyl residue must epimerize to the D form. But the failure to observe incorporation of ^{3}H into the penicillin from the labelled DLD tripeptide suggests that the epimerization occurs at a subsequent stage of biosynthesis. This could be a stage at which the pathways for the *Cephalosporium* and *Penicillium* types of fermentation diverge, for the isopenicillin N produced by the latter has an L-α-aminoadipyl side chain. It may be that the retention of the L configuration in this side chain is essential for the production of the common penicillins, such as benzylpenicillin, by *P. chrysogenum*.

THE LATE STAGES OF BIOSYNTHESIS

Preliminary experiments with the protein fraction of a crude extract of *P. chrysogenum*, obtained by grinding the mycelium with sand, indicated that this extract could bring about the incorporation of ^{14}C from added [^{14}C]phenylacetyl coenzyme A when isopenicillin N (but not penicillin N) was also added (Loder, 1970). Subsequent work with isopenicillin N and penicillin N labelled with ^{3}H in the 2-β-methyl group of the ring system has confirmed these results (Usher *et al.*, 1975; Fawcett *et al.*, 1975*b*). When *P. chrysogenum* was grown in the presence of N-methyl phenylacetamide and phenylacetate as side-chain precursors and the labelled isopenicillin N added to a crude extract of the mycelium, ^{3}H was incorporated into a solvent-soluble compound which behaved like benzylpenicillin on paper chromatography and electrophoresis, and which was susceptible to hydrolysis by penicillinase (Figure 1.2). When a

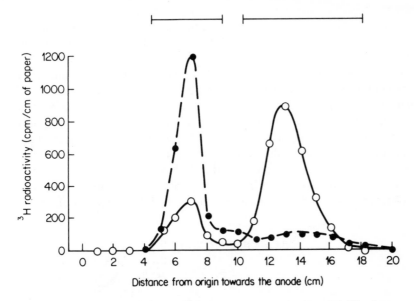

Figure 1.2 Incorporation of ^{3}H into solvent-soluble penicillin from isopenicillin N labelled in its 2-β-methyl group. Paper chromatography was carried out in butan-1-ol–ethanol–water (4:1:5, by vol): O, solvent-extractable material; ● material after treatment with penicillinase. The bars indicates the positions of markers benzylpenicillin (right) and benzylpenicilloate (left). From Fawcett *et al.* (1975*b*). Reproduced by permission of the Biochemical Society.

protein fraction of the crude extract was used, from which small molecules, including side-chain precursors, had been removed by filtration through Sephadex, significant incorporation was observed after addition of phenylacetyl-CoA, but not in its absence. In a further experiment, the crude extract was incubated with phenylacetyl-CoA and [^{3}H]isopenicillin N, and the crystalline potassium salt of radioactive benzylpenicillin was isolated after addition of non-radioactive benzylpenicillin as a carrier. In contrast to these results, no significant incorporation of ^{3}H into a solvent-soluble penicillin was observed when labelled penicillin N, instead of isopenicillin N, was added to the extract.

These results indicate that isopenicillin N is a substrate for an acyl transferase in *P. chrysogenum* and are consistent with the view that isopenicillin N is a precursor of benzyl and similar penicillins. If this is so, what is the origin of the 6-aminopenicillanic acid which is found in fermentations of this organism and what is its role in biosynthesis? Extracts of *P. chrysogenum* contain an acylase which catalyses the formation of benzylpenicillin from 6-aminopenicillanic acid and phenylacetyl-CoA (Gatenbeck and Brunsberg, 1968; Fawcett *et al.*, 1975*b*); the hydrolysis of benzylpenicillin by a number of microbial penicillin acylases is reversible. But it has still to be determined whether 6-aminopenicillanic acid is a free or enzyme-bound intermediate in a pathway from isopenicillin N to benzylpenicillin, or whether its appearance in the free state is a consequence of the hydrolysis of penicillins with non-polar side chains.

In the *Cephalosporium* type of fermentation, penicillin N is found in place of isopenicillin N and no penicillins with non-polar side chains, such as phenylacetyl, have yet been reported to be produced. Although such fermentations may also produce a number of compounds with the cephalosporin ring system, these cephalosporins all have a δ-(D-α-aminoadipyl) side chain and differ from each other in the nature of the group on the exocyclic methylene at C3. It now appears likely that the first cephalosporin to be formed is deacetoxycephalosporin C (XIII), that is subsequently converted to deacetyl-acephalosporin C, and that the latter is then acetylated to yield cephalosporin C

$$NH_3^+ \quad \overset{D}{\diagdown} CH.CH_2.CH_2.CH_2.CO.NH$$

(XIII)

itself. Deacetoxycephalosporin C is produced by a variety of fungi and by *Streptomyces* (Kitano *et al.*, 1974). Mutants of *C. acremonium* have been isolated which accumulate deacetylcephalosporin C (Kanzaki *et al.*, 1974) and others which accumulate deacetoxycephalosporin C, either alone or together with its deacetyl derivative (Queener *et al.*, 1974). Moreover, in the presence of a labile hydroxylase and acetyltransferase from *C. acremonium*, deacetoxycephalosporin C is converted to cephalosporin C (Liersch *et al.*, 1976); cephalosporin C produced by *C. acremonium* in the presence of molecular oxygen enriched with $^{18}O_2$ has been shown by mass spectroscopic analysis of the methyl ester of its N-acetylderivative to contain ^{18}O in its acetoxy group (Stevens *et al.*, 1975). Whether the oxygen at C7 in the methoxycephalosporins (VI) also comes from molecular oxygen, or whether it is introduced immediately after the formation of the fused ring system, is not yet known.

The hypothesis that δ-(L-α-aminoadipyl)-L-cysteinyl-D-valine is a precursor of deacetoxycephalosporin C, as well as of penicillin N, is consistent with the finding that the isotopic ratios of the valinyl fragments of penicillin N and cephalosporin C labelled from 2S-[^{15}N]-3S-[$^2H_3$]valine in *C. acremonium* are very similar, although the valine undergoes considerable transamination (Huang *et al.*, 1975). If the tripeptide is indeed a common intermediate, at what stage do the pathways diverge to lead finally to the antibiotics in fermentation fluids? One long-recognized possibility was that intracellular penicillin N (or conceivably isopenicillin N) is excreted partly as penicillin N and converted partly to cephalosporin C. This hypothesis became more attractive with the discovery of a non-enzymic ring expansion for the conversion of the sulphoxide of phenoxymethylpenicillin ester to the corresponding deacetoxycephalo-sporin (Morin *et al.*, 1963). But an attempt to test it by the addition of [^{14}C] penicillin N to suspensions of mycelium of *C. acremonium* was frustrated by the failure of the penicillin to be taken up by the mycelial cells, and kinetic data neither supported nor excluded a precursor–product relationship between the penicillin and cephalosporin C (Warren *et al.*, 1967). However, it seems likely that the relationship can now be clarified. Kohsaka and Demain (1976), using a cell-free system similar to that of Fawcett *et al.* (1973, 1976) from protoplasts of *C. acremonium* and conditions of high aeration, found that the formation of an antibiotic which is destroyed by a cephalosporinase, but not by a penicillin-ase, could be detected by assay with a strain of *Escherichia coli* supersensitive to β-lactam antibiotics. Cephalosporin synthesis in this system is markedly stimulated by the addition of penicillin N, but not of benzylpenicillin or 6-aminopenicillanic acid.

CONCLUSION

On the basis of the information obtained during the last few years a plausible outline of the biosynthetic pathways to the main β-lactam antibiotics is that shown in Figure 1.3. Whether stages in the biosynthesis of substances such as

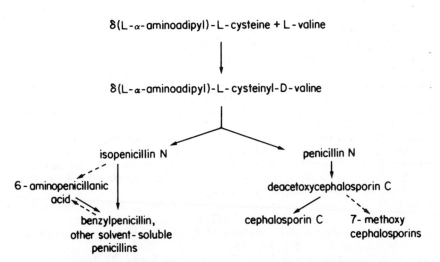

Figure 1.3 Biosynthetic pathways to β-lactam antibiotics.

clavulanic acid (VII) and nocardicin (VIII) will fit into this or a closely related scheme has yet to be determined. Some of the reactions shown in Figure 1.3, including those catalysed by acylases or transacylases, can be detected in cell-free extracts obtained by conventionenal methods and attempts may now be made to isolate the enzymes concerned for more detailed study. Some light has recently been thrown on features of the reactions involved in the closures of the β-lactam, thiazolidine, and dihydrothiazine rings by the use of chirally labelled amino acids as precursors followed by mass spectroscopic and nuclear magnetic resonance analyses of the products (for review see Fawcett and Abraham, 1976). But the enzyme systems involved in the formation of the fused-ring systems have so far only been liberated in an active form from the mycelial cells by formation and lysis of protoplasts. More needs to be learned about the factors which determine the stability of these enzymes before attempts to isolate them in quantity are likely to be profitable and before the mechanisms by which they function can be studied at the molecular level.

REFERENCES

Abraham, E. P., and Newton, G. G. F. (1961) *Biochem. J.*, **79**, 377.

Adriaens, P., Meesschaert, B., Wuyts, W., Vanderhaeghe, H., and Eyssen, H. (1975) *Antimicrob. Ag. Chemother.*, **8**, 638.

Aoki, H., Sakai, H., Kohsaka, M., Konomi, T., Hosoda, J., Kubochi, Y., Eguchi, E., and Imanaka, H. (1976) *J. Antibiotics*, **29**, 492.

Arnstein, H. R. V., and Crawhall, J. C. (1957) *Biochem. J.*, **67**, 180.

Arnstein, H. R. V., and Morris, D. (1960) *Biochem. J.*, **76**, 357.

Batchelor, F. R., Chain, E. B., and Rolinson, G. N. (1961) *Proc. Roy. Soc., Series B*, **154**, 478.

Batchelor, F. R., Doyle, F. P., Naylor, J. H. C., and Rolinson, G. N. (1959). *Nature (London)*, **183**, 257.

Behrens, O. K., Corse, J., Edwards, J. P., Garrison, L., Jones, R. G., Soper, Q. F., van Abeele, F. R., and Whitehead, C. W. (1948) *J. Biol Chem.*, **175**, 793.

Beecham Group Limited (1975) German Pat. 2 517 316.

Brotzu, G. (1948) *Lav. Ist. Igiene, Cagliari*, Cagliari-Tip C.E.L.

Cama, L. D., and Christensen, B. G. (1974) *J. Am. Chem. Soc.* **96**, 7582.

Cole, M., and Batchelor, F. R. (1963). *Nature (London)*, **198**, 383.

Fawcett, P. A. and Abraham, E. P. in *Biosynthesis* (J. D. Bu'Lock, ed.), (Specialist Periodical Reports) Chem. Soc., 1976, Vol. 4, p. 248.

Fawcett, P. A., Loder, P. B., Duncan, M. J., Beesley, T. J., and Abraham, E. P. (1973) *J. Gen. Microbiol.* **79**, 293.

Fawcett, P. A., Queener, S., Abraham, E. P. (1975a) unpublished results.

Fawcett, P. A., Usher, J. J., and Abraham, E. P. (1975b) *Biochem. J.* **151**, 741.

Fawcett, P. A., Usher, J. J., and Abraham, E. P. (1976) in *Second International Symposium on the Genetics of Industrial Microorganisms* (Macdonald, K. D., ed.) Academic Press, London and New York, p. 129.

Fawcett, P. A., Usher, J. J., Huddleston, J. A., Bleaney, R. C., Nisbet, J. J., and Abraham, E. P. (1976) *Biochem. J.* **157**, 651.

Flynn, E. H., McCormick, M. H., Stamper, M. C., De Valeria, H., and Godzeski, C. W. (1962) *J. Am. Chem. Soc.*, **84**, 4594.

Gatenbeck, S., and Brunsberg, U. (1968) *Acta Chem. Scand.*, **22**, 1059.

Goulden, S. A., and Chattaway, F. W. (1968) *Biochem. J.* **110**, 55P.

Guthikonda, R. N., Cama, L. D., and Christensen, B. G. (1974) *J. Am. Chem. Soc.*, **96**, 7584.

Hodgkin, D., and Maslen, E. N. (1961) *Biochem. J.*, **79**, 393.

Howath, T. T., Brown, A. G., and King, T. J. (1976) *J. Chem. Soc. Chem. Comm.* 1976, 266.

Huang, F. C., Chan, J. A., Sih, C. J., Fawcett, P., and Abraham, E. P. (1975) *J. Am. Chem. Soc.* **97**, 3858.

Kanzaki, T., Shirafugi, H., Fujisawa, Y., Fukita, T., Nara, K., Kitano, K., and Kida, M. (1974) *Abstracts 2nd International Symposium on the Genetics of Industrial Micro-organisms*, Sheffield, UK, Academic Press.

Kato, K. (1953) *J. Antibiotics, Japan*, **130**, 184.

Kitano, K., Kintaka, K., Suzuki, K., Katamoto, K., Nara, K., and Nakao, Y. (1974) *Agr. Biol. Chem.*, **38**, 1761.

Kohsaka, M., and Demain, A. L. (1976). *Biochem. Biophys. Res. Comm.*, **70**, 465.

Liersch, M., Nüesch, J., and Treichler, H. J. (1976) *Chem. Soc. Spec. Period. Rep. Biosyn.* **4**, 179.

Loder, P. B. (1970) D.Phil thesis, University of Oxford.

Loder, P. B., and Abraham, E. P. (1971a) *Biochem. J.*, **123**, 471.

Loder, P. B., and Abraham, E. P. (1971b) *Biochem. J.*, **123**, 477.

Loder, P. B., Abraham, E. P., and Newton, G. G. F. (1969) *Biochem. J.*, **112**, 389.

Masurekar, P. S., and Demain, A. L. (1974) *Appl. Microbiol.*, **28**, 265.

Morin, R. B., Jackson, B. G., Müller, R. A., Lavagnino, E. R., Scanlan, W. B., and Andrews, S. L. (1963) *J. Am. Chem. Soc.*, **85**, 1896.

Nagarajan, R., Boeck, L. D., Gorman, M., Hamill, R. L., Higgens, C. E., Hoehn, M. M., Stark, W. M., and Whitney J. G. (1971) *J. Am. Chem. Soc.*, **93**, 9.

Newton, G. G. F., and Abraham, E. P. (1954) *Biochem. J.*, **58**, 103.

Newton, G. G. F., and Abraham, E. P. (1955) *Nature (London)*, **175**, 548.

Queener, S. W., Capone, J. J., Radue, A. B., and Nagarajan, R. (1974) *Antimicrob. Agents Chemother.*, **6**, 334.

Sakaguchi, K., and Murao, S. (1950). *J. Agric. Chem. Soc., Japan*, **23**, 411.

Stapley, E. O., Jackson, M., Hernandez, S., Zimmerman, S. B., Currie, S. A., Mochales, S., Mata, J. M., Woodruff, H. B., and Hendlin, D. (1972) *Antimicrob. Ag. Chemother.*, **2**, 122.

Stevens, C. M., Abraham, E. P., Huang, F. C., and Sih, C. J. (1975) *Abstracts, Annual Meeting of the Federation of American Societies for Experimental Biology and Medicine*.

Usher, J. J. (1974) D.Phil. thesis, University of Oxford.

Usher, J. J., Loder, P. B., and Abraham, E. P. (1975) *Biochem. J.*, **151**, 729.

Warren, S. C., Newton, G. G. F., and Abraham, E. P. (1967) *Biochem. J.*, **103**, 902.

DISCUSSION

Professor Sir Derek Barton

What do you think is the role of the thioaldehyde in the synthesis of the penicillin antibiotics?

Professor Abraham

What seems to be clear is that no dehydrovaline is involved here, but we can't eliminate the possibility of the oxidation to a thioaldehyde.

Dr. M. Tishler

I have often wondered if we had gone ahead with penicillin F what the consequences would have been?

Professor Abraham

You went ahead with penicillin G because it was easier to produce.

Dr. M. Tishler

Yes, but take the data comparing penicillins G and F, for example, in the treatments of infections; when the difference was discovered, there was a big discussion in the States as to which was the penicillin of choice.

Professor Abraham

Their specific activities were not very different, but it was the ability to produce high yields of the benzylpenicillin which decided the issue. Some penicillins are hydrolysed by enzymes much more easily than others, as shown by Vanderhaeghe.

Sir Ernst Chain

This whole field is bedevilled by the fact that it is impossible to get materials to survive during isolation. The enzymes destroy everything during the isolation and unless we find a means of stopping these enzymes this will always be a difficulty. It would be interesting to see whether proteolytic inhibitors would be any help, although they are expensive.

Professor Abraham

My impression is that this same problem arises even in the much simpler system of synthesis of gramicidin S.

Dr. M. Tishler

It seems curious to me that the β-lactam structure was such a novelty when chemists proposed it. Many favoured an azlactone structure. There was a lot of discussion about this question but now we have four β-lactams that have come from nature.

Professor Abraham

Yes, there is a β-lactam ring in one of the bleomycins. Also there is a toxin with a β-lactam structure which is more remote from the antibiotics. Incidentally, it isn't true to say that all organic chemists were sceptical about the β-lactam structure.

Dr. M. Tishler

Yes, in particular the Merck chemists were more willing to accept it.

Sir Ernst Chain

We had a tremendous struggle at the beginning of this work between the organic chemists and other groups. In addition, many chemists such as Sir Robert Robinson were absolutely convinced this molecule would be synthesized in six months. It is very difficult to transfer observations from biological systems to matters of synthetic organic chemistry. May I ask how far we have gone in the synthesis of cephalosporins?

Sir Derek Barton

Sir Ernst, I must take up your implication that there is a difference between organic chemists and other people studying nature! We are really all studying the same thing. One mustn't hang the faults of some organic chemists in the past on the subject of organic chemistry. As to the synthesis of cephalosporins this is already a very large-scale industrial process.

2
Biological Properties of
β-Lactam Antibiotics

G. N. Rolinson

Beecham Pharmaceuticals Research Division, Betchworth, Surrey, U.K.

INTRODUCTION

In this tribute to Sir Ernst Chain a review of the biological properties of the β-lactam antibiotics is especially fitting because it was the demonstration of the remarkable activity of penicillin as a systemic chemotherapeutic agent, as well as the isolation and purification of the antibiotic, which distinguished the work carried out by Sir Ernst and his colleagues at Oxford in late 1939 and in the early 1940s. Since that time the penicillin field has expanded very considerably indeed, and again, this owes much to Sir Ernst not only because of his pioneering work, but also for his continued involvement in these developments, not least in the biological aspects.

The way in which the β-lactam field has developed during the past 35 years has taken several forms. Firstly, there have been important advances in the understanding of the nature of the antibacterial properties of penicillin and its mode of action in biochemical terms. Secondly, there has been the discovery of new naturally occurring substances, related in structure to penicillin, and thirdly, there has been the exploitation of these substances largely by chemical means in order to obtain new chemotherapeutic agents.

At a relatively early stage in the work on penicillin it was realized that the fermentation carried out with *Penicillium chrysogenum* yielded a mixture of antibiotics all closely related in chemical structure and differing only in the nature of an acyl group attached to a fused β-lactam thiazolidine ring system (Table 2.1). From this group of naturally occurring penicillins, benzylpenicillin (penicillin G) was selected as the preferred member for commercial production and clinical use. Two attempts were then made to exploit the penicillin molecule with a view to improving the biological properties. One approach was chemical modification of one of the naturally occurring penicillins, penicillin X, the *p*-hydroxy group in the benzene ring in this particular penicillin facilitating substitution by halogens and various azo radicals (Coghill *et al.*, 1949). Some of the novel penicillins prepared in this way were more active *in vitro* than benzylpenicillin, but the antibacterial spectrum is not improved and none was considered likely to be superior in clinical practice. The other approach was the

Table 2.1 Penicillins

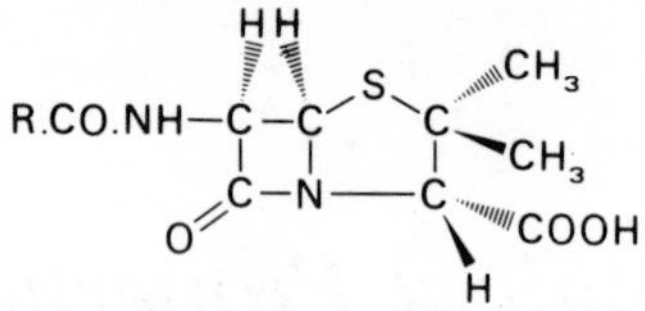

Compound	R

Naturally occurring penicillins

benzylpenicillin (penicillin G)

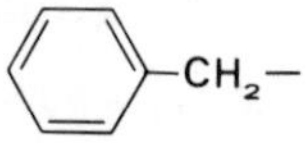

penicillin N

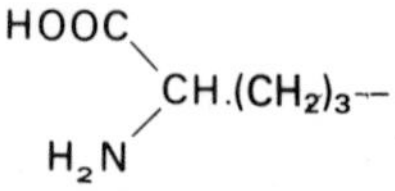

Biosynthetic penicillins

penicillin V

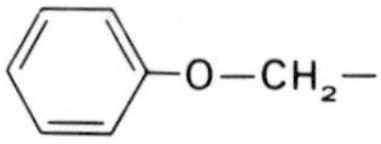

Semisynthetic penicillins

ampicillin

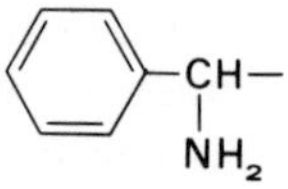

methicillin

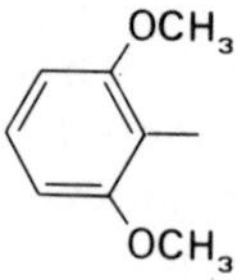

cloxacillin

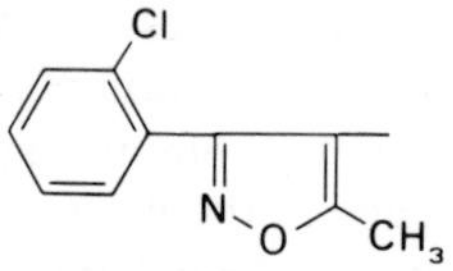

carbenicillin

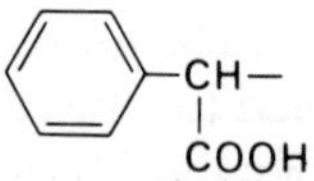

Non-acylamino derivatives of 6-amino penicillanic acid

mecillinam (FL 1060)

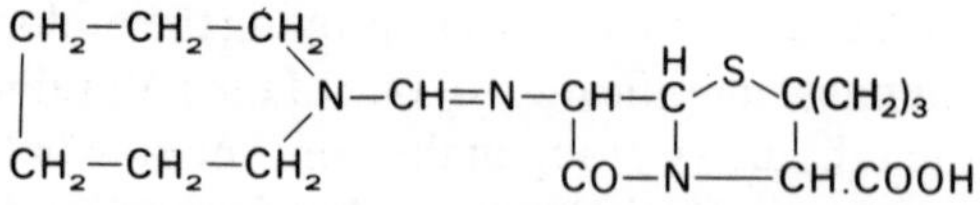

addition to the fermentation of substances which could serve as precursors for the acyl substituent in the penicillin molecule and in this way result in the biosynthesis of penicillins not otherwise available as naturally occurring products (Behrens *et al.*, 1948). One of the penicillins produced in this way was penicillin V, phenoxymethylpenicillin (Table 2.1), which shows the important property of acid stability and absorption when administered by mouth. Apart from this compound none of the penicillins obtained by biosynthetic means succeeded in finding a place in clinical practice.

A new aspect of the penicillin field was revealed in 1953, however, when the antibiotic cephalosporin N, produced by species of *Cephalosporia*, was shown by Abraham and co-workers to be a new type of penicillin in which the side chain was derived from a-aminoadipic acid (Abraham *et al.*, 1953; Abraham *et al.*, 1954) (Table 2.1). The biological properties of this penicillin were so different from those of the penicillins produced by species of *Penicillia* that interest was again stimulated in the possibility of extending and improving the therapeutic usefulness of the penicillin family by preparing members with novel side chain structures. The opportunity for this came with the discovery and isolation of the penicillin nucleus, 6-aminopenicillanic acid (Batchelor *et al.*, 1959). Using this substance, 6-APA, as a starting point, a very large number of semisynthetic penicillins has been prepared, many of which have found important places in clinical practice.

Extension of the β-lactam field in a different direction occurred as a result of the work on cephalosporin C, which was first detected as an impurity in partially purified preparations of cephalosporin N (Newton and Abraham, 1955). Structural determination showed that this compound also contained a fused β-lactam ring system but one in which the thiazolidine ring of the penicillin molecule was replaced by a dihydrothiazine ring. The discovery of cephalosporin C was of considerable interest not only because of the novelty of its structure but also because it proved to be highly stable to inactivation by staphylococcal penicillinase. From this compound a family of semisynthetic cephalosporins has been developed in an analogous manner to the semisynthetic penicillins (Table 2.2).

More recently another family of β-lactam antibiotics has been discovered, the members of which differ in structure from the cephalosporins in having a methoxy group in the 7-position on the β-lactam ring (Nagarajan *et al.*, 1971; Stapley *et al.*, 1972). These compounds, the cephamycins, are produced not by fungi but by species of *Streptomyces*, and like the penicillins and cephalosporins have also led to the preparation of semisynthetic analogues (Table 2.3).

Very recently, yet another naturally occurring β-lactam has been discovered, clavulanic acid (Figure 2.1) (Brown *et al.*, 1976), which is structurally different from the penicillins, cephalosporins and cephamycins (Howarth *et al.*, 1976). This compound extends still further the biological properties of the β-lactam group.

All the compounds referred to so far contain a fused β-lactam ring. In addition, however, there are a number of naturally occurring monocylic β-

Table 2.2 Cephalosporins

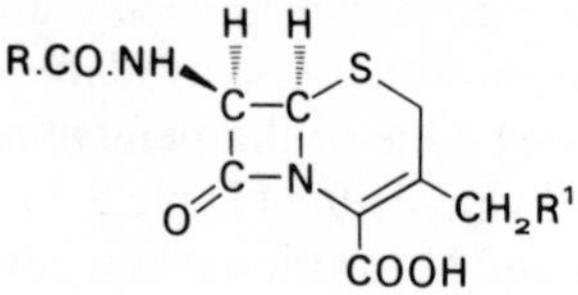

Compound	R	R^1
Naturally occurring cephalosporin		
cephalosporin C	$H_2N(HOOC)CH(CH_2)_3-$	$-O.CO.CH_3$
Semisynthetic cephalosporins		
cephalothin	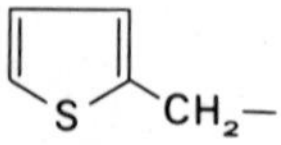	$-O.CO.CH_3$
cephaloridine	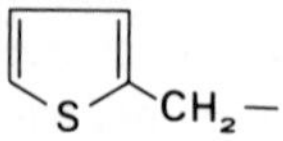	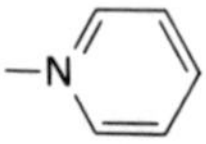

Table 2.3 Cephamycins

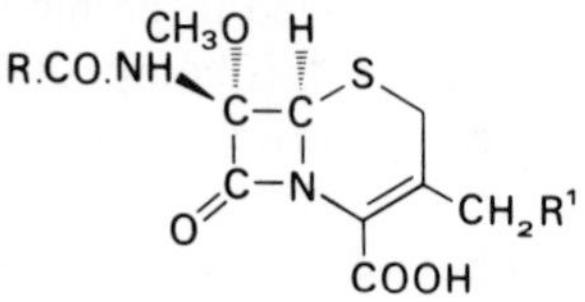

Compound	R	R^1
Naturally occurring cephamycins		
cephamycin C	$H_2N(HOOC)CH(CH_2)_3-$	$-O.CO.NH_2$
Semisynthetic cephamycins		
cefoxitin	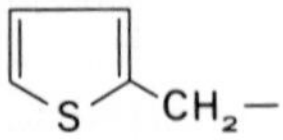	$-O.CO.NH_2$

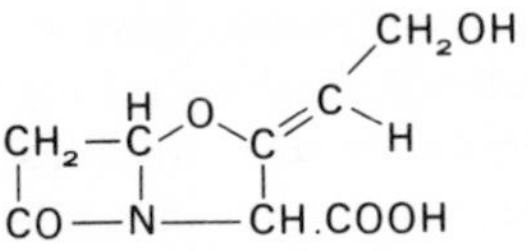

Figure 2.1 Clavulanic acid

lactam compounds, for example the wildfire toxin produced by *Pseudomonas tabaci* (Stewart, 1971). Some of these monocyclic β-lactams also display antibacterial activity, for example the metabolite of certain *Streptomyces* species reported by Scannell *et al.* (1975) and also the substance nocardicin A (Aoki *et al.*, 1976) which is produced by the actinomycete *Nocardia uniformis.* Furthermore, there are examples of quite complex structures, such as bleomycin, which nevertheless contain a monocylic β-lactam ring. There are some difficulties therefore in defining the scope of the term β-lactam antibiotics. For the purposes of this essay, however, it is proposed to limit the term β-lactam antibiotics to those substances in which the β-lactam ring is fused to some other ring system. These compounds all show some degree of antibacterial activity, and in most cases this is the principal biological property which these compounds show.

Antibacterial activity can be considered from a number of different points of view. Firstly, there is the nature of the antibacterial effect on the individual cell in terms of inhibition of growth, loss of viability, morphological changes and so on and these effects are the consequence of the particular mode of action of the substances. Secondly, there is the effect of the antibiotic on populations of bacterial cells, that is to say the kinetics of the antibacterial effect and the extent to which individual members of a bacterial population may respond differently to the rest. And thirdly, there is the chemotherapeutic aspect of antibacterial activity which is expressed in terms of the type of bacteria which are inhibited and the concentration of antibiotic required to bring about this effect.

EFFECT OF β-LACTAM ANTIBIOTICS ON THE BACTERIAL CELL

Different species of bacteria are by no means uniform in their sensitivity to particular β-lactam antibiotics and the latter also differ markedly one to another in their potency as well as in their spectra of antibacterial activity. It is exactly for this reason that the β-lactam antibiotics have been exploited so as to extend and improve their therapeutic usefulness and the result has been the development of a large family of antibiotics with considerable diversity in antibacterial properties. Nevertheless, the β-lactams do have a great deal in common with respect to their effect on the bacterial cell and there is no evidence that these antibiotics differ fundamentally one to another in their mode of action or that the action is basically different with different types of bacteria.

The property which these compounds have in common is a bactericidal action and there is good evidence that this results from an effect on cell-wall synthesis. Continued growth under such conditions then leads to death and lysis of the cell. This is consistent with the observation made as early as 1941 by Sir Ernst and his colleagues (Abraham *et al.*, 1941) that penicillin does not exert a bactericidal effect when the cells are in a resting phase. Numerous authors have subsequently confirmed that penicillin is only bactericidal under conditions which, in the absence of the drug, would allow growth. Observations more directly indicating an effect on the cell wall were made by Gardner (1940) who noted changes in the morphology of bacteria grown in subinhibitory concentrations of penicillin.

Large and irregular-shaped cells were frequently seen in experiments using cocci, and long filamentous cells were seen in the case of bacilli. The observation by Lederberg (1956) that penicillin results in the formation of osmotically fragile spheroplasts also indicated an effect on the cell wall but more direct evidence for the wall as the target site has come from biochemical studies on the effect of penicillin on mucopeptide synthesis, and in particular, the inhibition of cross linking in this structural component of the cell wall. In bacteria, the wall maintains the characteristic shape of the cell and prevents damage to the cytoplasmic membrane which would otherwise result from the relatively high internal osmotic pressure. It follows, therefore, that if the mechanical strength of the wall were to be impaired, under conditions which nevertheless allowed cell growth to continue, the wall itself might physically rupture. This indeed occurs with many Gram-negative bacilli when they are exposed to penicillins and related β-lactams. In *Escherichia coli*, for example, a localized rupture of the wall occurs allowing the cytoplasm to bulge out forming a spheroplast. The latter is osmotically fragile and soon bursts resulting in the sudden lysis of the cell. Most, if not all, of the penicillins and cephalosporins have this effect on *E. coli*, provided the antibiotic is present in adequate concentration. From such observations it might be concluded that the bactericidal effect of penicillin is the direct result of the rupture of the wall and the loss of cytoplasmic contents. On the other hand, lysis could be a secondary phenomenon and loss of viability might occur before the cell wall actually ruptures.

This is certainly the case with the Gram-positive cocci as was evident from the results of Chain and Duthie (1945). In their experiments with *Staphylococcus aureus*, exposure to three units of penicillin per ml for five hours resulted in less than a two-fold reduction in the total cell count but over 99 per cent of these bacteria were no longer viable. This observation was confirmed by others with the conclusion that since most of the organisms in a culture could be killed before lysis began the latter must be considered a secondary phenomenon. However this is not at variance with the view that inhibition of cell wall synthesis is the primary mode of action of penicillin. A weakening of the cell wall might well result in damage to the cytoplasmic membrane which could result in loss of the normal semipermeable characteristics and this in turn could cause loss of viability and death of the cell. The appearance of staphylococci which have been rendered non-viable by exposure to penicillin is certainly not inconsistent with such an effect. Many of the cells seem to have lost their normal turgor and are somewhat shrivelled although the wall does not appear to be ruptured. In this connection, it is of interest that Gale and Taylor (1947) showed that penicillin-treated cells fail to take up glutamic acid from the surrounding medium and also lose viability without necessarily undergoing lysis.

Loss of viability without obvious lysis is also seen with *E. coli* when the cells are exposed to the compound mecillinam which is a non-acylamino derivative of 6-aminopenicillanic acid (Table 2.1). Exposure to mecillinam first results in generalized changes to the cell surface. On further incubation, the cells appear to divide, with each half becoming more rounded, until after approximately two hours the culture consists of spherical cells, much increased in volume with irregular pitted surfaces (Greenwood and O'Grady, 1973). During this time, extensive loss of viability occurs in the culture, but this not accompanied by any simple and obvious rupture of the wall. The effect of mecillinam on the morphology of the cell, therefore, is quite different from that of the penicillins and cephalosporins, which typically cause cell-wall rupture. In this connection it is of interest that mecillinam does not inhibit any of the enzymic activities of *E. coli* which have been reported to be sensitive to penicillin, such as mucopeptide transpeptidase, D-alanine carboxypeptidase, and endopeptidase (Matsuhashi *et al.*, 1974). Furthermore, mecillinam does not appear to bind to any of the proteins to which [14C]benzylpenicillin binds, and mutants of *E. coli* resistant to mecillinam show no increased resistance to ampicillin for example (Matsuhashi *et al.*, 1974). Nevertheless, the bactericidal effect of mecillinam is again consistent with damage of some nature to the cell wall. This is apparent from microscopic observation of mecillinam-treated cells and from the fact that the lethal effect is also influenced by the osmolality of the culture medium. As with the penicillins and cephalosporins, mecillinam also fails to exert a lethal effect on resting cells.

The biological effect of impaired cell-wall synthesis by β-lactam antibiotics is not confined to loss of viability and cell-wall rupture. In staphylococci, sub-inhibitory concentrations of penicillins result in a failure of daughter cells to separate after cross-wall formation has taken place. Continued growth and septation under these conditions leads to the formation of abnormally large forms which are aggregates of cells in which cross-wall formation is to some extent disorganized and in which the septa have failed to separate (Lorian, 1975). The cells are not killed, however, and there is no significant alteration in the peripheral wall. When transferred to a penicillin-free medium these clusters separate to give cells of normal appearance and growth rate. This is certainly a biological effect of penicillin on the cell but not one which results in cell death or lysis.

Penicillins and cephalosporins also inhibit cross-wall formation in bacilli without necessarily resulting in rupture of the outer cylinder or inhibition of growth. At subinhibitory concentrations, the rate of cross-wall formation is inhibited such that it fails to keep pace with cell growth and the result is the formation of a population of short filaments. As the concentration of the β-lactam antibiotic is increased a point is reached where cross-wall formation is inhibited completely. When this occurs such cells are all destined to lyse eventually but, depending on the particular β-lactam antibiotic and the concentration present, this may not occur until after several hours incubation. Growth under these circumstances results in the formation of filamentous cells which may be up to 20 times the normal length or more. Examination of ultra-thin sections of such cells reveals that they are indeed single cells, in which septation has been prevented, and not chains of cells which have failed to separate. Although cross-wall formation has been prevented in such filaments, inactivation of the antibiotic with β-lactamase results in a rapid resumption of septation with the formation of a population of cells of normal morphology. It is of interest to speculate, however, whether such cells are identical in all respects with the original cell from which the filament arose in the first place.

EFFECT OF PENICILLIN ON POPULATIONS OF BACTERIA

The effect of penicilllin on bacterial populations depends to some extent on the concentration of antibiotic present and on the species of bacterium. When staphylococci and streptococci are exposed to relatively low concentrations of penicillin growth may not be arrested at once, and the viable count may increase appreciably over the first two to three hours before a bactericidal effect becomes apparent (Figure 2.2). With higher concentrations of penicillin the onset of bactericidal action is more rapid and a fall in viable count may

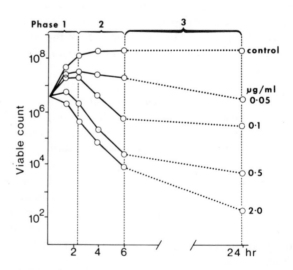

Figure 2.2 Effect of ampicillin on time course of growth of *Staph. aureus*. The concentration of the penicillin is indicated on the ordinate

occur shortly after the addition of the antibiotic. Under these circumstances, however, although the viable count may fall the total cell count may remain constant for a few hours, due to the fact that loss of viability of staphylococci and streptococci is not immediately accompanied by lysis, and under these conditions measurement of turbidity may even show some increase as a result of swelling of the cells. With Gram-negative bacilli, such as *E. coli*, the onset of bactericidal action tends to be more rapid than it is with Gram-positive cocci and loss of viability is more closely accompanied by cell lysis. With relatively low concentrations of penicillin however, during the first few hours a lag period can again be recognized during which time the rate of killing may be slow. This lag period is then followed by a phase of logarithmic killing, the rate of bactericidal action depending on the concentration of penicillin present. This phase of rapid bactericidal action generally lasts some two to three hours after which time the kinetics then follow one of three courses; the viable count may continue to fall, but at a slower rate, or the count may remain constant, or the viable count may increase. The situation in which the number of viable cells remains relatively constant following a phase of rapid bactericidal action is seen very commonly and the term 'persisters' was coined by Bigger (1944) to describe these cells. Persisters are not genotypically resistant mutants but show the same penicillin sensitivity when transferred to a drug-free medium as does the rest of the population. Moreover, they resume growth without any lag when the penicillin is removed. Bigger concluded that the persisters are cells which are in a phase of growth analogous to the resting phase and because of this would not be expected to be susceptible to penicillin. Whatever the true explanation of the phenomenon may be the persisters do represent a stationary population of viable cells in which the bacteriostasis is caused or at least maintained by the presence of penicillin.

Related to the persister phenomenon is the recovery period, first described by Parker and Marsh (1946). These authors showed that when staphylococci were exposed to penicillin and the antibiotic then removed this was followed by a period during which the count of the number of viable cells remained constant. At the end of this period bacterial multiplication was then resumed. The duration of this recovery period was found to be dependent on the concentration of penicillin and on the period of time the cells were exposed to the antibiotic. Recently we have reinvestigated this phenomenon in our own laboratories. Our results show that although the recovery period can be demonstrated with benzylpenicillin and with ampicillin, using *Staph. aureus* and *Strep. pyogenes*, a recovery period is not seen with the Gram-negative bacilli. For example, with *E. coli* exposed to ampicillin or with *Pseudomonas* exposed to carbenicillin, the viable count increases immediately after removal of the antibiotic.

A bactericidal effect is characteristic of the β-lactam family of antibiotics. However, the rate at which cells are killed is not always in direct proportion to the antibiotic concentration. In 1945, Kirby showed that low concentrations of penicillin ($0 \cdot 1$ μg/ml) killed staphylococci more rapidly than did high concentrations (100 μg/ml) and this paradoxical effect or 'zone phenomenon' was investigated in more detail by Eagle and Musselman (1948) using various bacteria. The paradoxical effect of concentration was found with some streptococci but not with others. Similarly, with *Staph. aureus* some strains showed the zone phenomenon while others did not. The significance of this paradoxical effect of penicillin concentration on rate of killing has not been established. However, in our own laboratories we have confirmed recently that this phenomenon does occur using the Oxford *Staphylococcus*, although the effect was only apparent when the inoculum was in the resting phase; when an inoculum of actively growing cells was used the rate of killing increased directly with the increase in antibiotic concentration.

The maximum rate at which bacteria are killed by penicillin varies with the particular species. With *Strep. faecalis*, for example, the rate of killing is frequently slow regardless of the concentration of antibiotic used and for a given multiple of the minimum inhibitory concentration (MIC) staphylococci are killed more slowly than, for example, is *E. coli*. Different members of the β-lactam family also differ markedly in the rate at which they kill cells when tested at a given multiple of their respective MIC values. For example, at a concentration of twice the MIC the bactericidal action of amoxycillin against *E. coli* is considerably more rapid than that of ampicillin, which in turn is more rapid than that of carbenicillin. Similarly, among the cephalosporins at twice the MIC cephaloridine results in a rapid loss of viability of *E. coli*, while cephalexin shows a very slow rate of bactericidal action.

ANTIBACTERIAL ACTIVITY FROM THE CHEMOTHERAPEUTIC STANDPOINT

A high level of activity of a penicillin, or a high degree of susceptibility of a particular bacterium, results from readiness of the drug to reach the site of action (permeability), a facility to react with the target site (intrinsic activity), and stability of the compound to β-lactamase, if this enzyme should be present. Exploitation of the β-lactam field to provide compounds with greater activity has certainly been successful as a result of improving stability to β-lactamase. Success has also been achieved in improving intrinsic activity, although in most cases it is difficult to determine whether this is the result of increased permeability or increased reactivity with the target site.

Some indication of the way in which the antibacterial activity of penicillin has been exploited for chemotherapeutic ends is given in Table 2.4.

An early success in this field of work was the preparation of penicillins stable to staphylococcal penicillinase and, as a consequence, active against the penicillin-resistant strains of *Staph. aureus*. The first compound of this type to be introduced into clinical practice was methicillin which owes its β-lactamase stability to an extremely high K_m value (Novick, 1962). The intrinsic level of antibacterial activity of methicillin, however, is not high and the compound is not absorbed when given by mouth. Further work with penicillins stable to

Table 2.4 Antibacterial spectra of semisynthetic penicillins

	MIC (μg/ml)			
	Penicillin G	Methicillin	Ampicillin	Carbenicillin
Staph. aureus				
penicillin-sensitive	0·02	.1·25	0·05	1·25
penicillin-resistant	>250	2·5	>250	25
Strep. pyogenes	0·01	0·25	0·02	0·5
Strep. pneumoniae	0·02	0·25	0·05	1·25
Strep. faecalis	2·5	25	1·25	25
N. gonorrhoeae	0·01	0·1	0·02	0·05
N. meningitidis	0·02	0·25	0·02	0·05
H. influenzae	0·5	2·5	0·25	0·25
E. coli	50	>250	5·0	5·0
Salm. typhi	5·0	>250	0·5	5·0
Sh. sonnei	50	>250	2·5	12·5
P. mirabilis	5·0	250	1·25	2·5
Proteus				
—indole-positive	>250	>250	250	5·0
Ps. aeruginosa	>250	>250	>250	50
Enterobacter sp.	>250	>250	250	12·5
K. aerogenes	250	>250	250	250

staphylococcal penicillinase resulted in the introduction of the isoxazolyl penicillins which, in addition to being more active than methicillin against *Staph. aureus*, also show the property of being absorbed from the gastrointestinal tract, and are therefore suitable for oral administration.

Improved activity against the Gram-negative bacilli was first realized with the penicillin, ampicillin. This compound largely retains the high activity which benzylpenicillin shows against the Gram-positive and Gram-negative cocci but in addition there is significantly improved activity against many of the *Enterobacteriaceae* and also against *Haemophilus influenzae*. Unlike benzylpenicillin, ampicillin is also moderately well absorbed when given by mouth and very much better oral absorption is seen with the *p*-hydroxy analogue of ampicillin, amoxycillin, introduced more recently.

Carbenicillin, introduced in 1967, also shows increased activity against many of the *Enterobacteriaceae* compared with benzylpenicillin, but the most notable property of this particular compound is the activity displayed against *Pseudomonas aeruginosa*. This activity is not of a very high order in terms of the MIC, but the extremely low toxicity of carbenicillin allows the compound to be administered in high doses thus enabling inhibitory levels to be obtained in the body. The significance of this activity against *Pseudomonas* is also accentuated by the fact that the number of antibiotics available for the treatment of infection caused by this pathogen is very limited.

Mecillinam, which is also a derivative of 6-aminopenicillanic acid, departs even more markedly from the antibacterial spectrum traditionally associated with a penicillin in that it is considerably more active against certain Gram-negative bacilli than it is against the Gram-positive cocci. Many strains of *E. coli*, *Klebsiella*, and *Proteus* are inhibited by mecillinam at concentrations as low as $0.1 \mu g/ml$, although it must also be said that other strains of these pathogens are highly resistant (Lund and Tybring, 1972). Activity is also very dependent upon inoculum size and it has been reported that there is a ready emergence of phenotypically resistant variants which retain their resistance over a number of generations (Greenwood and O'Grady, 1973).

At the present time, as many as 11 different semisynthetic penicillins are now in widespread clinical use and their diversity of antibacterial spectra is considerably greater than might have been anticipated when the work on the semisynthetic penicillins first began.

A similar exploitation of antibacterial activity has taken place in the cephalosporin field. Here the natural compound is cephalosporin C which shows a relatively low level of activity against both Gram-positive and Gram-negative bacteria. However, replacement of the α-aminoadipyl side chain, and also the acetoxy group at C3 with other structures, has resulted in semisynthetic cephalosporins with greatly increased activity, and many of these compounds, including cephalothin and cephaloridine, have an important place in chemotherapy.

Cephalosporin C itself shows marked stability to staphylococcal penicillinase and this property is largely retained in the semisynthetic cephalosporins. The latter differ from the penicillins, therefore, in that activity against the penicillin-resistant *Staphylococci* tends to be a characteristic of these compounds whereas this property is only achieved in the penicillin family by the introduction of particular side-chain structures. In general, the cephalosporins also show activity against *Klebsiella* whereas the penicillins do not. On the other hand, the cephalosporins at present in clinical use show relatively low activity against *H. influenzae* and also *Strep. faecalis*, while these organisms are highly susceptible to certain of the semisynthetic penicillins. The different members of the penicillin and cephalosporin groups, therefore, have their advantages and their disadvantages.

Many bacteria of clinical significance produce the enzyme penicillinase which opens the β-lactam ring by hydrolysis, resulting in inactivation of the antibiotic molecule. In this way, bacteria which produce this enzyme may be penicillin-resistant. Both penicillins and the cephalosporins are potential substrates for this enzyme and in recent years the term β-lactamase has been adopted in preference to the original name penicillinase. Since the original discovery of this enzyme by Abraham and Chain (1940) it has become clear that a number of different β-lactamases are produced by different bacteria and that these enzymes differ in their β-lactam substrate specificity. A given penicillin or cephalosporin may thus be relatively stable to one β-lactamase but inactivated by another and the converse may be the case with a different β-lactamase produced by some other organism. The β-lactam family of antibiotics, therefore, cannot simply be divided into two groups, one β-

lactamase stable and the other β-lactamase unstable, except with respect to one particular β-lactamase.

Although many bacteria do bring about inactivation of particular penicillins and cephalosporins, β-lactamase is not the only mechanism of bacterial resistance to the β-lactam antibiotics. Some bacteria, for example certain strains of the *Gonococcus*, show diminished sensitivity to penicillin yet do not produce β-lactamase. Again, strains of *Staph. aureus* which are resistant to methicillin although they do produce penicillinase, nevertheless do not bring about significant inactivation of methicillin, because the latter is highly stable to this particular β-lactamase. In such cases, the resistance to the antibiotic may be the result of diminished permeability of the bacterial cell, or the target site may show diminished reactivity with the antibiotic. Certain bacteria thus show an intrinsic type of resistance to particular penicillins and cephalosporins. However, with the majority of bacteria of clinical importance, resistance to penicillins and cephalosporins is indeed the result of β-lactamase production and inactivation of the antibiotic. Attempts to overcome such resistance have been one of the main objectives of the work on semisynthetic penicillins and cephalosporins. The first success in this direction was the preparation of methicillin, which has already been referred to. More recently, certain cephalosporins have been described, notably cefoxitin, cephamandole, and cefuroxime which show increased stability to the β-lactamases produced by certain Gram-negative bacteria and which, as a result, are active against these otherwise resistant organisms.

Another approach to the problem of β-lactamase production and bacterial resistance has been *via* inhibition of β-lactamase action. Certain penicillins, notably methicillin and the isoxazolyl penicillins, are competitive inhibitors of the β-lactamase produced by certain Gram-negative bacilli. Although such compounds themselves have little antibacterial activity against these organisms they are capable of protecting other penicillins which are intrinsically active but labile to the β-lactamase in question. The novel β-lactam clavulanic acid which has been reported recently (Brown *et al.*, 1976) is of particular interest as an inhibitor of β-lactamase and may offer a means of overcoming bacterial resistance to the penicillins and cephalosporins now in clinical use.

REFERENCES

Abraham, E. P., and Chain, E. B. (1940) *Nature (London)*, **146**, 837.

Abraham, E. P., Chain, E. B., Fletcher, C. M. Florey, H. W., Gardner, A. D., Heatley, N. G., and Jennings, M. A. (1941) *Lancet*, **241**, 177.

Abraham, E. P., Newton, G. G. F., Crawford, K., Burton, H. S., and Hale, C. W. (1953) *Nature (London)*, **171**, 343.

Abraham, E. P., Newton, G. G. F., and Hale, C. W. (1954) *Biochem. J.*, **58**, 94.

Aoki, H., Sakai, H., Kohsaka, M., Konomi, T., Hosoda, J., Kubochi, Y., Iguchi, E., and Imanaka, H. (1976) *J. Antibiotics*, **29**, 492.

Batchelor, F. R., Doyle, F. P., Nayler, J. H. C., and Rolinson, G. N. (1959) *Nature (London)*, **183**, 257.

30

Behrens, O. K., Corse, J., Edwards, J. P., Garrison, L., Jones, R. G., Soper, Q. F., Van Abeele, F. R., and Whitehead, C. W. (1948) *J. Biol. Chem.*, **175**, 793.

Bigger, J. W. (1944) *Lancet*, **247**, 497.

Brown, A. G., Butterworth, D., Cole, M., Hanscomb, G., Hood, J. D., Reading, C., and Rolinson, G. N. (1976) *J. Antibiotics*, **29**, 668.

Chain, E. B., and Duthie, E. S. (1945) *Lancet*, **248**, 652.

Coghill, R. D., Stodola, F. H., and Wachtel, J. K. (1949) in *The Chemistry of Penicillin* (Clarke, H. T., Johnson, J. R., and Robinson, R., eds.), Princeton University Press, Princeton, pp. 680–687.

Eagle, H., and Musselman, A. D. (1948) *J. Exp. Med.*, **88**, 99.

Gale, E. F., and Taylor, E. S. (1947) *J. Gen. Microbiol.*, **1**, 314.

Gardner, A. D. (1940) *Nature (London)*, **146**, 837.

Greenwood, D., and O'Grady, F. (1973) *J. Clin. Path.*, **26**, 1.

Howarth, T. T., Brown, A. G., and King, T. J. (1976) *J. Chem. Soc. Chem. Comm.*, **1976**, 266.

Kirby, W. M. M. (1945) *J. Clin. Invest.*, **24**, 165.

Lederberg, J. (1956) *Proc. Nat. Acad. Sci., U.S.A.*, **42**, 574.

Lorian, V. (1975) *Antimicrob. Ag. Chemother.*, **7**, 864.

Lund, F., and Tybring, L. (1972) *Nature (New Biol.)*, **236**, 135.

Matsuhashi, S., Kamiryo, T., Blumberg, P. M., Linnett, P., Willoughby, E., and Strominger, J. L. (1974) *J. Bacteriol.*, **117**, 578.

Nagarajan, R., Boeck, L. D., Gorman, M., Hamill, R. L., Higgens, C. E., Hoehn, M. M., Stark, W. M., and Whitney, J. G. (1971) *J. Am. Chem. Soc.*, **93**, 2308.

Newton, G. G. F., and Abraham, E. P. (1955) *Nature (London)*, **175**, 548.

Novick, R. P. (1962) *Biochem. J.*, **83**, 229.

Parker, R. F., and Marsh, H. C. (1946) *J. Bacteriol.*, **51**, 181.

Scannell, J. P., Pruess, D. L., Blount, J. F., Ax, H. A., Kellett, M., Weiss, F., Demny, T. C., Williams, T. H., and Stempel, A. (1975) *J. Antibiotics*, **28**, 1.

Stapley, E. O., Jackson, M., Hernandez, S., Zimmerman, S. B., Currie, S. A., Mochales, S., Mata, J. M., Woodruff, H. B., and Hendlin, D. (1972) *Antimicrob. Ag. Chemother.*, **2**, 122.

Stewart, W. W. (1971) *Nature (London)*, **229**, 174.

DISCUSSION

Sir Ernst Chain

I was fascinated by the paper of Dr. Rolinson; he has done his work *in vivo* in infected muscle. This is a very striking example of a general point which I have often made, that even in a relatively simple system, like antibacterial action, there may be simple *in vitro* events, but it turns out that the situation is infinitely more complex *in vivo*. Dr. Rolinson has shown that you can inject the same amount of antibiotic *in vivo* and yet you get a completely different effect. In immunosuppressed animals, for example, something is lacking and antibacterial effects may be very low *in vivo*. This shows that it is not just enough to have a good antibiotic available, but that there are other forces in the body, largely non-specific, which are just as important. This biological aspect has been neglected. This point applies not only to antibiotics but to all drugs. Therefore, model building and other such exercises may be amusing, but their significance *in vivo* may not be great.

Dr. A. Dixon

In this section on biologically active substances derived from penicillin, it is important to record that Sir Ernst also gave us d-penicillamine, which has proved life-saving in Wilson's disease and cystinuria, and is now used in very considerable amounts for the relief of suffering in rheumatoid arthritis. The search for antibiotics for the acute infectious diseases has been an exciting story, but the main diseases medicine has to deal with today are the chronic diseases, such as rheumatoid arthritis. It is a pleasure to note that Sir Ernst's medical 'Midas-touch' has contributed here too.

3

Biochemical Engineering in the Production of Fungal Metabolites

R. Falini

Steril-Pharmaceutical Engineering Company, Milan, Italy

INTRODUCTION

If I remember correctly the term 'biochemical engineering' did not exist in 1949 when I started to work with Professor Chain at the State Institute of Health in Rome and I, as a chemical engineer, approached biochemistry and microbiology for the first time. However, as told by Hoogerheide (1973) during the Symposium on Microbiological Engineering in Prague, that period, with the development of the production of antibiotics, changed the initially weak link between chemists, microbiologists, and engineers. Thus, a more serious co-operation developed from which a bioengineer was born.

It was an important opportunity for biochemical engineering to start dealing with the production of penicillin, a chance which contributed to its success. In fact, the production of this antibiotic, gave and still does give, rise to a lot of difficulties as it illustrates the main problems which may be encountered by a bioengineer. The most significant are (*i*) contamination, particularly by micro-organisms producing penicillinase; (*ii*) rheological properties of the broth which can reduce the oxygen supply; (*iii*) sensitivity to variations in temperatures of the growth and production stages; and (*iv*) thermal and chemical lability of the product in aqueous phase.

The years from 1946 to 1955 were primarily devoted to the research and development of facilities capable of ensuring reliable operation of the plants to be used for antibiotic production or for microbiological transformation, to steroids, organic acids, or alkaloids. In those years Professor Chain confined me and my colleagues to the study of the basic problems connected with biotechnology. His coworkers in Rome will always remember with deep gratitude Professor Chain for he was one of the most passionate and successful supporters of biochemical engineering.

At the end of the 1950s and during the following 10 years biochemical engineering concentrated its efforts on an in-depth understanding of the kinetic problems connected, at the initial stage, with metabolite production, and more recently, with biomass production.

PRODUCTION OF MICRO-ORGANISMS AND THEIR METABOLITES

a. Basic production problems

Even at the initial stages of antibiotic production it seemed essential to use a method of the deep culture rather than a surface one. This created the problem of providing sufficient oxygen to the micro-organisms suspended in the broth in order not to limit their growth and metabolite production. The air distribution–agitator system turned out to be the determining factor and the studies made in the 1950s brought a remarkable improvement of such systems, thanks to a better comprehension of the geometrical ratio of the agitator to the fermenter, which finally led to a better sizing of the fermenter itself. To overcome this problem, in 1950–52, Professor Chain organized in Rome a task-force of young engineers who succeeded in finding some original solutions both from a geometrical and a mechanical viewpoint, such as a fully baffled or open-vortex system and bottom-fitted stirrers, and from a mass-transfer viewpoint.

They considered the overall efficiency factor of the oxygen transfer, defined as the ratio of the whole mechanical work employed for air compression and liquid stirring to the quantity of the oxygen transferred from the air to the broth. Furthermore, original analytical instruments, including a system for measurement of dissolved oxygen due to Professor Gualandi and a dynamometric coupling, were developed. The mass-transfer problem, which is accepted as a classic of bioengineering, was further enriched by the work of some English researchers, including Calderbank, Pirt, Hockenhull, and Blakebrough, who found more and more adequate solutions to the new problems. Even at the end of the first 10 years of work in this field it was evident the behavioural differences of the various broths were partly due to their different rheological properties. In fact, the filamentous micro-organisms may produce non-Newtonian conditions, although this is not necessarily true for the non-filamentous ones such as bacteria and yeasts.

This variation in behaviour gives rise to remarkable differences in the formation of the air/liquid transfer surfaces and in their transport within the bulk of the liquid. According to the Danckwert's theories, this may further affect the boundary-transfer coefficients. Thus, for the non-filamentous micro-organisms it is possible to use oxygen transfer devices other than those adopted for the production of fungal metabolites. In fact, direct air distribution without agitation, air-lift, and tower fermenters are successfully used for the production of biomasses from single-cell organisms. Nevertheless, fermenters with agitators are still used for the production of fungal metabolites.

This problem is however more complex than already described, since the agitator, in addition to creating surfaces for oxygen transfer and distribution of the organisms within the bulk of the liquid, may exert a negative mechanical action on the organisms. Furthermore, the intensity of the agitation influences the costs incurred in temperature and foam control, as well as for the solid–

liquid separation and product recovery (Zhvkovskaya *et al.*, 1974). Consequently, the initial problem of how to supply oxygen during the aerobic fermentation, solved in principle and improved through the evaluation of the energetic yield of the process, finally became a problem of minimum cost. Therefore, the search began for the optimal solution to minimize not only the cost of the oxygen transfer, but also the total cost of the final product.

Figure 3.1 highlights an attempt to outline schematically the interrelationship between the cost of the end product and the above-mentioned factors. This figure also shows how the behaviour of the overall mass-transfer coefficient, as a function of the agitator speed which is roughly associated with the specific production, influences the depreciation allowance of the fermentation unit.

Sterility is the second problem which worried—and in some cases still does concern—the bioengineers. The aim is to prevent any micro-organisms from contaminating the selected culture ensuring, in the meantime, the in and out communications of the culture equipment. Some of these difficulties are promptly removed by the adoption of some simple techniques, such as steam seals, suffing boxes of special type, and maintenance of a positive pressure inside the fermenter; other problems are still not entirely eliminated. This applies to the fluids, like air and liquid nutrients, to be added continuously during fermentation. There are no economical methods capable of ensuring a 100 per cent safe continuous sterility; the means presently available may bring the contamination level down to very low values, but at proportionally increased costs. Assuming that the contamination level of a fermenter of about 150 m^3 useful volume (cycle length, say, 200 hour) receiving 10^6 m^3 of air per cycle, should not exceed 1 per cent, only one micro-organism every 10^8 m^3 of air can be allowed to enter the fermenter. As the micro-organism level present in the atmosphere is of the order of 10^3 m^3 it is necessary to remove 10^{11} micro-organisms. This may be achieved by two procedures.

(*i*) Filtration through paper or deep fibrous beds capable of fixing the submicron particles onto the fibres of inertial impaction or by particle adhesion to the fibres.

(*ii*) Filtration through porous membranes whose mean pore size is smaller than that of the particles to be separated.

In the first case the ratio between the particles passing through each elementary filtering layer and the particles captured by this layer being constant, the number of layers required to remove the remaining particles proportionally increases. This involves an increase in the cost due to both the air pressure drop through the filtering bed, and the more complex design of the filter. Figure 3.2 shows a filter of this type, engineered 25 years ago after careful tests carried out under the supervision of Professor Chain in Rome. It is still one of the most reliable filters in use.

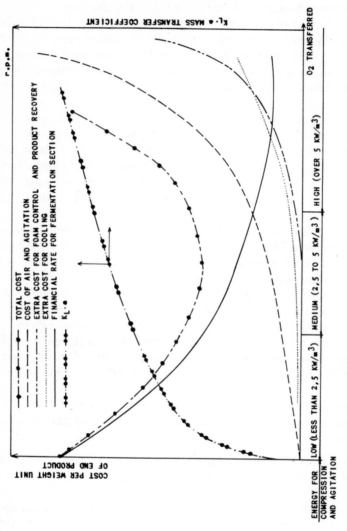

Figure 3.1   Influence of the factors related to the oxygen transfer rate on the end product cost

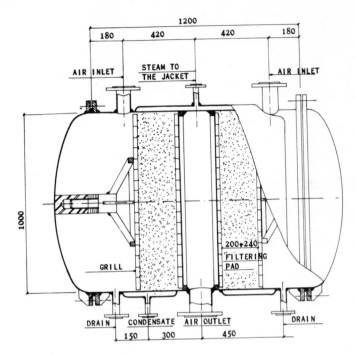

Figure 3.2 Air filter with two glass filtering pads. Filtering material: glass-wool 5–7 μm. Pad density: 300 g/cm³

As far as the microporous membranes or the cartridge filters are concerned, the risk of anomalous pore sizes, particularly after repeated sterilization, makes it necessary to adopt membranes whose pore size will be lower than theoretically required. This leads to a demand for a careful prefiltration and an increase in the compression costs caused by the higher pressure drop. Therefore, in this case a minimum cost problem also has to be considered. If the increasing cost of micro-organism removal is plotted against the decreasing cost due to production losses caused by the contamination, the contamination rate which is economically acceptable is obtained. Figure 3.3 shows how a contamination rate below 10^{-11}, equivalent to 1 per cent loss, would involve no economical advantage. The same figure shows that the position of the total cost curve is a function of the cost of the filtration system compared with the value of a fermentation cycle.

The sterility problem is of slightly less importance in the production of the tetracycline group of antibiotics thanks to the self-protecting ability of these substances and to their chemical stability. Greater problems arise in the production of non-antibiotic metabolites. The most difficult problem concerns the production of alkaloids in submerged culture, because of the length of the fermentation cycles and the necessity for carrying out the filtration of the broth

38

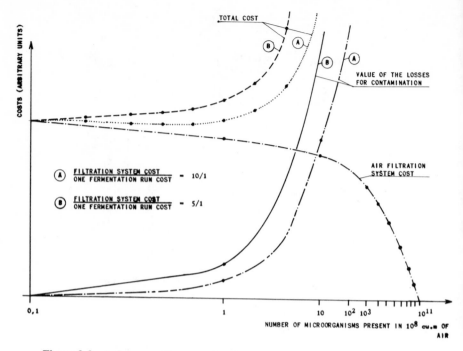

Figure 3.3   Influence of factors related to air filtrations on the end product cost

for the recycling of the mycelial masses under sterile conditions. Fortunately, when with Professor Chain at the end of the 1950s, this problem was considered. It was possible to apply knowledge previously gained in the batch production of penicillin and in the repeated attempts at continuous production of antibiotics. This experience confirmed that achievement of sterility depends both on the plant design and on operation by restricting to a minimum the intervention by personnel.

b. Kinetics of fermentation

After solving the most important problems connected with the production of the required metabolites at any cost, in the 1960s biochemical engineering turned its attention to production kinetics.

The mycelial mass during a batch fermentation grows according to the well-known laws governing the growth of any biological aggregate with limited availability of space and nutrients. It was not so easy to find a clear relationship between the biomass formation, the substrate consumption, and the metabolite production, particularly when this relationship is the final result of a complex series of reactions rather than the result of a direct microbiological transformation, for example to ethanol.

During a batch fermentation the following features may be observed.

(*i*) The derivative of the production curve of biomasses and, in many cases, of the metabolites, (see Fig. 3.4) defined as the specific production rate, has a maximum, before and after which the process does not occur under optimal conditions.

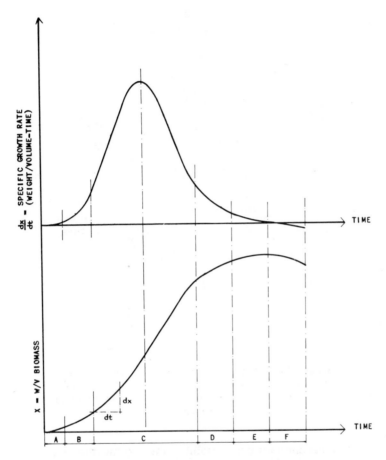

Figure 3.4 Biomass concentration and specific growth rate

(*ii*) During phase A (lag phase), as well as the steady phase E and the decreasing phase F, no significant biomass or metabolite production takes place. A slow increase is observed during stages B and D.

(*iii*) When examining metabolite production, it appears that the specific rate of maximal biomass formation does not coincide with that of the metabolite, either when it shows a direct relationship with the substrate consumption (Figure 3.5), or when such a relationship is not clearly identifiable (Figure 3.6). The first observations resulted in an attempt to replace the batch production

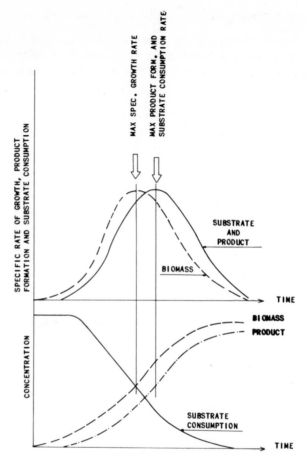

Figure 3.5 Biomass and product concentration and specific rate of growth product formation and substrate consumption (product related to the substrate consumption)

with a continuous one in order to stabilize the specific production rate at its maximum by achieving the advantages schematically shown in Figure 3.7.

Unfortunately this goal of the biochemical engineers, supported by the elegant Monod theory, and thoroughly investigated by Pirt and Callow among others, has not been reached in the case of many industrial productions of antibiotics while it is fully satisfied when producing the biomasses. The failure could depend upon the above-mentioned non-coincidence of the various maximal production rates.

One of the solutions suggested by the bioengineers to overcome this problem is to separate the biomass production from that of metabolites, by subdividing the fermentation unit into several subunits connected in series. Thus, each

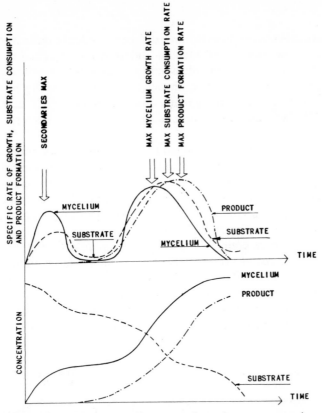

Figure 3.6 Biomass, substrate, and product concentration and specific rate of growth, substrate consumption, and product formation (product not directly related to the substrate consumption)

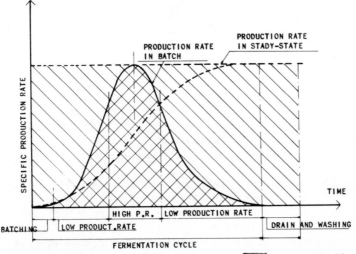

Figure 3.7 Production in batch: short cycle ▨ compared with continuous ⬚ stabilized at the maximal specific production rate

subunit has a different volume to allow different residence times when inserted in a constant flow system, and each has different working conditions, such as temperature, pH, and oxygen diffusion rate. This problem proved to be much more complex than expected, both because of the difficulty in reaching a simultaneous steady-state in the many interconnected vessels, and, probably, because of the washing-out of some of the intermediates from the individual subunits.

In the meantime, it was ascertained that the fermentation process could be prolonged through the continuous addition of the exhausted nutrients, thus maintaining the specific production rate during most of the cycle. In other cases the so-called replacement technique has been applied, which can be partially identified with the variable volume continuous process recently considered theoretically by Dunn and Mor (1975).

Both these methods seem able to achieve the main advantage of continuous production—the greater productivity of the system—due both to the maintenance of the production at the maximal rate, and to the removal of the batching and discharging times affecting the production.

During long-term fermentation the down-time problem is of less importance (Figure 3.8) as the production rate can be stabilized at relatively high levels

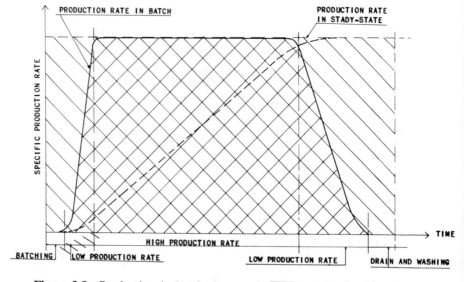

Figure 3.8 Production in batch: long cycle ▨ compared with continuous ▧ stabilized at the maximal specific production rate

over a long period. On the other hand, the replacement method, which is kinetically similar to the continuous one (Malek *et al.*, 1966), has both these advantages, by allowing the removal of down-time and the maintenance of a high production rate (Figure 3.9). Therefore a multistage continuous production of fungal metabolites would offer presently only negligible advantages—if any—in terms of the cost of the end product.

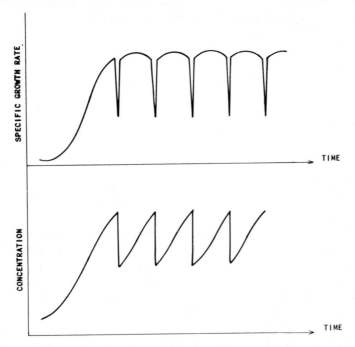

Figure 3.9 Specific growth rate in a semicontinuous fermentation

I like to recall my attempts of 20 years ago, when, contrary to Professor Chain's opinion, I enthusiastically tackled the study of the continuous production of penicillin, obtaining, true to his expectations, huge amounts of mycelium but negligible quantities of penicillin.

METABOLITE RECOVERY

No other vital problems, including sterilization or oxygen transfer, have prompted such wide bioengineering research in this field dominated by the organic chemists, as metabolite recovery. I would mention Podbielniak's continuous countercurrent solvent extractor, a typical development of biochemical engineering, adopted at the initial stage of penicillin production to replace the mixing–settling method. The rapid improvement of such machines in conjunction with the high water–solvent partition coefficient of this antibiotic raised the total yield of the extraction process to very high levels.

Again, it is without doubt that the difficulties encountered in the production of penicillin, due to its chemical and thermal lability, have been greater than those arising from the production of other metabolites in particular the tetracyclines. In the latter case in fact, the increase in the concentration of the metabolite in the broth has allowed its direct precipitation in the filtered broth, thus avoiding the need for a solvent-extraction phase. However, I can not abandon this subject without mentioning the exciting ultrafiltration method which has provided a revolutionary simplification of the product-recovery process. This could be achieved by the use of membranes of different permeability, providing a means of solid–liquid separation, as well as product concentration and purification.

PLANT—GENERAL PROBLEMS

a. Sizing

There are two problems, namely the determination of the total fermentation capacity and its subdivision into fermentative subsystems, to be considered in the plant design.

The fermentation capacity should be determined automatically when the total production required by the market and the specific production rate are known. However, the latter may only be assumed as, contrary to most chemical productions, it is increasing for many metabolites, including antibiotics; for penicillin the average annual rate has increased from 10 to 20 per cent over the last 25 years. Therefore, sizing should be based on the rate which could be actually obtained at the time of the plant start-up rather than on the rate predicted at the plant-design stage, otherwise, the plant tends to be oversized. Many of the price fluctuations which have occurred in the antibiotics market in the past 15 years have been caused by some plants being too large, due to a lack of evaluation of the specific production rate, particularly when the production, in absence of patents, is determined purely by the market.

The next problem is the subdivision of the total capacity into several fermentation subsystems. The following factors will affect the problem.

(i) The cost of the fermentation section is proportional to the number of fermentation sybsystems. A single unit, having a capacity equal to the total production capacity would permit the achievement of the lowest depreciation allowance.

(ii) The sizing, and consequently the cost of the batching, filtration, and extraction sections, follows the dimension of fermentation subunits, it being unprofitable to store over a long period the culture medium and the broth discharged from the fermenters.

(iii) The manpower cost, partially related to the number of manipulations to be carried out, is interrelated to the number of units and to the duration of the cycles.

(iv) The cost of automation is proportional to the number of subunits and to its complexity, which in turn may reduce the manpower cost.

(*v*) The cost of the losses due to contamination is directly proportional to the number of operations and of subunits, and inversely proportional to the automation grade.

b. Economics

The above analysis emphasizes the increasing tendency of bioengineers to formulate the problems on an economic basis, being basically committed to an industry which cannot omit the problem of manufacturing cost. The recent attempts of Aiba and Okabe (1976) to optimize the extraction and filtration phases in the process for antibiotics production illustrate this.

Figure 3.10 shows the behaviour of an arbitrary parameter (ϕ) as a function of the total cost of the end product, in connection with the total yield expected for one of these two phases (filtration) (Y_{FL}) the second parameter being the total yield of both filtration and extraction ($Y = Y_{FL} \times Y_{EX}$). According to Aiba's hypothesis the increase in ϕ connected with the increase in the total yield is more significant, making the adoption of too sophisticated methods for

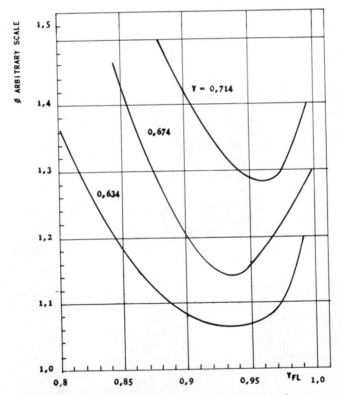

Figure 3.10 ϕ as affected by filtration yield (Y_{FL}) and extraction yield (Y_{EX}): $Y = Y_{FL} \times Y_{EX}$, according to Aiba and Okabe (1976)

improving the process unprofitable. Aiba would like this method to be extended to the entire process, including fermentation and effluent treatment. This extension, however, may be extremely complex, because of the interference of each phase with the next one, as shown in the case of agitation which influences the product-recovery phases. This complexity may partially explain the lack of in-depth research in this field to date. Other factors explaining the lack of studies may be the predominance of basic problems such as oxygen transfer, sterilization, and continuous production.

FALL-OUT BIOTECHNOLOGY

Perlman (1975) recently outlined the influence of penicillin production on the processes evolved for the production of other antibiotics. Furthermore, in other fields biochemical engineering methods have been integrated with processes developed by other industries to give significant results. One of these is the application of the sterility technology to the pharmaceutical, food, and hospital sectors. Also, sterile area construction, allowed by simultaneous application of the asepsis standard and the air purification procedures, has been adopted by the electronic industry. This industry employs large volumes of clean air to keep working areas under controlled conditions (laminar flow). Thus, the biological cleanliness of the air, obviously irrelevant for electronics, is carefully controlled by the methods widely employed in fermentation.

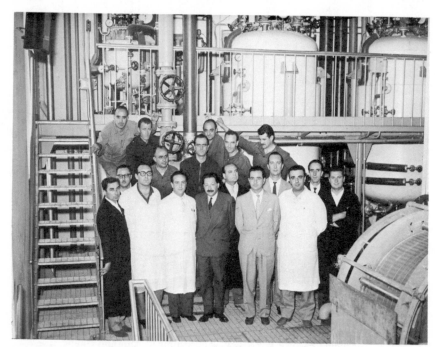

Figure 3.11 Sir Ernst Chain and coworkers, Rome, 1957

Looking at the future, I would like to mention the role to be played by bioengineers as promoters of traditional processes in respect to those developed in the post-war period, when the hydrocarbon costs were low. Reference is made, in particular, to ethanol, whose production process from carbohydrates is being re-examined as Solomons (1976) has recently reviewed. The work of biochemical engineers may become of significant importance and they may be expected to suggest new technologies capable of substantially modifying the process kinetics and the economic terms.

In this report, no mention has been made of the pilot plants crucial to the success of biochemical and genetic research, and indispensable for the scale-up of the experimental data to the industrial scale. The absolute necessity of the pilot plant in this branch of the chemical industry was stressed by Professor Chain in such a way that those developed under his leadership in Rome and at Imperial College were among the most important in Europe. Figure 3.11 shows Sir Ernst and his coworkers at the Rome pilot plant, in 1957, while Figure 3.12 shows the pilot plant at Imperial College.

Figure 3.12   Pilot plant at Imperial College

ACKNOWLEDGEMENTS

I think that this Symposium, which has gathered many people who have had the chance to work with Professor Chain, is the best expression of the scale-up of his own life.

48

REFERENCES

Aiba, S., and Okabe, M. (1976) *Process Biochem.*, **11** (3), 25.
Dunn, I. J., and Mor, J. R. (1975) *Biotechnol. Bioeng.*, **17**, 1805
Hoogerheide, J. C. (1973) 1st International Symposium on *Advances in Microbial Engineering*, John Wiley and Sons, New York and London.
Malek, I. (1972) *Continuous Culture of Micro-organisms*, (Eds. A. C. R. Dean, S. J. Pirt and D. W. Tempest), Academic Press, New York and London, p. 65.
Perlman, D. (1975) *Process Biochem.*, **10** (9), 23.
Solomons, G. L. (1976) *Process Biochem.*, **11** (3), 32.
Zhvkovskaya, S. A. *et al.* (1974) 2nd International Symposium on *Advances in Microbial Engineering*, John Wiley and Sons, New York and London, p. 935.

4

The Claviceps *Fermentation and the Development of New Ergoline Drugs*

F. Arcamone

Farmitalia, Gruppo Montedison, Milan, Italy

INTRODUCTION

Officially ergot comprises the sclerotium, which is the resting stage of the fungus *Claviceps purpurea*. The ergot alkaloids constitute the largest known group of nitrogenous fungal metabolites. The biological activities of the ergot-active compounds, which are also the basis of their established applications in gynaecology, internal medicine, and psychiatrics, have been classed in six distinct categories. Categories one to four are concerned with peripheral effects. Uterine contraction and vasoconstriction are the consequence of a direct action on smooth muscle, while serotonin antagonism and the α-adrenolytic effects are related to an interference with amines at the receptor sites. Categories five and six are concerned with central actions, namely bulbomedullary and mesodiencephalic effects, and are related to a direct action at the brain level. Bulbomedullary effects include vomiting, bradycardia, inhibition of vasomotor centre, and baroceptive reflexes, while mesodiencephalic effects include the so-called 'excitatory syndrome', mydriasis, hyperglycaemia, and hyperthermia (Cerletti, 1959).

Figure 4.1 shows the structure of the classical ergot alkaloids. The compounds can be divided in two classes, the lysergic acid derivatives and the so-called clavines, a group of compounds which, although possessing the tetracyclic ergoline system, are not amide derivatives of lysergic acid. The lysergic acid derivatives include the simple amides (I), and the compounds of the ergotamine group (II), and of the ergotoxin group (III), which differ according to the substitution on the peptide portion of the molecule. The clavines (IV) are exemplified by the group possessing a double bond between C8 and C9; however compounds having an unsaturated bond between C9 and C10, or a completely hydrogenated D ring are also known. The well-known biologically inactive isolysergic acid derivatives display structures I–III but the centre at C8 is inverted. These compounds are easily formed by isomerization of the corresponding lysergic acid derivatives.

In testing any ergot alkaloid a whole battery of assays must be performed. According to this a spectrum can be designed for each compound which allows

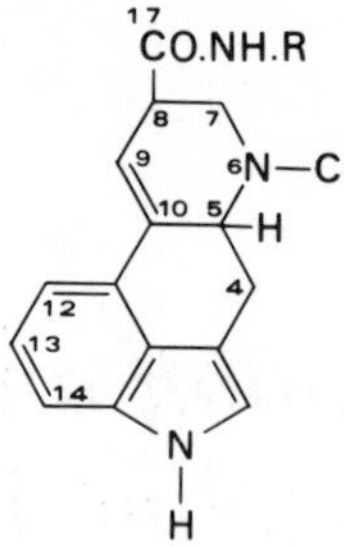

Figure 4.1 The structures of the classical ergot alkaloids. Lysergamide: I, R = H; ergometrine: I, R = CH$_3$(CH$_2$OH)CH; ergotamine: II, R = C$_6$H$_5$CH$_2$; ergosine: II, R = (CH$_3$)$_2$CH.CH$_2$; ergocristine: III, R = C$_6$H$_5$CH$_2$; ergocornine: III, R = (CH$_3$)$_2$CH; ergocryptine: III, R = (CH$_3$)$_2$CH.CH$_2$; agroclavine: IV, R^1 = R^2 = H; elymoclavine: IV, R^1 = H, R^2 = OH; molliclavine: IV, R^1 = R^2 = OH

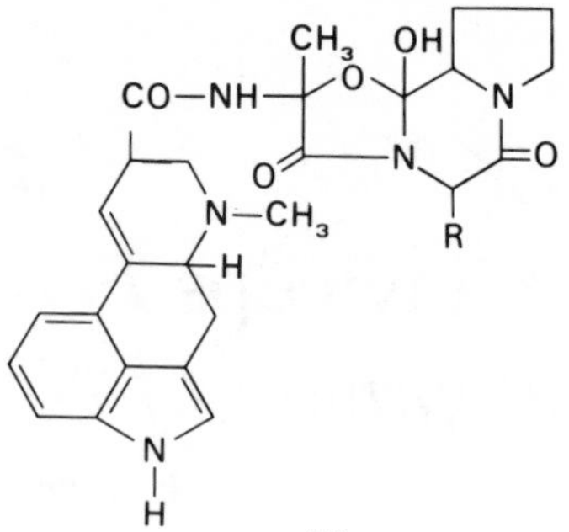

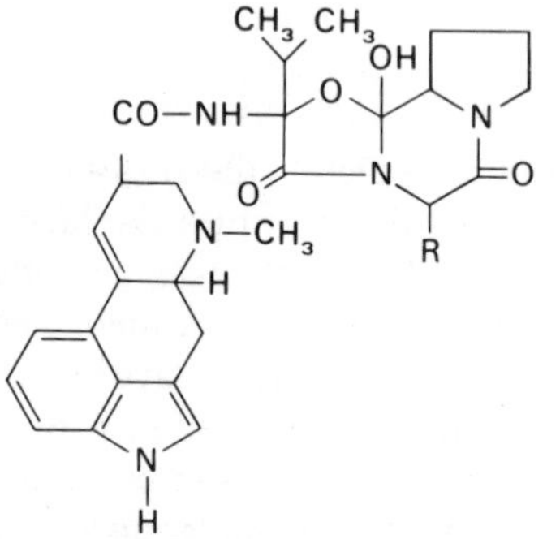

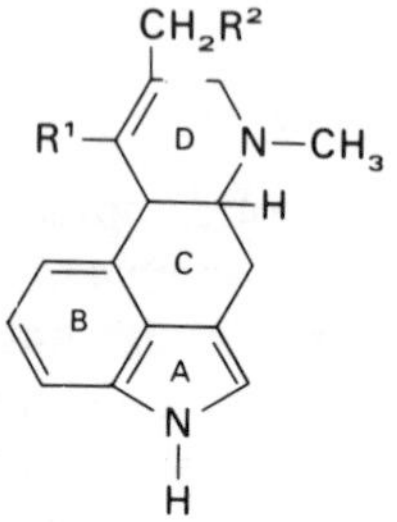

the estimation of the relative importance of a given category of effects within the overall efficacy of any of these drugs. For instance, ergometrine displays a pronounced action on uterine contraction and as a serotonin antagonist, while ergotamine, in which peripheral and central effects are somewhat balanced, approximately possesses the classic pharmacology of the natural mixtures which were used in the medical practice before purified alkaloids were introduced during the second quarter of the present century. Both ergometrine and ergotamine are clinically useful drugs. Dihydroergotamine shows a selectivity as far as adrenergic blockade and bulbomedullary effects are concerned, and provides an example of a semisynthetic derivative of the natural ergot alkaloids.

A number of such derivatives was already known in the late 1950s which appeared to be endowed with a good separation of the original pharmacological activities of ergot. Among the most important, reference will be made here to methylergometrine [lysergic acid-(+)-butanolamide-(2), methergine], an oxytocic drug; lysergide (lysergic acid diethylamide, LSD), the well-known psychomimetic agent; methysergide (1-methyl-lysergic acid butanolamide), a serotonin antagonist used for the prophylaxis of vascular headache; and dihydroergotoxin (a mixture of equal parts of dihydroergocornine, dihydro-ergocristine, and dihydroergocryptine as the methansulphonates), an adrenergic blocking agent (Hofmann, 1964).

The only known practical source of the pharmacologically important ergot alkaloids before 1960 was from the sclerotia of *C. purpurea* grown on the rye. The possibility of obtaining these valuable compounds was therefore restricted to field infection procedures, and the final yields were obviously subject to seasonal variations. Moreover, these methods of production did not allow much opportunity for optimization studies. The production of lysergic acid derivatives by different strains of *C. purpurea* (Fr.) Tul., in surface or in submerged culture, had been attempted in many laboratories. However, none had so far been successful in obtaining more than trace amounts. Alkaloids belonging to the clavine series had instead been obtained in submerged culture from *C. purpurea* (Fr.) Tul. strains after incubation periods of several weeks (for a comprehensive review see Abe and Yamatodami, 1964). These were the first successful alkaloid-producing fermentations, and provided the biological system with which most of the biosynthetic studies were performed. However, the clavine alkaloid-producing fermentations, as well as other natural sources of the ergot alkaloids, were unsuitable for practical developments (Kelleher, 1968).

THE *CLAVICEPS PASPALI* FERMENTATION

Many years have elapsed since the publication of detailed results on the production of new lysergic acid derivatives (LAD) in submerged culture by a strain of *C. paspali* Stevens and Hall (Arcamone *et al.*, 1961*a*). This publication, which followed a preliminary report by Arcamone *et al.* (1960) described the production, in submerged culture and in reasonable yields, of lysergic acid α-hydroxyethylamide, a new simple lysergic acid derivative, after incubation for six to nine days. From this derivative lysergic acid amide and lysergic acid itself could be obtained readily and in high yield.

This report was the culmination of two years effort by a group of research workers headed by Professor Chain, at that time Director of the Biochemical Department and of the International Centre for Chemical Microbiology at the Istituto Superiore di Sanità in Rome. Co-ordinated effort by both academic and industrial scientists was necessary because of the high importance of the goal which meant that limitless amounts of intermediates would be available for the development of the chemistry and pharmacology of the ergoline derivatives. Prior to this, production was hampered by the cumbersome procedures involved in parasitic production of sclerotia in the field. I had the great good fortune to be included as a natural-products chemist in Sir Ernst's department and to be an active witness of these and subsequent developments. In those two very happy years I could share Sir Ernst's personal approach to biochemical research, consisting of the investigation of biological phenomena which could be explained in terms of the action of well-defined chemical substances, as well as of the study of structure and mode of action of these substances. It was always borne in mind that the final goal was the potential practical usefulness—in this case the development of important new drugs for the relief of human illnesses—of the findings. Strict schedules for the coworkers were also an important part of the approach, this aspect being actively pursued by Sir Ernst with a well-timed alternation of strict supervision and stimulating discussion.

a. Morphology and alkaloid production

First mention must be made of the important observation by Tonolo (1959) that when rye embryos are infected *in vitro* with different strains of *Claviceps*, some of the strains tested are non-infective, some cause infection but grow in the form of vegetative mycelium without formation of sclerotia, whereas others give rise to both infection and sclerotia formation. Among the last group is one, isolated from a sclerotium found on an infected plant of *Paspalum distichum* L. and identified as *C. paspali* Stevens and Hall, which is able to infect about 20 per cent of the embryos and form sclerotia. One of these was made to germinate on agar, and hyphal subcultures were prepared from the resulting mycelium. A subculture was isolated which proved to be more infective to the rye embryos than the parent strain, infecting about 90 per cent of embryos and giving rise to ample sclerotia formation. This strain, when grown in submerged culture in shake flasks, produces about 10–20 μg/ml of lysergic derivatives. This, and other observations, allowed a relationship to be established between virulence, sclerotia formation, colour of the mycelium in submerged culture, and alkaloid production. Selection of the cultures based on one or more of these criteria afforded the high-yielding strain which was investigated in detail.

During the subsequent stages the approach used in Sir Ernst's department for the study of fermentation processes was applied. Typical of this approach was the establishment of correlations between the morphology of the micro-organism, the cultural parameters, and the production. In addition, great attention was given to sophisticated methods involving engineering, physical chemistry, and biochemical analysis. Such an approach, which was derived from established experience in the penicillin fermentation as well as in other bioprocesses, proved to be successful in the case now being considered.

A common morphological feature of the producing strains of *C. paspali* used in this study is the presence of hyphal structures and hyphal aggregates (synnemata) resembling the natural sclerotial tissue. Figure 4.2(1) shows a colony of strain F-550, seven days old, grown on potato–glucose agar, charac-terized *inter alia* by the presence of sectors constituted by hyphae of 3–4 μm diameter, with septa 20–50 μm apart, containing fat droplets and generally grouped into synnemata. The morphological appearance of the same strain in submerged culture varies when mannitol is the main carbon source (Figure 4.2, 2*a–c*, indicating synnemata (2*b*) and simple synnemata, 2*c*).

Figure 4.2 Morphology of *C. paspali* strain F-550 grown on potato–glucose agar (1) and in submerged culture containing mannitol (2). Reproduced by permission of the Royal Society

b. The full achievement

Figure 4.3 shows the course of a typical fermentation with *C. paspali* strain F-550 in shake flasks and in a medium containing 5 per cent mannitol, 3 per cent of succinic acid neutralized to pH 5·2 with ammonia, 0·1 per cent KH_2PO_4, 0·03 per cent $MgSO_4.7 H_2O$, and tap water. The carbon sources appear only partially consumed while ammonia is in excess up to the end of the fermentation; high alkaloid production is correlated with the rapidity of phosphorus uptake. The alkaloid production is stimulated markedly by tryptophan, a known precursor of ergoline alkaloids, but not by a number of other amino acids. Adequate aeration is an important requirement for both growth and alkaloid production.

The recovery of the lysergic acid derivatives from the fermentation broths affords generally four products; lysergic acid amide (I) (Figure 4.1), isolysergic

54

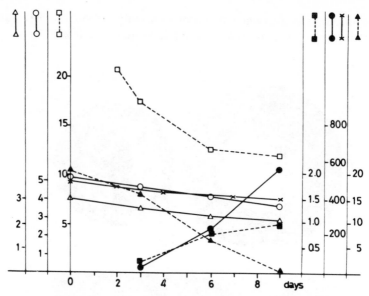

Figure 4.3 Course of a typical lysergic acid derivatives fermentation by *C. paspali* strain F-550 in shake flasks in the mannitol–ammonium succinate medium. △, succinic acid (g/100 ml); ○, mannitol (g/100 ml); □, QO_2; ■, dry weight (g/100 ml); ▲, inorganic phosphate (mg P/100 ml); ●, lysergic acid derivatives (μg/ml); ×, ammonia (mg N/100 ml)

acid amide, lysergic acid methylcarbinolamide (V), and isolysergic acid methyl-carbinolamide (VI) (Figure 4.4). However, it has become evident that compound V is the only alkaloid actually produced by this strain of *C. paspali*, but it is subsequently transformed into the other derivatives during the working-up operations carried out over a prolonged period at room temperature. Thus, the isolation of compound V was attempted at a lower temperature and with the minimum of delay. Compound V was shown to readily undergo cleavage to acetaldehyde and lysergic acid amide under different conditions. Isomerization of V in warm diluted acetic acid leads to the isolysergic isomer (VI) with concomitant formation of lysergic acid amide and isolyergic acid amide.

The structure of V was confirmed by reduction with lithium aluminium hydride to 6-methyl-8-ethylaminomethyl-Δ^9-ergolene (VIIa), which in turn was converted to the corresponding acetyl derivative (VIIb). The identity of the latter compounds was proved by their independent synthesis from VIII (Arcamone *et al.*, 1967). In the same study it was shown that compound V as well as its 9,10-dihydro derivative (IXa) undergo another type of isomerization when in acid solution at room temperature. This reaction shows specific proton catalysis and leads to two isomeric α-hydroxymethylamides which, in the case of the 9,10-dihydro derivative are readily cleaved to dihydrolysergic acid amide, thus proving that they are epimeric compounds which differ only in the spatial arrangement of the substituents around the asymmetric carbon in the

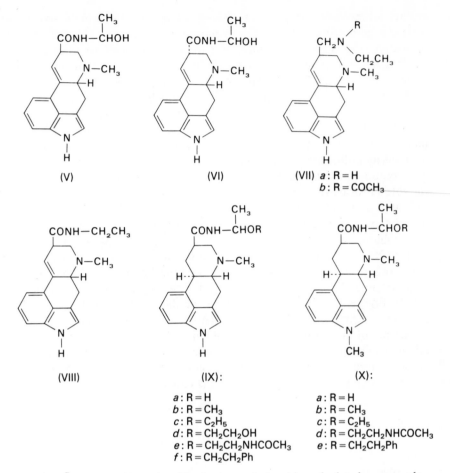

Figure 4.4 Structure of lysergic acid α-hydroxyethyl amide and related compounds

side chain. When the α-hydroxyethylamides (V) or (IXa) are treated with alcohols in the presence of a weak acid, the reaction results in the formation of O-alkyl derivatives which are easily cleaved to lysergic acid amide by heating in either acid or alkaline aqueous solution. The O-alkyl derivatives of the dihydro series have been studied in some detail, owing to their interesting pharmacological properties. Compounds IXb–f have been obtained in the two diastereoisomeric forms, having opposite configurations at the asymmetric carbon in the side chain (Arcamone et al., 1967). They can be methylated in the 1-position to yield the corresponding O-substituted derivatives of 1-methyl-9,10-dihydro-lysergic acid α-hydroxyethylamide (Xb–e). Compound Xb gives, by acid hydrolysis, 1-methyl-dihydro-lysergic acid α-hydroxyethylamide (Xa).

Compounds Xb–e exhibit significant antiserotonin activity and reduced toxicity, as compared with ergometrine. The natural alkaloid lysergic acid methylcarbinol amide (V) appears pharmacologically similar to the structurally related ergometrine, albeit distinctly more toxic (Glaesser, 1961). Its dihydro derivative (IX) is instead 10 times less toxic than ergometrine but displays a marked antireserpine effect when administered intraperitoneally to reserpinized mice. The ED_{50} is 40 mg/kg while, when administered by the same route, the LD_{50} was 220 mg/kg. Similar results have been obtained in other species, including rat, cat, and dog (Arcamone and Ferretti, 1966).

Our studies on the *C. paspali* fermentation also included other aspects of the metabolism of the micro-organism. 2,3-Dihydroxybenzoic acid (XI, Figure 4.5) was identified as a metabolite of major importance in submerged cultures. The compound is also formed in replacement cultures in which tryptophan is the sole substrate (Arcamone *et al.*, 1961*b*). This was the first time that XI was indicated as a metabolite of tryptophan in a biological system. These results have been confirmed later by other authors (Tyler *et al.*, 1964), who using L-tryptophan-[indole-^{3}H] as substrate obtained high incorporation rates of the ^{3}H into XI in feeding experiments with a strain of *C. paspali*. In a subsequent study, other catabolites of tryptophan, namely anthranilic acid (XII), formylanthranilic acid (XIII), and kynurenine (XIV), were detected (Arcamone *et al.*, 1962). Figure 4.5 shows the structures of the products of the tryptophan-feeding experiments. Although the isolation of these compounds may indicate the nature of the pathway from tryptophan to XI, even taking account of later studies by Gröger *et al.* (1965) and by Floss *et al.* (1969) demonstrating the high conversion rate of labelled anthranilic acid to XI by *C. paspali*, no conclusion can be drawn as to the exact mode of the conversion in this organism.

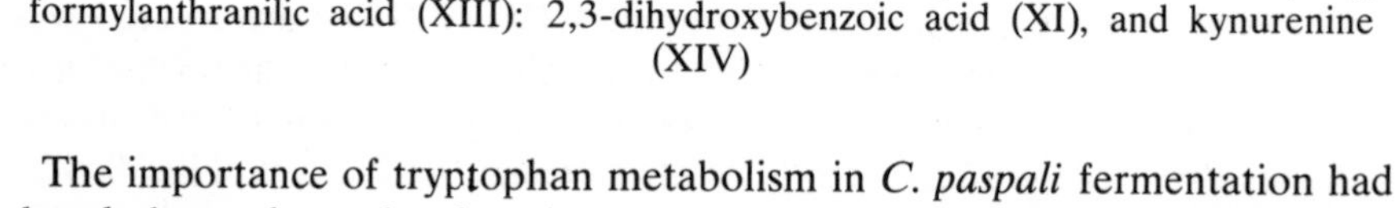

Figure 4.5 Products of tryptophan metabolism in *C. paspali*. Anthranilic acid (XII), formylanthranilic acid (XIII): 2,3-dihydroxybenzoic acid (XI), and kynurenine (XIV)

The importance of tryptophan metabolism in *C. paspali* fermentation had already been shown by the stimulation of the production of D-lysergic acid α-hydroxyethylamide by this amino acid in shake-flask cultures. This stimulation is accompanied by a high rate of incorporation of radioactivity when [3-^{14}C]-DL-tryptophan is fed to cultures. Although the incorporation rate is remarkably high—about 54 per cent of fed radioactivity—the phenomenon is not surprising due to the fact that tryptophan is a precursor of ergoline derivatives in *C. purpurea* (Arcamone *et al.*, 1962). In the same study, the effect of methyltryptophans on alkaloid production and fungal growth was investigated. 4-Methyltryptophan specifically inhibits the production of lysergic derivatives without any effect on mycelial dry weight. In contrast, 5-

methyltryptophan significantly affects growth but specific production of alkaloids is increased. 6-Methyltryptophan has no effect on mycelial growth and considerable alkaloid production occurs in its presence. These results would indicate that the effect of tryptophan, or of tryptophan analogues such as 5-methyltryptophan, can be at least partially related to a mechanism of induction of enzymes involved with the synthesis of lysergic acid derivatives. However, it was subsequently found that exogenous tryptophan displays no effect on alkaloid production in other strains of *C. paspali* which produce high yields of lysergic acid derivatives. Also, the incorporation rate of $[2,3-^3H]$-DL-tryptophan into strain 22 of *C. paspali* appears much less than that observed in the above-mentioned study, that is, less than 5 per cent of fed radioactivity is recovered in the extracted alkaloids (Vicario *et al.*, 1967). It seems therefore that, although other workers have more recently disclosed interesting features of tryptophan metabolism in *Claviceps* strains or have presented evidence for its involvement in induction processes related to ergoline biosynthesis (Floss *et al.*, 1974), the stimulation of the production of lysergic acid derivatives by exogenous tryptophan is limited to a restricted number of strains.

OTHER *CLAVICEPS* FERMENTATIONS

a. Production of ergotamine and other peptide ergot alkaloids

The results of the above-mentioned studies on *C. paspali* fermentation made available a process of industrial importance for the biosynthetic preparation of simple lysergic acid derivatives from which lysergic acid could be obtained in limitless amounts for chemical derivatization. These results also indicated that ergot alkaloid production in saprophytic culture under submerged conditions with the techniques normally employed in antibiotic production is possible. Investigations were therefore undertaken, both at the Farmitalia Research Institute and at Imperial College with the object of studying similar processes for the preparation of the therapeutically useful and commercially important peptide derivatives of lysergic acid. These investigations were successful, and the first announcements concerning the production of peptide alkaloids, mainly consisting of ergotamine, in mg/ml amount by cultivation of *C. purpurea* in submerged conditions, appeared in 1966 (Tonolo, 1966; Amici *et al.*, 1966, 1967). These results, together with the publication by Amici *et al.* (1969) reporting that three new strains of *C. purpurea* (Fr.) Tul., isolated from sclerotia grown on rye, produced under submerged conditions high yields of ergocryptine and ergotamine, ergocornine and ergosine, and ergocristine, respectively, indicated that the objective of the investigations had been fully attained. General features concerning the high-producing strains and those concerning the corresponding process exemplified by the ergotamine fermentation will be summarized because they represent a valuable development in the fields of industrial microbiology and of fermentation technology.

58

The genetic problems related to the production of ergot alkaloids have been thoroughly reviewed and discussed in detail (Spalla, 1973). An important characteristic of the species of *Claviceps* studied so far in different laboratories is their variability, which is however remarkably decreased in highly productive strains obtained through selection. The variability involves both the morphology and the amount of alkaloid produced and has been related to the heterokaryotic nature of the corresponding strains. The individual strains supporting the heterokaryotic condition have been isolated from the different sectors of giant colonies, by unbalanced growth, or by inducing the cultures to form uninucleate conidia. The fact that the alkaloid-producing strains do not normally form conidia must reflect their requirement for stable existence as heterokaryons, as this condition is obviously not compatible with reproduction through uninucleate conidia. It has already been mentioned that in nature alkaloid production takes place only in the sclerotial stage of *Claviceps*. It has been clearly shown that sclerotia are mostly heterokaryotic (Spalla *et al.*, 1969).

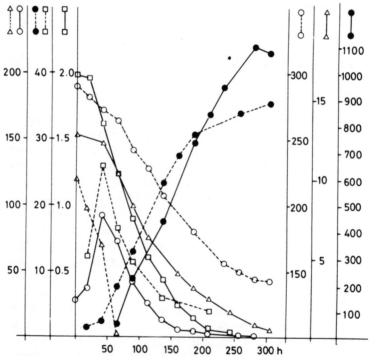

Figure 4.6 The ergotamine fermentation with strain 275 FI in 8001 fermenter in the sucrose–ammonium citrate sodium. Dry weight (●- - -●); free glucose (O——O); total carbohydrate (O- - -O); citric acid (△——△); NH$_3$ (□——□), mg/l; Pi (△- - -△), μg/ml; QO$_2$ (□- - -□), μl O$_2$/mg dry weight hr^{-1}; LAD (●——●), μg/g whole culture. Reproduced by permission of the National Research Council of Canada from the *Canadian Journal of Microbiology*, Volume 16, 1970, pp. 923–931.

Figure 4.6 shows the course of the ergotamine fermentation with strain 275 FI in a 800 l fermenter on a standard sucrose–ammonium citrate medium (Arcamone *et al.*, 1970*a*). Three phases of growth are observed. The first ends at about 70 hours, when inorganic phosphate disappears from the medium and is characterized by a high QO_2 value, by exponential growth, and by active ammonium nitrogen uptake. The second linear growth phase (70–180 hours) corresponds to a transition phase between the time of exhaustion of phosphate and that of nitrogen. In the typical ergotamine fermentation, free glucose originating from sucrose in the early stage of growth is exhausted before ammonium nitrogen but other carbon sources and citric acid are still available. The third phase (180–280 hours) appears to be a kind of 'maintenance' phase during which the dry weight increases at a slower rate with concomitant moderate uptake of carbohydrate. Approximately one-half of total lysergic acid derivatives are synthesized during the third phase.

The changes observed in the chemical composition of mycelium between 64 and 112 hours are consistent with the transition of the culture from a state of high metabolic and proliferative activity to one of reduced cellular synthesis (the transition phase) supported wholly by use of the internal reserve of phosphate.

The ergotamine fermentation is clearly phosphorus-limited fermentation. The use of nitrogen for protein synthesis during the second and third phases of growth is limited and simple nitrogenous precursors, such as amino acids, are made available for the synthesis of lysergic acid derivatives. At higher concentrations of phosphate in the medium the second phase becomes shorter and production of derivatives is strongly reduced.

Figure 4.7 shows the morphological appearance of the organism. The inoculated mycelium, appearing as aggregates of elongated hyphae (*a*) shows thickening and swelling during the first phase of growth (*b*), this process becoming more evident during the third phase (*c*). In the late stages of the fermentation, the whole mycelium consists of short and thick vacuolated elements, the vacuoles being filled with fat (*d*).

b. Mechanism of sucrose utilization

The metabolism of sucrose in the ergotamine fermentation is of particular interest. Utilization of sucrose is a fundamental metabolic feature of *C. purpurea* in both saprophytic and parasitic conditions. Experiments in which ergot-infected rye has fixed $^{14}CO_2$ have shown that the principal sugar supplied by the host to the fungus is sucrose (Basset *et al.*, 1972). This sugar is also preferred in fermentations as it gives the highest alkaloid yield. Moreover, it has been shown that the honeydew produced under saprophytic conditions has the same sugar composition as that produced under parasitic conditions (Grein, 1967).

The first step of sucrose metabolism in ergotamine fermentation is the liberation of glucose produced by a β-fructofuranosidase which transfers the

60

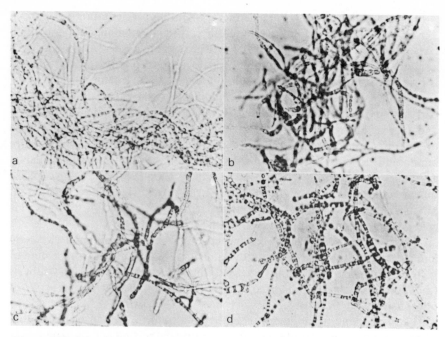

Figure 4.7 Morphological appearance of mycelium of *C. purpurea* strain 275 FI grown in submerged culture in stirred fermenters: (*a*) inoculum; (*b*) 40 hours old; (*c*) 112 hours old; (*d*) 184 hours old (magnification × 360)

fructose component of sucrose to form fructo-oligosaccharides as shown by the chemical structure of the products. In fact, three reducing oligosaccharides and D-fructose accumulate in the medium when *C. purpurea* strain 275 is grown aerobically on a sucrose–ammonium citrate medium in shake flasks or in stirred fermenters (Arcamone *et al.*, 1970*b*). Isolation of these compounds by preparative chromatography and crystallization has yielded fructose and three oligosaccharides whose structures are presented in Figure 4.8.

In all three oligosaccharides, D-glucose is the reducing unit as shown by the titration of the aldose using the sodium hypoiodite method and by the formation of D-fructose and D-glucitol upon acid hydrolysis of the products of borohydride reduction. The oligosaccharides are also completely hydrolysed by yeast invertase, which is a typical β-D-fructofuranosidase, thus establishing that the fructose units are present as β-D-fructofuranosyl groups. Complete knowledge of the structures of the oligosaccharides has been obtained by periodate oxidation studies performed on the alcohols obtained following borohydride reduction, by full methylation of the oligosaccharides followed by identification of the methylated compounds after acid hydrolysis, and on the basis of the results of partial enzymic hydrolysis (Arcamone *et al.*, 1970*a*). Compound XV is a known product of the action of levansucrase on sucrose and of yeast invertase on a mixture of sucrose and D-glucose. Compounds XVI and XVII are novel oligosaccharides. Nuclear magnetic resonance studies on the

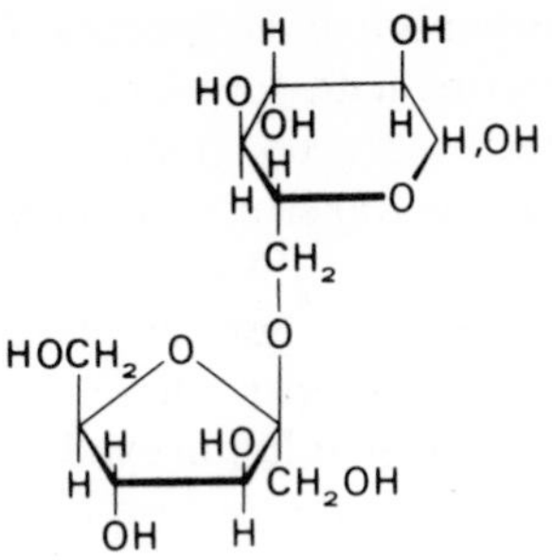

(XV)

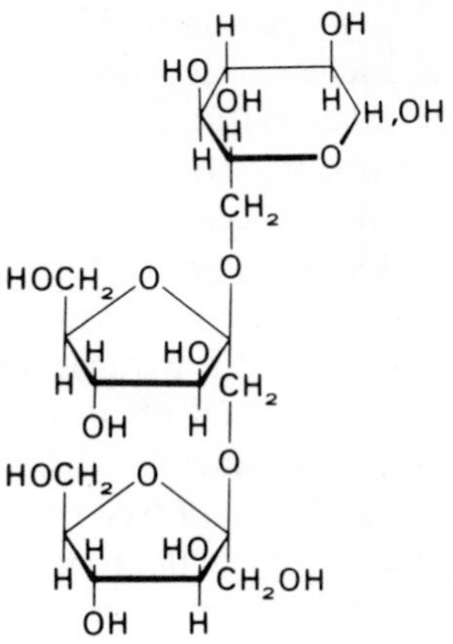

(XVI)

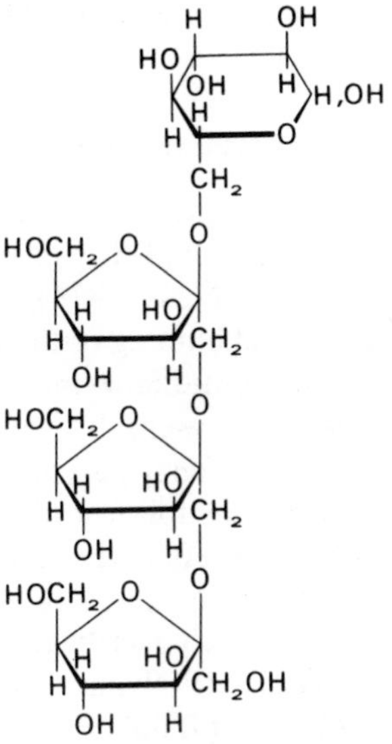

(XVII)

Figure 4.8 The oligosaccharides produced by the action of *β*-D-fructofuranosidase on sucrose in cultures of *C. purpurea* strain 275 FI: 6-*O*-*β*-D-fructofuranosyl-D-glucose (XV); *O*-*β*-D-fructofuranosyl-(2→1)-*O*-*β*-D-fructofuranosyl-(2→6)-D-glucose (XVI); and *O*-*β*-D-fructofuranosyl-(2→1)-*O*-*β*-D-fructofuranosyl-(2→1)-*O*-*β*-D-fructofuranosyl-(2→6)-Dglucose (XVII)

peracetylated oligosaccharides (Arcamone *et al.*, 1970*a*), as well as mass spectrometric analysis (Kamerling *et al.*, 1971), are in full agreement with the assigned structures.

The above-mentioned studies also allow a differentiation of *C. purpurea* *β*-D-fructofuranosidase from other mould and yeast invertases as the action of these enzymes is primarily hydrolytic. In a subsequent study (Dickerson, 1972), the enzyme was recognized as being mainly associated with the cells of

C. purpurea strain 117/2 and being inducible. The mechanism of the utilization of sucrose was also investigated and the early intermediate formation of 6^G-fructosylsucrose, 1^F-fructosylsucrose, 6^G-(1^F-fructosylfructosyl)-sucrose, sucrose itself behaving as the primary acceptor in the transfructosylation reaction, was shown.

Oligosaccharides formation plays an important role in the fermentation process as well as in the parasitic growth of the fungus on its host, where the young parasitic tissue is surrounded by a concentrated sucrose solution exuded by the infected plant. Formation of oligosaccharides allows the release of a consistent amount of free glucose, while at the same time preventing the accumulation of free fructose which, when present in high amounts near free glucose, has an unfavourable effect on growth. The use of the oligosaccharides as a glucose source in the late stage of the fermentation allows the extension of the transition phase of growth, which is the most active stage for the production of lysergic acid derivatives.

c. Biosynthetic relationships between the different lysergic acid derivatives

Although the whole reaction sequence leading to the formation of the lysergic acid moiety of the ergot alkaloids is well established, the same is not true for the side-chain biosynthesis (Floss, 1976). In the peptide alkaloids, it is currently believed that a sequential binding of the constituent amino acids (in activated form) takes place onto a multienzyme complex starting from an L-prolyl–enzyme up to, for instance, lysergyl-L-valyl-L-phenylalanyl-L-prolyl–enzyme. Subsequent release of the enzyme could be concomitant with the formation of the lactam ring, while the following hydroxylation and cyclization should yield the final alkaloid (for recent reviews, see also Thomas and Basset, 1973; Gröger, 1975). The origin of the side chain of lysergic acid α-hydroxyethylamide, a problem which has been an object of study in the author's laboratory (Minghetti *et al.*, 1969) and at Imperial College (Castagnoli *et al.*, 1970; Basset *et al.*, 1973), is still unknown.

d. Dihydroergosine fermentation

A further achievement is represented by the work carried out at Imperial College concerning the identification of dihydroergosine as the main alkaloid produced by *Sphacelia sorghi* (Mantle and Tonolo, 1968; Mantle 1968*b*) and its production in stationary surface culture of the same micro-organism (Mantle, 1973). *S. sorghi* as studied by Mantle was derived from a sexually defective—the sclerotia were unable to germinate to a sexual stage—Nigerian strain of this organism. Yields exceeding 0·5 mg/ml have been described.

e. Clavine alkaloids fermentation

The importance of agroclavine, which prevents implantation in mice when administered orally during the first two to three days of pregnancy (Mantle,

1969*a*) and which inhibits lactation when administered to mice during late pregnancy (Mantle, 1968*b*), prompted the study of a large-scale production of clavine alkaloids by *C. fusiformis*. Yields of alkaloids (mainly agroclavine) of up to 4 mg/ml within six days were obtained in 4000 l stirred fermenters using a sucrose–ammonium succinate–inorganic salts medium (Banks *et al.*, 1974). Improved yields (6 mg/ml) were obtained by using a half-replacement multi-stage fermentation process.

A characteristic feature of alkaloid-producing strains of both *C. paspali* and *C. purpurea* is their instability, whereby they revert to non-producing forms after only a few subcultures (Kobel, 1969; Mantle, 1969*b*). In constrast, the clavine alkaloid-producing strains of *C. fusiformis* are usually more stable in submerged culture (Banks *et al.*, 1974). In the large-scale production process, alkaloid synthesis closely follows growth, as expressed by dry weight accumulation and, although the growth form of the cells resembles those of naturally occurring sclerotia *C. fusiformis*, alkaloid synthesis by this species appears not as closely related to sclerotial cells as had been demonstrated in *C. purpurea* (Mantle and Tonolo, 1968, Mantle, 1969*c*). Clavine alkaloids have also been obtained by chemical synthesis from lysergic acid (Bernardi *et al.*, 1974).

NEW SEMISYNTHETIC ERGOLINE DERIVATIVES

The chemical development of natural lysergic acid derivatives, aimed at the exploitation of the wide potential therapeutic value of this class of compounds, was directly connected with the above-mentioned biochemical and micro-biological studies from the very beginning of this line of research. In fact, the easy availability of the well-known lysergic acid derivatives, some of which, however, are of significant therapeutic and commercial value, does not repre-sent *per se* an advance in the field of medicine. The main objective of the author's work has been instead the exploitation of the limitless amount of material obtainable by fermentation for the synthesis and pharmacological evaluation of new derivatives in the search for more selective and useful drugs for the treatment of human diseases. The ready availability of lysergic acid led to a consideration, in the first instance, of the chemical modification of this moiety. This approach was also based on the hypothesis, which proved largely correct, that the peptide moiety of the more complex ergot alkaloids was not essential for the typical pharmacological activity of these substances.

a. New modifications of the C8 side chain

The presence of the carboxyl group at C8 in lysergic acid allowed the development of a chemical approach in which two important classical reactions of the ergoline derivatives, namely the reduction of the 9–10 double bond and the N-methylation at position 1, were considered together with an extensive modification at the C8 side chain. In Figure 4.9, the general structure of the new derivatives, all possessing the *trans* configuration at C5 and C10, is shown.

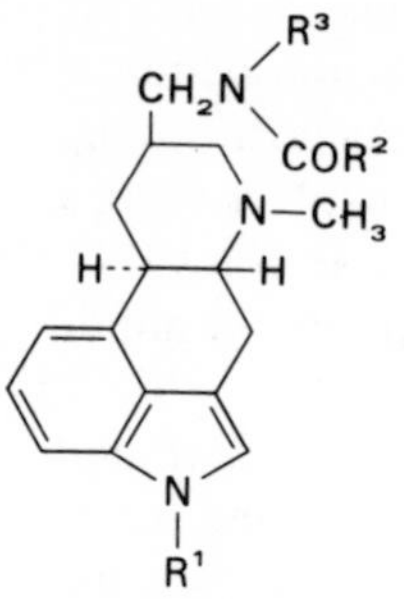

Figure 4.9 Ergoline derivatives modified at C8 side chain (XVIII–XXIII, R^1 = H, CH_3) and at the C10 configuration (XXIV, XXV)

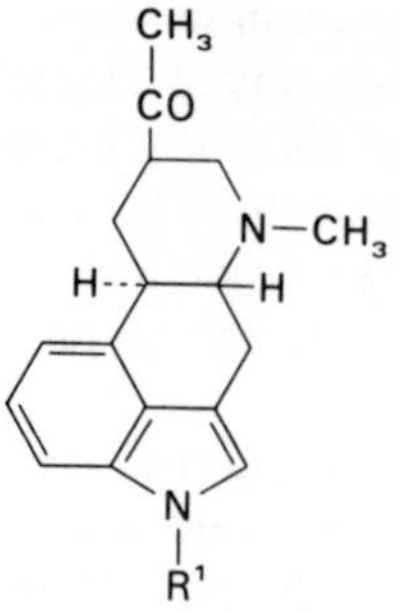

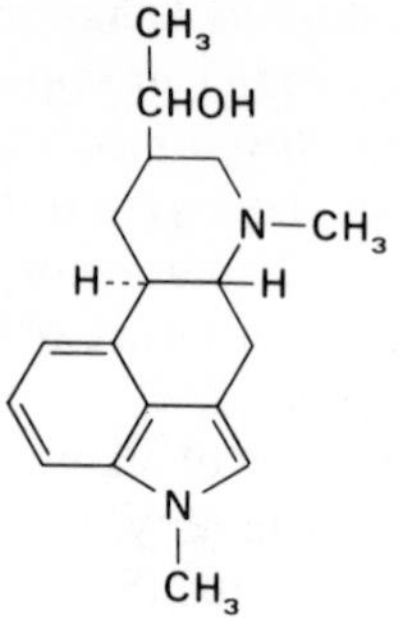

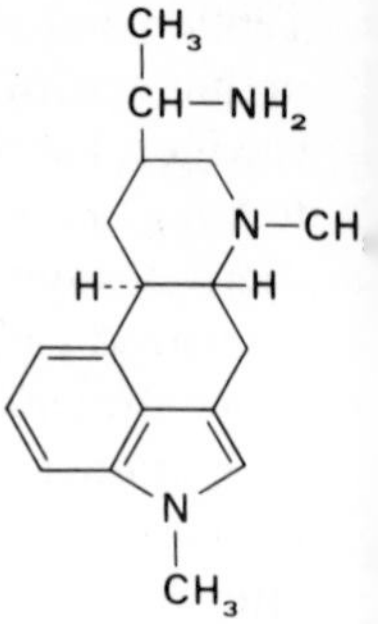

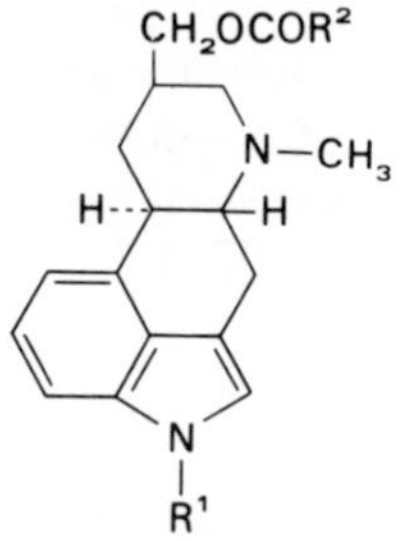

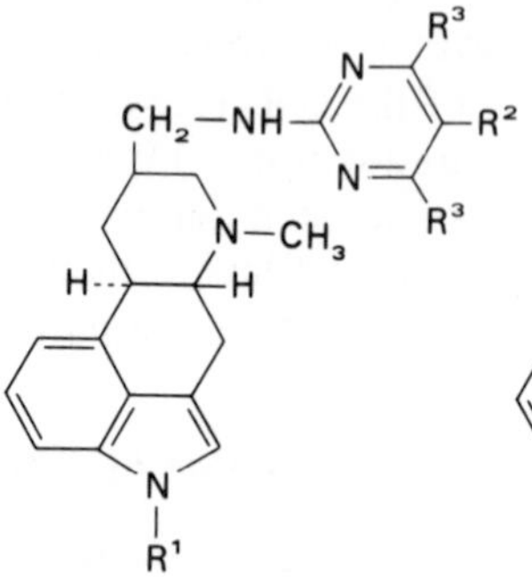

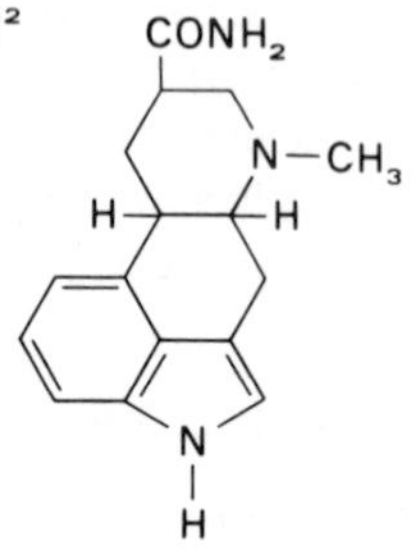

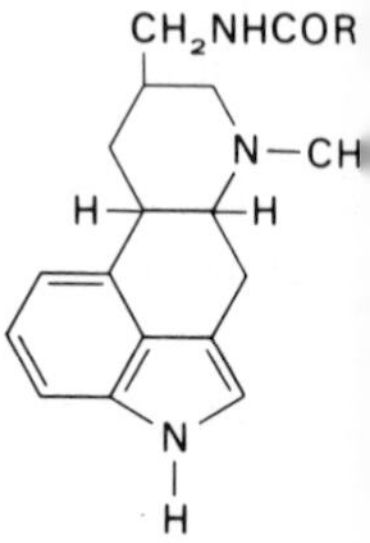

It should be recalled that the saturation of the 9–10 double bond leads, in the field of the peptide ergot alkaloids, to a reduction of uterotonic activity while the adrenolytic activity is strongly enhanced. Alkylation of the indole nitrogen is also known to improve the antiserotonin activity, in respect to the non-alkylated derivative (Hofmann, 1964).

The derivatives of structure XVIII (Figure 4.9) obtained starting from the known dihydrolysergamides, in which R^1 = H, display considerable oxytocic activity, which contradicts the former belief that reduction of the 9–10 double bond in the lysergic acid derivatives abolished this type of pharmacological effect. This effect is however absent, as expected, in the 1-methylated compounds among which the urethanes, such as metergoline (Lyserdol®:, R^1 = CH_3, R^2 = OCH_2Ph, R^3 = H), displays noticeable antiserotonin activity (Bernardi et al., 1964b).

A Grignard reaction on dihydrolysergamide derivatives to give XIX opened the way to epimeric 8β-(α-hydroxyethyl)-10α-ergoline (XX) and 8β-(α-aminoethyl)-10α-ergoline (XXI), and their derivatives (Bernardi et al., 1964a, Bernardi and Bosisio, 1964). Among the compounds of general structure XXII, the benzoic and nicotinic esters display a consistent α-adrenolytic activity, higher than that exhibited by the corresponding acylated dihydrolyser-gamines (Bernardi and Goffredo, 1966). The pyrimidine derivatives of general structure XXIII were also prepared and found to behave as α-adrenolytic agents provided that the 1-methyl group was present (Arcari *et al.*, 1972*b*).

b. *Cis* derivatives of 9,10-dihydroergolines

Compounds XVIII–XXIII belong to the 5,10-*trans*-dihydrolysergic acid series, which implies the following configurations: 5β, 8β, 10α. The epimeric series 5β, 8β, 10β corresponding to the 5,10-*cis*-dihydrolysergic acid series appeared to be practically unexplored. The establishment of a reaction of preparative value for the conversion of dihydroisolysergamide (*cis*) to di-hydrolysergamide (*cis*) XXIV (Figure 4.9) affords a suitable entry into the new series (Bernardi and Goffredo, 1964). Among the compounds belonging to this series, however, none display interesting pharmacological activity. The activities of derivatives of general structure XXV appear to be distinctly lower than those displayed by the corresponding derivatives in the 10α series (Bernardi *et al.*, 1964*c*).

c. Modification of the indole moiety

The substitution at C2 and C3 of the indole ring was already known to be of importance following the work of the Sandoz group who prepared the 2-halo derivatives of simple lysergic acid derivatives, as well as of the peptide alkaloids, and of the corresponding dihydro derivatives, the 2,3-dihydro compounds, and the 2-oxo and 2-oxo-3-hydroxy derivatives of some phar-macologically important representatives of these series (Hofmann, 1964).

In Figure 4.10, chemical modifications concerning the indole ring of the ergoline system performed in the author's laboratory are reported. Position 2 of ergoline is highly susceptibile to electrophilic reagents, and therefore nitration and aminomethylation affords new substituted derivatives bearing, respectively, a nitro group or an aminomethyl group α to the indole nitrogen. Catalytic reduction yields 2-amino derivatives in the first case and 2-methyl derivatives in the second one (Franceschi *et al.*, 1965; Bernardi and Temperilli, 1972). The biological activity of these analogues was however found to be remarkably lower than that of the corresponding unsubstituted compounds. Bromination of ergoline derivatives gave 2,13-dibromo compounds which could be converted upon debromination to 13-bromoergolines. This substitu-tion allows the full retaining of the typical antiserotonin and adrenolytic properties of the parent ergolines (Arcari *et al.*, 1974).

The catalytic reduction at C2,3 in the presence of fluoboric acid of 1,6-dimethyl-8β-aminomethyl-10α-ergoline (XXX, Figure 4.11) followed by acy-lation affords a new series of highly active antiserotonin agents (Arcamone and Franceschi, 1971). The 2,3-dihydro compounds have been used also as inter-mediates for the synthesis of 12-hydroxyergolines (Figure 4.11). The latter

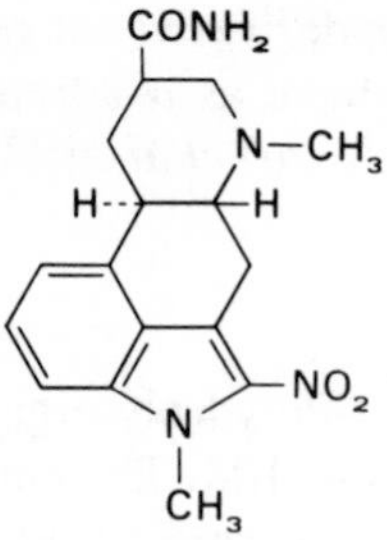

Figure 4.10 Representative ergoline derivatives showing substitution of the indole ring: 1-methyl-2-nitro-9,10-dihydrolysergamide (XXVI); diethylamide of 2-amino-9,10-dihydrolysergic acid (XXVII); 1,2-dimethyl-9,10-dihydrolysergamide (XXVIII); 13-bromo-1,6-dimethyl-8β-hydroxymethyl-10α-ergoline (XXIX)

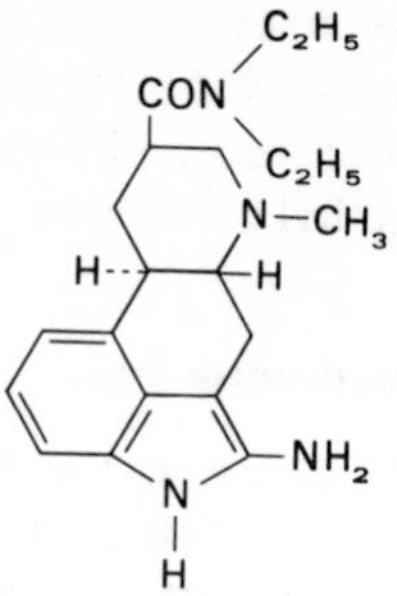

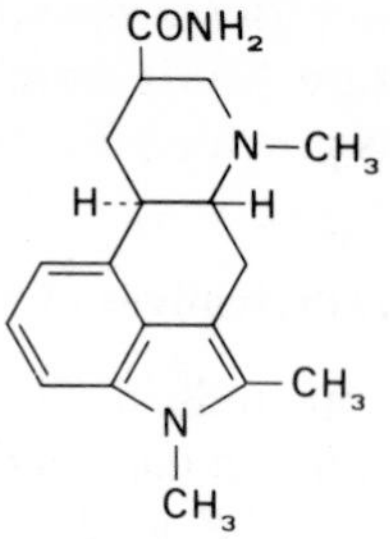

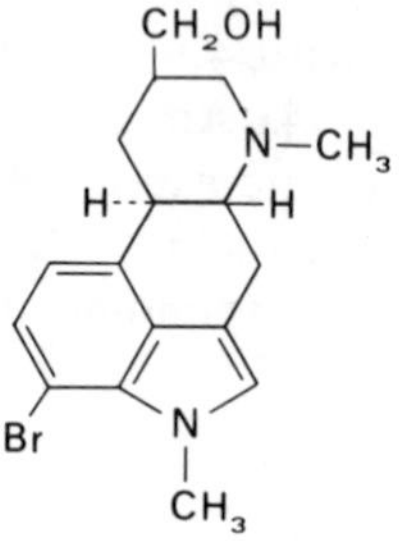

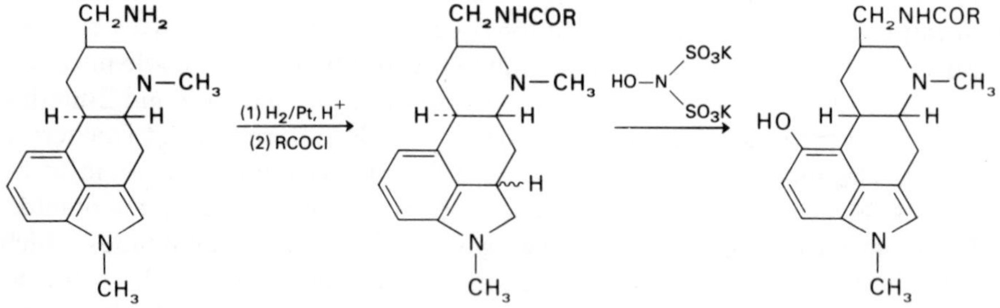

R = CH₃, CH₂CH₂ — (cyclopentyl), Ph, OCH₂PH, — (pyridyl)

Figure 4.11 Synthesis of 12-hydroxyergoline derivatives

compounds were of interest for two reasons. Firstly, the presence of a hydroxyl at C12 was of interest in the search for active anti-serotonin agents because of the obvious similarity of this substitution with that of 5-hydroxytryptamine. Secondly, the hydroxylation at C12 has been suggested as a reaction involved in the metabolism of lysergic acid derivatives in the mammals (Slaytor *et al.*, 1962). It does actually appear that compounds of structure XXXII are endowed with an extraordinarily high antiserotonin activity both *in vitro* and *in vivo* (Arcamone *et al.*, 1972*a*).

d. Substitutions in the quinuclidine portion of the ergoline system

Lysergic acid derivatives add, in the presence of light and in acid solution, a molecule of water across the 9–10 double bond to give the 10-hydroxy derivatives, the so-called lumi derivatives (Hofmann, 1964; Bernardi *et al.*, 1965).

The 10-methoxy derivatives can be obtained from the corresponding 10-hydroxy compounds upon treatment with methanol containing sulphuric acid or by direct irradiation in acid methanolic solution of the corresponding ergolenes (Barbieri *et al.*, 1969; Arcamone *et al.*, 1971*a*). Owing to the noticeable adrenolytic activity of 1-methyldihydrolysergol benzoate and nicotinate the corresponding 10α-methoxy esters were investigated (Figure 4.12). Nicotinate is remarkably active, whereas the picolinate, the isonicotinate, and the 3-pyridylacetate are practically devoid of adrenolytic activity. In the same study (Arcari *et al.*, 1972*a*), a number of other esters was prepared, and it was eventually found that a particularly high α-adrenolytic activity is associated with those substituted nicotinate esters bearing an electron-withdrawing group at position 5. The 5-bromonicotinic acid ester was chosen for further testing on the basis of its low toxicity, for example in rats the LD_{50} is 72 mg/kg after intravenous administration, and for the absence of any emetic effects in dogs. This compound is remarkable for its vasodilating and α-adrenergic blocking activity. From a study of 25 5-bromonicotinic acid esters related to XXXIII (Figure 4.12) it was concluded that only limited modifications of the structure and stereochemistry of nicergoline can be introduced without any great loss of activity (Bernardi and Bosisio, 1974; Bernardi *et al.*, 1975). It should be noted, however, that nicergoline displays an activity 70 times higher than ergotamine *in vitro*, and that 12 of these analogues are more active than ergotamine; α-receptor-blockade was determined against adrenaline using isolated guinea-pig seminal vesicle.

Compound XXXIV is an example of the 9,10-dihydro-10α-methoxy derivatives of the peptide ergot alkaloids. This compound, as well as its analogue lacking the N1 methyl group and those derived from other peptide alkaloids, was shown to possess the 10α-configuration on the basis of their conversion to the corresponding known 10α-methoxydihydrolysergamides. Compound XXXIV, as well as the corresponding analogue derived from ergocryptine, displays enhanced adrenolytic activity when compared with the natural

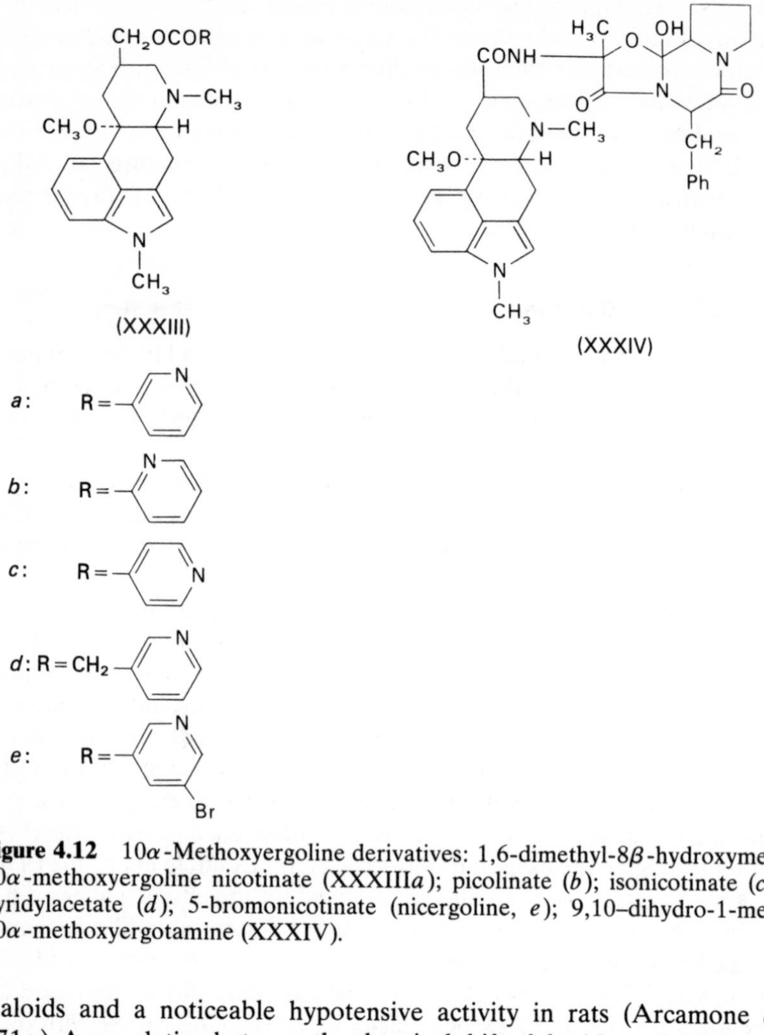

Figure 4.12 10α-Methoxyergoline derivatives: 1,6-dimethyl-8β-hydroxymethyl-10α-methoxyergoline nicotinate (XXXIIIa); picolinate (b); isonicotinate (c); 3-pyridylacetate (d); 5-bromonicotinate (nicergoline, e); 9,10–dihydro-1-methyl-10α-methoxyergotamine (XXXIV).

alkaloids and a noticeable hypotensive activity in rats (Arcamone *et al.*, 1971a). A correlation between the chemical shift of the 10-methoxy group and the stereochemistry of 10-methoxy-dihydrolysergic acid esters and amides has been proposed and interpreted in terms of the shielding effect of the indole system (Vigevani and Gandini, 1971).

NEW DRUGS AND DEVELOPMENTS

a. Nicergoline

It is well-known that pharmacological actions of ergot alkaloids are varied and complex. The ergot alkaloids have been classified as adrenolytic agents and attention has been focused on this property in the past, because both the natural and the hydrogenated peptide alkaloids produce a persistent α-adrenergic blockade. However, the presence of independent important pharmacological effects—mainly a direct stimulation of smooth muscle, and a complex excitatory and depressant action on the central nervous system—prevents the administration of doses which could produce more than minimal blockade in man (Goodman and Gilman, 1975). All members of the ergotoxine complex are potent α-adrenergic blockers and hydrogenation of ergotoxine to dihydroergotoxine (Hydergine®) increases the potency several fold. Dihydroergotoxine is a less effective smooth muscle stimulant than is dihydroergotamine, but the persistence of the side effects is demonstrable. Even the peripheral vasodilation and the fall in arterial blood pressure induced by dihydroergotoxine are due predominantly to central depression of vasomotor nerve activity, an action which is prominent with doses even lower than those required to produce significant α-adrenergic blockade (Nickerson and Hollenberg, 1967). Use of dihydroergotoxine as a peripheral vasodilator and antihypertensive agent has never been widespread in English-speaking countries, but it has recently received attention for the treatment of central and emotional disorders apparently related to inadequacy of cerebral blood flow in the aged. The efficacy of the drug in this application is, however, not recognized unanimously (Goodman and Gilman, 1975).

Good α-adrenolytic activity was demonstrated in the screening of semisynthetic derivatives such as 1-methyl-9,10-dihydrolysergol nicotinate and the corresponding 10α-methoxy derivative. Nicergoline (Sermion®), 1-methyl-10α-methoxy-9,10-dihydrolysergol-5-bromonicotinate, displayed an α-receptor block in the absence of vascular smooth muscle stimulation and of vomiting (Arcari et al., 1968). The same compound and dihydroergocryptine were found to inhibit selectively cardiac necrosis induced in rats by the α-adrenoceptor agent phenylephrine (Bellini and Glaesser, 1972). Nicergoline was also found to antagonize the modifications of biochemical parameters in rat heart induced by catecholamines, such as the impairment of oxidative phosphorylation (Moretti and Arcari, 1972), the accumulation of calcium, and the fall in glycogen concentration (Moretti et al., 1973). A pronounced pharmacological interest was devoted to the action of nicergoline on the brain as a consequence of clinical observations indicating favourable effects of the drug on cerebral and peripheral vascular insufficiencies, in agreement with results of acute animal studies. The latter suggested an action of the drug on the metabolism of neurones on the basis of the increased rate of post-hypoxaemic recovery induced by the drug measured by electrical and biochemical parameters (Suchowsky and Pegrassi, 1972; Moretti et al., 1972, 1973; Bienmüller and Betz, 1972; Boismare, 1972; Benzi, 1975). The mechanism of this action is practically unknown and, although the peripheral α-adrenolytic effect of nicergoline could be demonstrated by the phenylephrine-induced mydriasis test in humans (Trimarchi et al., 1974), no information is available concerning the relationships, if any, of the observed action at the cerebral level and of the α-adrenergic blocking activity of the drug. In rat cerebral cortical slices,

Table 4.1 Effect of different compounds on the accumulation of [³H]cyclic AMP in rat cerebral cortical slices. Data are expressed as per cent conversion of labelled ATP + ADP into labelled cyclic AMP after 10 minutes incubation in the presence of the drug (95 per cent confidence limits)

Compound	Conversion (per cent)
None	0.25 ± 0.02
Noradrenaline (10^{-5} M)	0.79 ± 0.16
Nicergoline (10^{-3} M)	1.16 ± 0.23
Noradrenaline (10^{-5} M) + Nicergoline (10^{-3} M)	1.51 ± 0.37
Dihydroergotamine (2×10^{-4} M)	0.51 ± 0.21
Dihydroergotoxine (2×10^{-4} M)	0.77 ± 0.27

nicergoline stimulates accumulation of cyclic AMP, behaving similarly to other ergoline derivatives, such as dihydroergotoxine and dihydroergotamine (Table 4.1) (Montecucchi, 1975). Another property of nicergoline, apparently related to its α-adrenolytic activity should be mentioned. The drug is a very effective inhibitor of adrenaline-induced platelet aggregation in man and in experimental animals, a property which opens the way to its possible use in the prevention of thromboembolic disorders (Pogliani *et al.*, 1975; Der Agopian *et al.*, 1973).

For the metabolic studies, ³H-labelled, and ³H and ¹⁴C double labelled nicergoline have been prepared (Figure 4.13). Absorption of radioactivity was

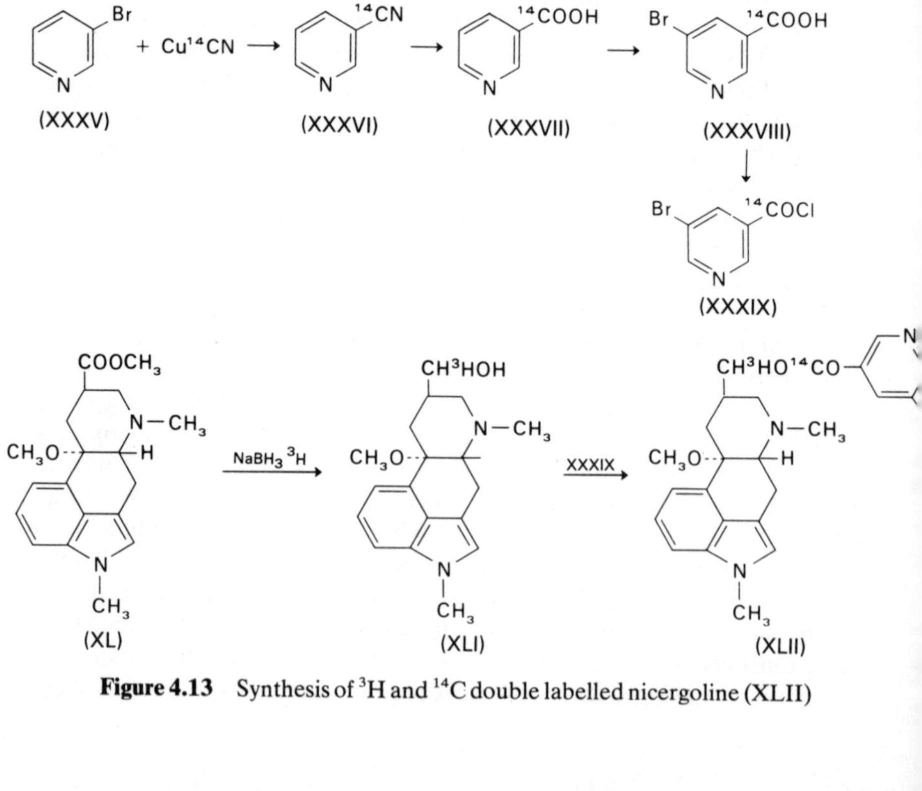

Figure 4.13 Synthesis of ³H and ¹⁴C double labelled nicergoline (XLII)

nearly complete after oral administration of {³H, ¹⁴C}nicergoline in man. Nicergoline appears to be transformed actively in all species tested by a hydrolysis of the ester function with the formation of 1,6-dimethyl-10α-methoxy-8β-hydroxymethylergoline and 5-bromonicotinic acid, and then by demethylation at position 1 of the ergoline nucleus (Figure 4.14). Glucuronic acid conjugation is also of importance in some species, particularly in the monkey (Arcamone *et al.*, 1972*b*).

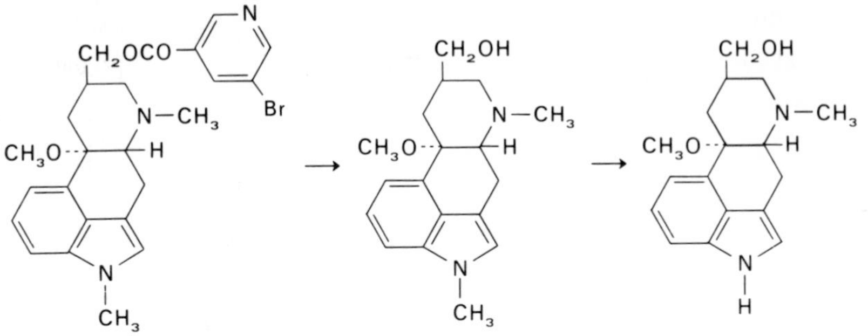

Figure 4.14 Metabolic inactivation of nicergoline in man

b. Metergoline

The drug 8β-carbobenzyloxyaminomethyl-1,6-dimethyl-10α-ergoline (metergoline, Lyserdol®), was shown to diplay a strong antagonism to serotonin *in vitro*. *In vivo*, the compound reduces local serotonin-induced oedema in the rat paw and powerfully antagonizes the serotonin-induced bronchospasm in guinea-pigs. Both effects are long lasting (Beretta *et al.*, 1965*a, b*). Metergoline was also found to be effective in the inhibition of serotonin-induced foetal death in pregnant rodents, reaching its maximal effect more slowly than methysergide but maintaining it for a much longer period (Baldratti *et al.*, 1965). Characteristics of metergoline are the powerful anti-serotonin activity, the higher selectivity of action when compared with the therapeutically useful methysergide (Deseril®), and the duration of activity and absence of emesis.

Labelled metergoline originally prepared from [9,10-³H]dihydrolysergic acid (Minghetti *et al.*, 1967) was used for the metabolic studies. Studies showed a remarkable absorption of the drug after oral administration. More recently, a higher specific radioactivity was obtained following a different synthetic scheme (Figure 4.15). Unchanged metergoline accounted for a small fraction of excreted radioactivity. Among the metabolites, 1-demethylmetergoline was isolated and the presence of 12-hydroxymetergoline, resulting from the hydroxylation of the indole nucleus, was demonstrated. The latter compound, also obtained by synthesis, displays a powerful anti-serotonin activity *in vitro* ($EC_{50} = 0·01$ pg/ml), a 100-fold more active than metergoline itself. In the experimental animal, 12-hydroxymetergoline displays a prompt effect which is

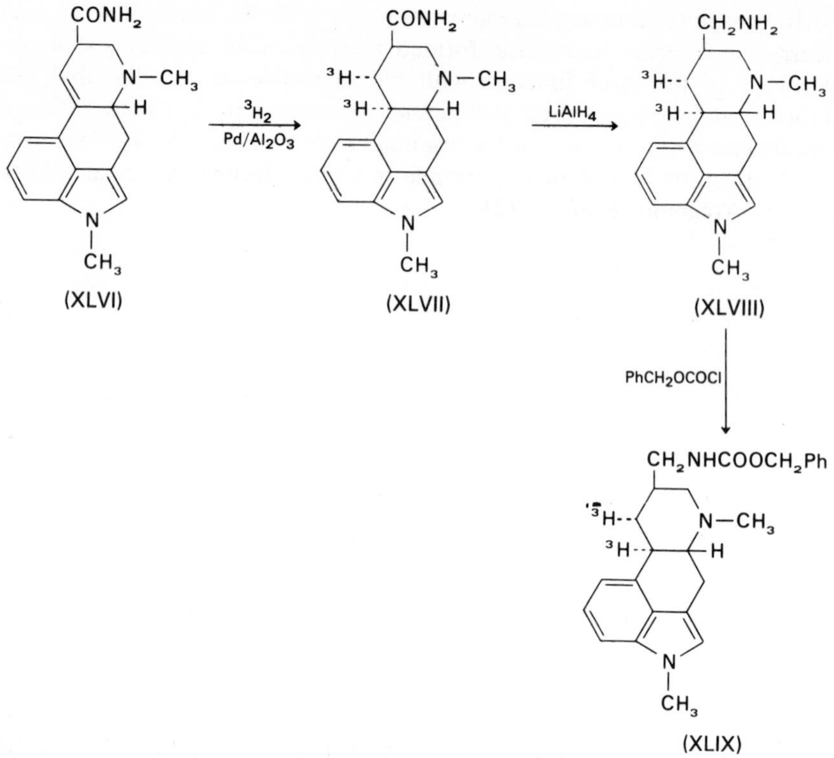

Figure 4.15 Synthesis of [³H]metergoline (XLIX)

however of short duration, probably as a consequence of a rapid glucuronidation and disposal (Arcamone *et al.*, 1971*b*).

Metergoline is by far the most potent of the serotonin antagonists studied (Clineschmidt and Lotti, 1974) and evidence has been presented suggesting that the drug may be a selective and potent blocker of at least some central post-synaptic serotonin receptors in the brain and in the spinal cord in rats (Fuxe *et al.*, 1975). The same authors have also found that the drug inhibits specific, high affinity [³H] LSD binding to homogenates of cerebral cortex. They concluded that it is possible that metergoline may be an antidote against hallucinogens, such as LSD in man, and may prove helpful in the treatment of certain types of schizophrenias.

c. New developments

The recent consideration of ergot alkaloids and their derivatives in endocrinology was initiated by the study of Shelesnyak who suggested that ergotoxine prevents implantation of the fertilized ovum in rats by suppressing prolactin secretion from the pituitary (Shelesnyak, 1958). The influence of ergot alkaloids on pituitary prolactin and prolactin-dependent processes has therefore received considerable attention (Floss *et al.*, 1973). A contribution to this field has also come from the Biochemistry Department of Imperial College with the identification of agroclavine as the toxic agent responsible for the inhibition of lactation in animals by ergot sclerotia of African origin (Mantle, 1968c). Agroclavine is, however, less effective and more toxic than 6-methyl-8-cyanomethylergoline (Mantle and Firm, 1971). These effects of ergot alkaloids are related to a dopaminergic activity, that is to a specific activation of dopamine receptors. The best known ergoline derivative displaying this action is 2-bromo-α-ergocryptine. This compound's clinical efficacy in suppressing puerperal lactation, in restoring fertility in patients with hyperprolactinaemia, in the treatment of acromegaly, and in Parkinsonism has been well established (Johnson et al., 1976). However, the side effects of bromocriptine are important and new ergoline derivatives with more selective effects are currently being screened in several laboratories. It has been recently reported (Delitala et al., 1976; Chiodini et al., 1976) that metergoline (4 mg/day), when administered to acromegalic patients, clearly reduces the levels of growth hormone and prolactin in plasma as measured by specific radioimmunoassay procedures. This observation opens the way to an extension of the therapeutic applications of the drug, and raises, among others, a question concerning the involvement of serotonin in prolactin secretion.

In the field of biosynthetic lysergic acid derivatives, the isolation of ergovaline, ergoptine, and ergonine, previously obtained by chemical synthesis and not yet found in nature (Stadlet and Stütz, 1975), from cultures of C. purpurea, has opened the way to further enlargement of the pharmacologically important family of natural peptide ergot alkaloids (Minghetti, personal communication).

As far as structure–activity relationships are concerned, interesting and rather surprising observations have been made recently in the author's laboratory. Compounds corresponding to the structural types reported in Figure 4.16 have been synthesized (Bernardi and Bosisio, 1977, Bernardi et al., 1976) and evaluated pharmacologically. Without entering into the details one cannot but be surprised to discover that compound L (Figure 4.16), which differs from

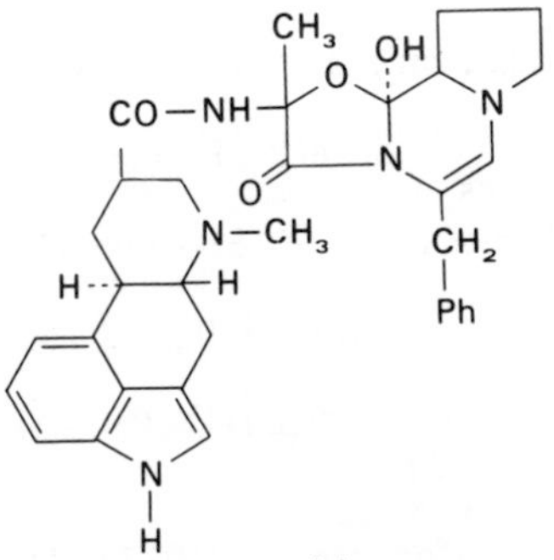

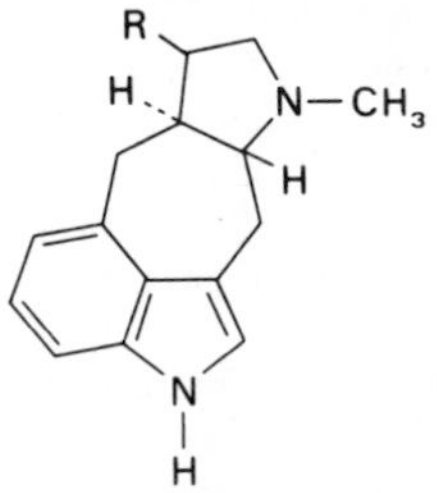

Figure 4.16 Chemical structure of 6'-deoxo-9,10-dihydroergotamine (L) and 5(10 → 9)abeo-9,10-didehydroergolines (LI)

dihydroergotamine by the absence of an oxygen atom, but which contains all the structural features hitherto associated with biological activity, displays only very slight pharmacological action. On the other hand, compounds of the general structure LI possess a high degree of adrenolytic activity which appears even greater than that exhibited by the corresponding ergolines, suggesting that further exploration of ergot-derived compounds is still required.

In summary, the possibilities opened in the field of ergot alkaloids by Sir Ernst and his group in 1960 have not only fulfilled their expectations, but have also extended them. It can be stated that in the foreseeable future new, useful ergoline compounds will be used in medicine in addition to old and new ergot-derived drugs.

ACKNOWLEDGEMENTS

I am greatly indebted to Drs. Giuliana Arcari, Luigi Bernardi, Paolo Pennella and Celestino Spalla for help in the preparation of this review. Labelled syntheses were performed by Dr. Gian Piero Vicario.

REFERENCES

Abe, A., and Yamatodami, S. (1964) *Prog. Ind. Microbiol.*, **5**, 203.

Amici, A. M., Minghetti, A., Scotti, T., Spalla, C., and Tognoli, L, (1966) *Experientia*, **22**, 415.

Amici, A. M., Minghetti, A., Scotti, T., Spalla, C., and Tognoli, L. (1967) *Appl. Microbiol.*, **15**, 597.

Amici, A. M., Minghetti, A., Scotti, T., Spalla, C., and Tognoli, L. (1969) *Appl. Microbiol.*, **18**, 464.

Arcamone, F., Barbieri, W., Cassinelli, G., and Pol, C. (1970a) *Carbohyd. Res.*, **14**, 65.

Arcamone, F., Bonino, C., Chain, E. B., Ferretti, A., Pennella, P., Tonolo, A., and Vero, L. (1960) *Nature (London)*, **187**, 238.

Arcamone, F., Camerino, B., Chain, E. B., Ferretti, A., and Redaelli, S. (1967) *Tetrahedron*, **23**, 11.

Arcamone, F., Cassinelli, G., Ferni, G., Penco, S., Pennella, P., and Pol, C. (1970b) *Can. J. Microbiol.*, **16**, 923.

Arcamone, F., Chain, E. B., Ferretti, A., Minghetti, A., Pennella, P., Tonolo, A., and Vero, L. (1961a) *Proc. Royal Soc., Series B*, **155**, 26.

Arcamone, F., Chain, E. B., Ferretti, A., and Pennella, P. (1961b) *Nature (London)*, **192**, 552.

Arcamone, F., Chain, E. B., Ferretti, A., Minghetti, A., Pennella, P., and Tonolo, A. (1962) *Biochim. Biophys. Acta*, **57**, 174.

Arcamone, F., Dorigotti, L., Glaesser, A., and Redaelli, S. (1971a) U.S. Pat. 3 585 201.

Arcamone, F., and Ferretti, A. (1966), U.S. Pat. 3 272 823.

Arcamone, F., and Franceschi, G. (1971) U.S. Pat. 3 557 118.

Arcamone, F., Franceschi, G., Glaesser, A., and Dorigotti, L. (1972a) U.S. Pat. 3 646 046.

Arcamone, F., Glaesser, A., Grafnetterova, J., Minghetti, A., and Nicolella, V. (1972b) *Biochem. Pharmacol.*, **21**, 2205.

Arcamone, F., Glaesser, A., Minghetti, A., and Nicolella, V. (1971b) Boll. Chim. Farm., 110, 704.

Arcari, G., Bernardi, L., Bosisio, G., Coda, S., Fregnan, G. B., and Glaesser, A. (1972a) Experientia, 28, 819.

Arcari, G., Bernardi, L., Foglio, M., Glaesser, A., and Temperilli, A. (1972b), Brit. Pat. 1 357 238.

Acari, G., Bernardi, L., Glaesser, A., and Patelli, B. (1974) Germ. Pat. 2 330 912.

Arcari, G., Dorigotti, L., Fregnan, G. B., and Glaesser, A. (1968) Brit. J. Pharmacol., 34, 700P.

Baldratti, G., Arcari, G., and Suchowsky, G. K. (1965) Experientia, 21, 396.

Banks, G. T., Mantle, P. G., and Szczyrbak, C. A. (1974) J. Gen. Microbiol., 82, 345.

Barbieri, W., Bernardi, L., Bosisio, G., and Temperilli, A. (1969) Tetrahedron, 25, 2401.

Basset, R. A., Chain, E. B., and Corbett, K. (1973) Biochem. J., 134, 1.

Basset, R. A., Chain, E. B., Corbet, K., Dickerson, A. G., and Mantle, P. G. (1972) Biochem. J., 127, 3P.

Bellini, O., and Glaesser, A. (1972) J. Pharm. Pharmacol., 24, 741.

Benzi, G. (1975) Jap. J. Pharmacol., 25, 251.

Beretta, C., Ferrini, R., and Glaesser, A. (1965a) Nature (London), 207, 421.

Beretta, C., Glaesser, A., Nobili, M. B., and Silvestri, R. (1965b) J. Pharm. Pharmacol., 17, 423.

Bernardi, L., and Bosisio, G. (1964) Gazz. Chim. Ital., 94, 969.

Bernardi, L., and Bosisio, G. (1974) Chem. Comm., 690.

Bernardi, L., and Bosisio, G. (1977) Paper submitted to Experientia.

Bernardi, L., Bosisio, G., and Camerino, B. (1964a) Gazz. Chim. Ital., 94, 961.

Bernardi, L., Bosisio, G., Elli, C., Patelli, B., Temperilli, A., Arcari, G., and Glaesser, A. (1975) Il Farmaco, Ed. Sci., 30, 789.

Bernardi, L. Bosisio, G., Goffredo, O., and Patelli, B. (1965) Gazz. Chim. Ital., 95, 384.

Bernardi, L., Camerino, B., Patelli, B., and Redaelli, S. (1964b) Gazz. Chim. Ital., 94, 936.

Bernardi, L., Elli, C., and Temperilli, A. (1976) Chem. Comm., 750.

Bernardi, L., Gandini, E., and Temperilli, A. (1974) Tetrahedron, 30, 3447.

Bernardi, L., and Goffredo, O. (1964) Gazz. Chim. Ital., 94, 947.

Bernardi, L., and Goffredo, O. (1966) U.S. Pat. 3 236 852.

Bernardi, L., Goffredo, O., and Patelli, B. (1964c) Gazz. Chim. Ital., 94, 955.

Bernardi, L., and Temperilli, A. (1972) Chim. Ind. (Milan), 54, 998.

Bienmüller, H., and Betz, E. (1972) Arzneim. Forsch., 22, 1367.

Boismare, F. (1972), Atti Acc. Med. Lombarda, 27, 20.

Castagnoli, N. Jr., Corbett, K., Chain, E. B., and Thomas, R. (1970) Biochem. J., 117, 451.

Cerletti, A. (1959) in Neuropsycopharmacology (Pradley P. P., Deniker, D., and Radonco T. C., eds.), Elsevier Publ. Co., Amsterdam, p. 117.

Chiodini, P. G., Liuzzi, A., Müller, E. E., Botella, L., Cremascoli, G., Oppizzi, G., Verde, G., and Silvestrini, F. (1976) J. Clin. Endocrin. Metab., 43, 356.

Clineschimidt, B. V., and Lotti, V. J. (1974) Brit. J. Pharmacol., 50, 311.

Delitala, G., Masala, A., Alagna, S., Devilla, L., and Lotti, G. (1976) J. Clin. Endocrin. Metab., 43, 1382.

Der Agopian, P., Rosa, A., Gautier, J. C., and Lhermitte, F. (1973) La Nouvelle Presse Med., 2, 2521.

Dickerson, A. G. (1972) Biochem. J., 129, 263.

Floss, H. G. (1976) Tetrahedon, 32, 873.

Floss, H. G., Cassady, J. M., and Robbers, J. E. (1973) J. Pharm. Sci., 62, 699.

Floss, H. G., Guenther, H., Groeger, D., and Erge, D. (1969) Archiv. Biochem. Biophys., 131, 319.

76

Flose, H. G., Robbers, J. E., and Heilstein, P. F. (1974) *Recent Adv. Phytochem.*, **8**, 141.

Franceschi, G., Mondelli, R., Redaelli, S., and Arcamone, F. (1965) *Chim. Ind. (Milan)*, **47**, 1334.

Fuxe, K., Agnati, L., and Everitt, B. (1975) *Interdisciplinary Workshop on Schizophrenia, Capri, Sept. 1975; Neuroscience Letters*, **1**, 283.

Glaesser, A. (1961) *Nature (London)*, **189**, 313.

Goodman, L. S., and Gilman, A. (1975) *The Pharmacological Basis of Therapeutics*, 5th Ed., The Macmillan Co., New York.

Grein, A. (1967) *Giorn. Microbiol.*, **15**, 217.

Gröger, D. (1975) *Planta Medica*, **28**, 37.

Gröger, D., Erge, D., and Floss, H. G. (1965) *Z. NaturForsch.*, **20**, 856.

Hofmann, A. (1964) *Die mutterkorn Alkaloide*, Ferdinand Enke Verlag, Stuttgart.

Johnson, A. M., Loew, D. M., and Vigouret, J. M. (1976) *Brit. J. Pharmacol.*, **56**, 59.

Kamerling, J. P., Uliegenthart, J. F. G., Vink, J., and de Ridder, J. J. (1971) *Tetrahedron Letters*, **(1971)**, 2367.

Kelleher, W. J. (1968) *Adv. Appl. Microbiol.*, **11**, 211.

Kobel, H. (1969) *Pathologia Microbiologia*, **34**, 149.

Mantle, P. G. (1968a) *Ann. Appl. Biol.*, **62**, 443.

Mantle, P. G. (1968b) *Trans. Brit. Mycol. Soc.*, **51**, 499.

Mantle, P. G. (1968c) *Proc. Roy. Soc., Series B.*, **170**, 423.

Mantle, P. G. (1969a) *J. Reprod. Fert.*, **18**, 81.

Mantle, P. G. (1969b) *Trans. Brit. Mycol. Soc.*, **52**, 381.

Mantle, P. G. (1969c) *Ann. Appl. Biol.*, **63**, 425.

Mantle, P. G. (1973) *J. Gen. Microbiol.*, **75**, 275.

Mantle, P. G., and Firm, C. A. (1971) *J. Reprod. Fert.*, **24**, 441.

Mantle, P. G., and Tonolo, A. (1968) *Trans. Brit. Mycol. Soc.*, **51**, 499.

Mantle, P. G., and Waight, E. S. (1968) *Nature (London)*, **218**, 581.

Minghetti, A., and Arcamone, F. (1969) *Experientia*, **25**, 926.

Minghetti, A., Arcamone, F., Nicolella, V., Dubini, M., and Vicario, G. P. (1967) *J. Lab. Comp.*, **3** (Suppl. 2) 491.

Montecucchi, P. (1975) *Il Farmaco, Ed. Prat.*, **31**, 10.

Moretti, A., and Arcari, G: (1972) *Il Farmaco, Ed. Sci.*, **27**, 800.

Moretti, A., Arcari, G., Laterza, L., and Suchowsky, G. K. (1973) *Il Farmaco, Ed. Sci.*, **28**, 3.

Moretti, A., Pegrassi, L., and Suchowsky, G. K. (1972) *Atti Acc. Med. Lombarda*, **27**, 36.

Nickerson, H., and Hollenberg, N. N. (1967) in *Physiological Pharmacology*, Vol. 4 (Root, W. S., and Hofman, F. G., eds.), Academic Press, New York and London, 243.

Pogliani, E., Della Volpe, A., Ferrari, R., Recalcati, P., and Praga, C. (1975) *Il Farmaco, Ed. Prat.*, **30**, 630.

Shelesnyak, M. C. (1958) *Acta Endocrinologica*, **27**, 99.

Slaytor, M. B., and Wright, S. E. (1962) *J. Med. Pharm. Chem.*, **5**, 483.

Spalla, C. (1973) *Genetics of Industrial Microorganisms* (Vanek, Z., Hostalek, Z., and Cudlin, J., eds.), Academia Prague, 393.

Spalla, C., Amici, A. M., Scotti, T., and Tognoli, L. (1969) in *Fermentation Advances*, Academic Press, New York, 611.

Stadler, P. A., and Stütz, P. (1975) in *The Alkaloids* (Manske, R. H. F., ed.), Academic Press, New York and London, 1.

Suchowsky, G. K., and Pegrassi, L. (1972) *Atti Acc. Med. Lombarda*, **27**, 30.

Thomas, R., and Basset, R. A. (1973) *Progress in Phytochemistry*, **3**, 47.

Tonolo, A. (1959) *Sel. Sci. Pap. Ist. Super. Sanità, Rome*, **2**, 386.

Tonolo, A. (1966) *Nature (London)*, **209**, 1134.

Trimarchi, F., Gelmi, C., and Marangoni, R. (1974) *IRCS*, **2**, 1640.

Tyler, V. E., Jr., Mothes, K., and Gröger, D. (1964) *Tetrahedron Letters*, **1964**, 593.
Vicario, G. P., Dubini, M., Minghetti, A., and Arcamone, F. (1967) *J. Label. Compd.*, **3** (Suppl. 2), 492.
Vigevani, A., and Gandini, E. (1971) *Chim. Ind.* (*Milan*), **53**, 841.

5

Fusicoccin Phytotoxins

K. D. Barrow and G. Mellows

Department of Biochemistry,
Imperial College of Science and Technology, London, U.K.

INTRODUCTION

The fusicoccins are a family of phytotoxic substances which are produced by the fungus *Fusicoccum amygdali* Del. This fungus is a pathogen of almond (*Prunus amygdalus* St.) and peach (*P. persica* (L.) St.) trees and causes cankers to develop around infected buds and nodes on the branches of the trees. As these cankers form, the leaves on the distal part of the infected branches wilt and die, leading in many cases to the desiccation of the branches which eventually fall away. The first signs of infection are the formation of necrotic spots on that side of the shoot having vascular connections to the site of infection. These effects have been attributed to the elaboration, by the fungus, of the fusicoccin phytotoxins at the site of infection. The phytotoxins are then thought to be transported to the more distal parts of the stem in the sap stream where wilting occurs. The disease is particularly prevelant in Southern Europe, where it was first recorded in 1905, and parts of North and South America.

The discovery of the fusicoccins dates back to the mid 1950s, when Grosclaude (1956) noted that the culture filtrate of *F. amygdali*, growing saprophytically, exhibited phytotoxic activity of a similar nature to the foliar symptoms observed under natural conditions of infection. Graniti (1962) confirmed these observations and drew the attention of research workers at the International Centre of Microbiological Chemistry, of which Sir Ernst Chain was Director, at the Istituto Superiore di Sanità, in Rome, to the existence of the phytotoxin (Graniti and de Leo, 1964). These researchers soon succeeded in isolating from laboratory cultures small amounts of the major phytotoxic principle in crystalline form, to which they ascribed the name fusicoccin (fusicoccin A). In the first publication by Ballio *et al.* (1964), sufficient evidence had been accumulated to show that the toxin was a glycoside.

At this time, Sir Ernst relinquished his position at the Institute and returned to England as Head of the Biochemistry Department at Imperial College, and he brought with him the fusicoccin problem. The outstanding question at the time was the nature of the toxin. This brought together the expertise of the Biochemistry and Chemistry Departments at Imperial College under the guidance of Sir Ernst Chain and Sir Derek Barton, respectively, in a collaborative study on the microbiological, biochemical, and chemical aspects of these substances. While the structure of fusicoccin was being unravelled at Imperial College, the Italian group, now under the direction of Professor Ballio, were also pursuing similar goals. As will be seen later the two teams arrived at the structure of fusicoccin simultaneously.

FUSICOCCIN FERMENTATION

The major phytotoxic metabolite isolated from the culture-fluid extract of *F. amygdali* is fusicoccin (Ia) (see Table 5.1 for list of isolates). Since its discovery and structural characterization, a number of structurally related cometabolites

Table 5.1 Fusicoccins isolated from cultures of *F. amygdali* Del.

Compound	Formula number
Fusicoccin	Ia
Isofusicoccin (fusicoccin B)	Ib
Monodeacetylfusicoccin (fusicoccin C)	Ic
Dideacetylfusicoccin (fusicoccin D)	Id
Allofusicoccin	Ie
Monodeacetylallofusicoccin	If
Monodeacetylisofusicoccin	Ig
12-*O*-Acetyldideacetylfusicoccin	Ih
12-*O*-Acetylfusicoccin	Ii
12-*O*-Acetylisofusicoccin	Ij
19-Deoxydideacetylfusicoccin (fusicoccin J)	XVIa
16-*O*-Demethyl-19-deoxydideacetylfusicoccin	XXVIa
16-*O*-Demethyl-19-deoxydideacetyl-3-*epi*fusicoccin	XXVIc
Fusicoccin H	VIa
3-Hydroxy-19-deoxydideacetylfusicoccin	XXVIb

have been identified. Several of these substances, which differ from fusicoccin (Ia) only in the number and/or position of the *O*-acetyl groups, are thought to be formed from fusicoccin by chemical rather than enzymic processes during the course of the fermentation, the pH of which is usually slightly alkaline (pH 7·5). The major byproducts are isofusicoccin (fusicoccin B) (Ib), monodeacetylfusicoccin (fusicoccin C) (Ic), and dideacetylfusicoccin (fusicoccin D) (Id) which are also formed together with allofusicoccin (Ie), a minor isolate, on incubation of fusicoccin in aqueous methanol at neutral or slight alkaline pH (Barrow *et al.*, 1971*a*; Barrow and Chain, 1969; Barrow *et al.*, 1968*a*; Ballio *et al.*, 1964; Ballio *et al.*, 1970*a, b*; Ballio *et al.*, 1972*a*). Other minor fermentation isolates having the same oxidation pattern as fusicoccin, which have been characterized, are monodeacetylallofusicoccin (If), monodeacetylisofusicoccin (Ig), 12-*O*-acetyldideacetylfusicoccin (Ih) (Ballio *et al.*, 1972*b*), 12-*O*-acetylfusicoccin (Ii), and 12-*O*-acetylisofusicoccin (Ij) (Ballio *et al.*, 1974). The above rearrangements in the sugar residue, which are thought to proceed intramolecularly *via* a labile *ortho*-ester, also take place in the dihydro series (reduced isopentenyl moiety) and do not appear to be influenced by modification of the aglycone (Ballio *et al.*, 1972). Kinetic studies of the rearrangement have shown that migration of the acetate residue from C2' and C3' to C4' proceeds faster than from either C4' to C3' or C3' to C2' (Ballio *et al.*, 1972*a*). Such rearrangements of acetyl groups in carbohydrates normally require stronger base. Cultures of *F. amygdali* buffered at pH 6·5 decrease the amounts of these substances and significantly increase the yield of fusicoccin (Barrow *et al.*, 1971).

The original strain of *F. amygdali* produced very low yields of total fusicoccins (approximately 20 μg/ml) when assayed by a colorimetric procedure following acid treatment. Hand-in-hand with the structural studies, yield improvement studies on the fermentation process were carried out in the pilot plant at Imperial College (Banks *et al.* unpublished results). A new strain of the fungus (designated 1–29) was obtained from the parent strain by ultraviolet mutation, using hyphal fragments, which gave yields of total fusicoccin of 200–300 μg/ml. However, this strain did not give reproducible yields due to culture degeneration and a more stable strain (1–29/29) was developed by a series of strain selections without mutations. This new strain was used in all subsequent medium formulation and biochemical studies. After an exhaustive study, the best nitrogen source for the fermentation was found to be 0·2 per

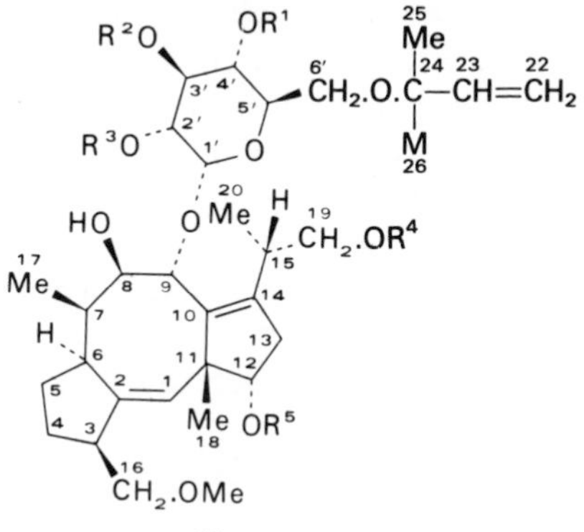

(I)

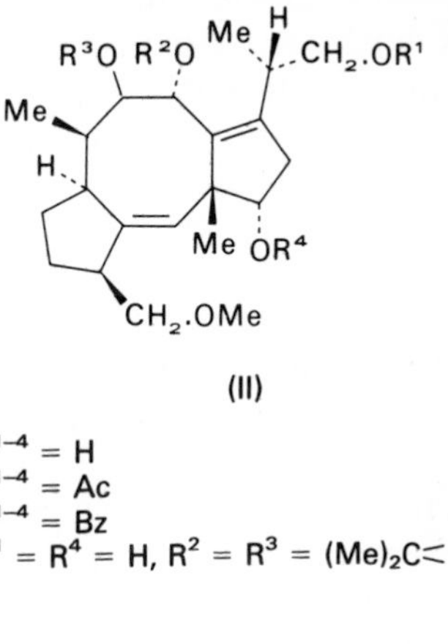

a: $R^1 = R^3 = R^5 = H, R^2 = R^4 = Ac$
b: $R^2 = R^3 = R^5 = H, R^1 = R^4 = Ac$
c: $R^1 = R^2 = R^3 = R^5 = H, R^4 = Ac$
d: $R^{1-5} = H$
e: $R^1 = R^2 = R^5 = H, R^3 = R^4 = Ac$
f: $R^1 = R^2 = R^4 = R^5 = H, R^3 = Ac$
g: $R^{2-5} = H, R^1 = Ac$
h: $R^{1-4} = H, R^5 = Ac$
i: $R^1 = R^3 = H, R^2 = R^4 = R^5 = Ac$
j: $R^2 = R^3 = H, R^1 = R^4 = R^5 = Ac$
k: $R^{1-5} = Ac$
l: $R^1 = R^3 = R^5 = Bz, R^2 = R^4 = Ac$
m: $R^{1-4} = H, R^5 = .SO_2.p.I.C_6H_4$
n: $R^1, R^{3-5} = H, R^2 = Ac$

(II)

a: $R^{1-4} = H$
b: $R^{1-4} = Ac$
c: $R^{1-4} = Bz$
d: $R^1 = R^4 = H, R^2 = R^3 = (Me)_2C{<}$

cent (w/v) soya bean meal. The highest yielding carbon source was sucrose in shaken-flask experiments and consequently beet molasses, which is rich in this carbohydrate, was subsequently used in pilot plant fermentations. In a typical fermentation, a 10 per cent by volume seed culture is inoculated into a stirred fermenter containing medium comprising the above ingredients and trace metal salts. The fermentation is carried out under defined aeration conditions at 24°C for four days, at which point maximal fusicoccin levels are attained. After removal of the mycelium by centrifugation, the fusicoccins are isolated conveniently from the broth by solvent extraction. Yields of total fusicoccin of 200–300 μg/ml are obtained consistently in 400 l fermenters. The fusicoccins are purified by column chromatography and crystallization.

CHEMISTRY OF FUSICOCCIN

a. The fusicoccin molecule

This basic molecule (Ia) is composed of a tricyclic diterpenoid aglycone unit which is bonded from C9, through an α-glycosidic linkage, to a substituted D-glucose residue. The aglycone moiety is variously substituted with hydroxyl groups (C8 and C12), a methoxy residue (C16), and an acetoxy group (C19) and contains unsaturated bonds at positions C1, C2 and C10, C14. The sugar residue contains an acetyl substituent at C3' and is additionally substituted at C6' with a 1,1-dimethylallyl group. Terpene glycosides are rare among the fungal metabolites. Others which have been characterized are the cotylenins, virescenoside (Cagnoli et al., 1967), and sordaricin (Hauser and Sigg, 1971).

The structure of (Ia) was established independently by the Italian (Ballio et al., 1968a) and Imperial College (Barrow et al., 1968a,b; Barrow et al., 1971a,b)groups. Both groups made extensive use of chemical degradative methodology and homonuclear spin–spin decoupling experiments on various derivatives of (Ia), and the structure of (Ia) was finally determined by X-ray crystallographic studies of two different derivatives.

Most of the known chemistry of fusicoccin was elaborated during the elucidation of its structure and only the salient features are discussed below. Fusicoccin forms a triacetate (Ik) and a tribenzoate (Il) derivative. The remaining, more sterically hindered secondary hydroxy group at C8, will acylate but only at elevated temperatures. Removal of the isolated isoprenoid residue can be accomplished by either hydrogenolysis or mild acid hydrolysis, the latter giving the higher yield, furnishing 3'-deacetyldesisopentenylfusicoccin (fusicoccin E) and dideacetyldesisopentenyl fusicoccin (fusicoccin F). More rigorous acid hydrolytic conditions generate the aglycone (IIa), D-glucose, and a mixture of 1,1-dimethylallyl alcohol and isoprene. A higher yielding procedure, generating IIa in 80 per cent yield, involves the dideacetylfusicoccin (Id), obtained from fusicoccin by base hydrolysis, with sodium periodate, sodium borohydride, and 0·4 N sulphuric acid in methanol. The aglycone readily forms a tetraacetate (IIb), a tetrabenzoate (IIc), and an acetonide (IId) derivative.

Most of the homonuclear magnetic resonance experiments were carried out on these derivatives during the structure elucidation. On reaction with mercuric acetate in methanol, followed by potassium bromide treatment, the aglycone (IIa) is readily converted into the mercuribromide derivative (IIIa) in which the C8 oxygen atom forms an ethereal bridge with C2. The structure and absolute stereochemistry of this derivative, as shown in IIIa, were determined by X-ray crystallography (Hough et al., 1968). Demercuration of IIIa was readily accomplished with sodium borohydride, generating a cyclic ether (IIIb). The latter can also be formed from the mercuribromide derivative (IV), formed from fusicoccin, by demercuration with borohydride followed by acid hydrolysis. These observations established the structure and absolute stereochemistry of fusicoccin as depicted in Ia. This structure is in full accord with the conclusions of an X-ray study carried out on the p-iodobenzene sulphonate derivative (Im) by the Italian group (Ballio et al., 1968a), and is further supported by the mass spectral fragmentation patterns of Ia and various derivatives.

Of the three double bonds in fusicoccin, only the one in the 1,1-dimethylallyl fragment is readily hydrogenated over Adams catalyst. The C1, C2 unsaturation is however reduced selectively in the aglycone (IIa) on treatment with lithium in liquid ammonia. While the C10, C14 double bond is unreactive

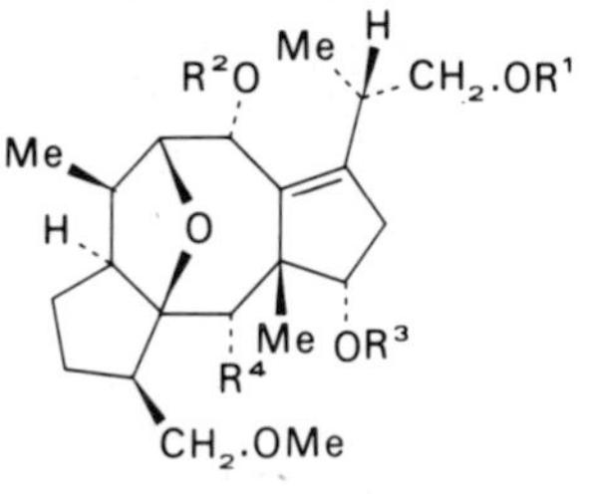

(III)

a: R^{1-3} = H, R^4 = .HgBr
b: R^{1-4} = H

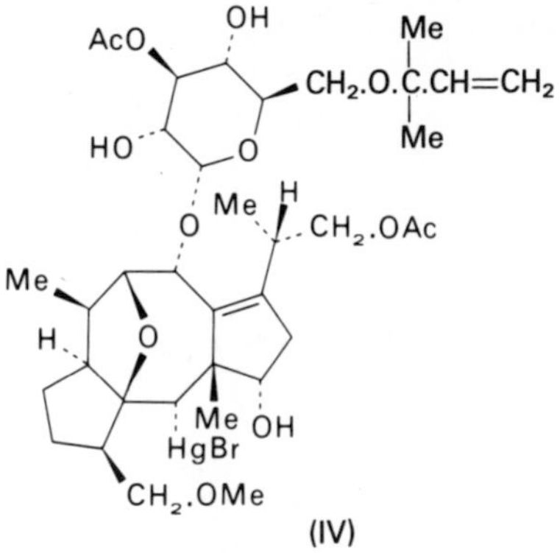

(IV)

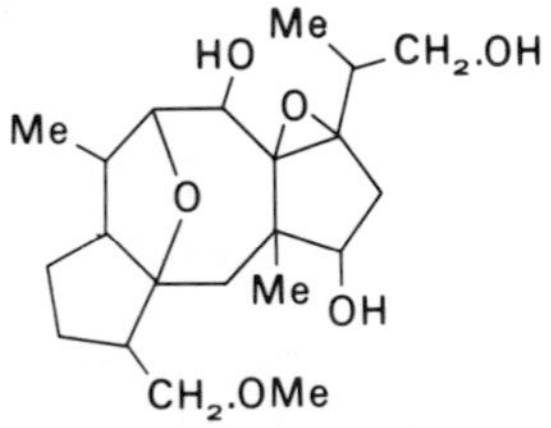

(V)

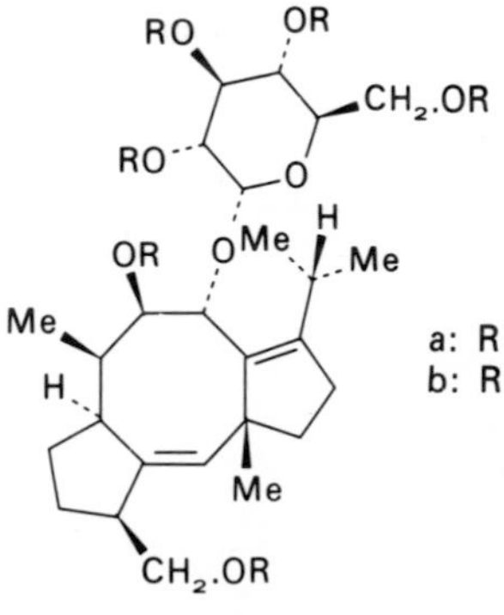

a: R = H
b: R = Ac

(VI)

under these conditions, it does however react with m-chloroperbenzoic acid in the cyclic ether series, generating the epoxide (V).

b. Fusicoccin H

Following the elucidation of the structure of fusicoccin, attention was next directed to other substances, with different oxidation levels to Ia, present in smaller amounts in the culture filtrate of *F. amygdali*. These substances incorporate radioactivity from $[2\text{-}^{14}\text{C}]$mevalonic acid and give colour reactions similar to fusicoccin (Ia). The first of these substances, fusicoccin H (VIa) (Barrow *et al.*, 1973) was shown to have the moelcular formula $C_{26}H_{42}O_8$. The mass spectrum of the hexaacetate derivative (VIb), in which all the hydroxy groups of VIa have been acetylated, clearly shows the characteristic fragmentation pattern of the tetra-O-acetylglycosyl residue which was observed in the mass spectrum of fusicoccin triacetate. The spectrum also indicates that the isolated isoprenoid residue is missing. Structure VIa seemed the most plausible of several alternatives, and this was confirmed by chemical degradation and correlation with a derivative obtained from fusicoccin, (Scheme 5.1).

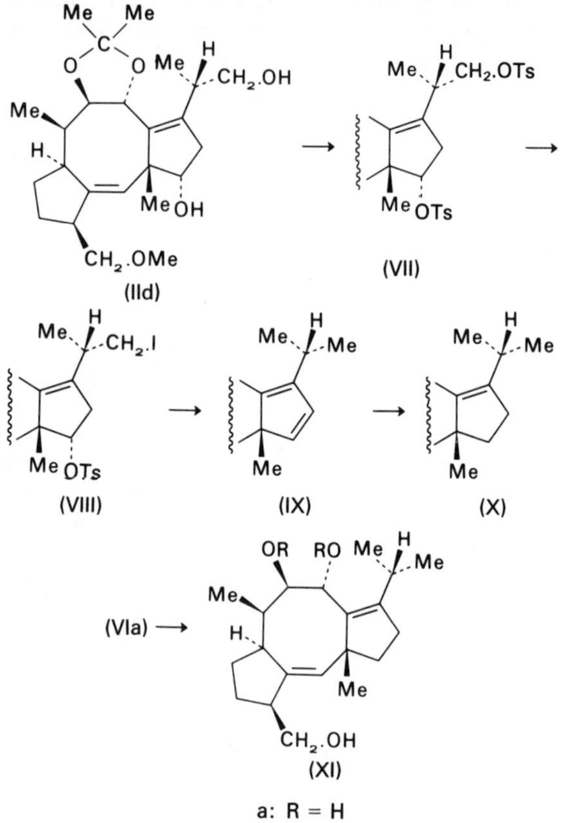

a: R = H
b: R = (Me)₂C<

Scheme 5.1

The aglycone acetonide derivative (IId), derived from Ia, was converted into the ditosylate (VII) by reaction with p-toluene sulphonyl chloride in pyridine. On treatment with sodium iodide in acetone, VII gave the iodotosylate (VIII) as the major product. Reductive displacement of the primary iodide group with sodium borohydride in dimethylsulphoxide also leads to the elimination of the tosyl residue in the five-membered ring affording the cyclopentadiene (IX). Hydrogenation of IX over palladium on strontium carbonate furnished the correlation compound (X).

To achieve the desired correlation, fusicoccin H was converted to its aglycone derivative (XIa) by the same procedure as used in forming IIa from Ia. The aglycone readily forms an acetonide derivative (XIb), which, on treatment with methyl iodide and sodium hydride in N,N-dimethylacetamide, generates the same derivative (X). These observations, while defining unambiguously the consitution of the aglycone of fusicoccin H, did not confirm the attachment of the sugar residue to C9. This was achieved by converting the aglycone (XIa) into the cyclic ether derivative (XII), via the mercuribromide (Scheme 5.2).

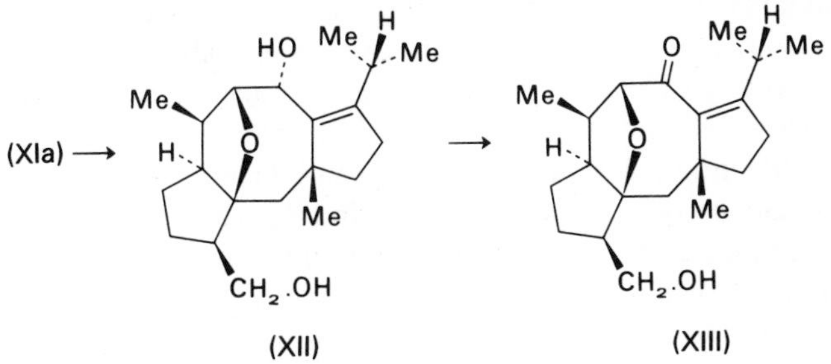

Scheme 5.2

Allylic oxidation of XII generated the α,β-unsaturated ketone (XIII), confirming the involvement of the C8 hydroxy group in the cyclic ether formation. The same cyclic ether (XII) was also formed directly from fusicoccin H by treatment of the mercuribromination product with borohydride, periodate, and strong base, thus confirming the glucosidic linkage to C9. The constitution of fusicoccin H was thus established as VIa, in full agreement with the independent studies of the Italian group (Ballio et al., 1972b).

Several attempts have been made to produce derivatives of the fusicoccin H series by direct demethylation of the methyl ether residue in fusicoccin. A smooth demethylation took place when Ik or IIb was reacted with boron trifluoride in the presence of acetic anhydride. Unfortunately, ring expansion also occurred producing, respectively, XIV and XV in which the sugar C_5 residue of Ik was lost.

c. Fusicoccin J

Fusicoccin J (XVIa) (Barrow et al., 1975a), was isolated originally from an acetylated culture-filtrate extract in only minute amounts as its pentaacetate

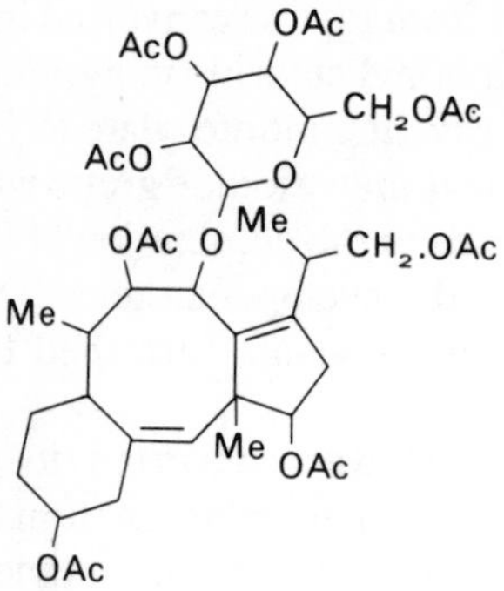

(XIV)

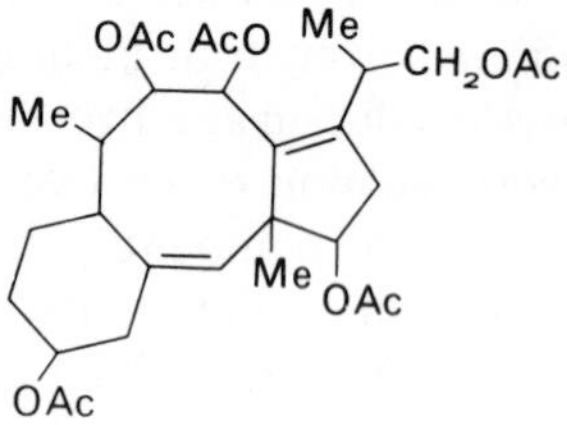

(XV)

(XVIb) and this hampered early attempts to elucidate its structure. In its mass spectrum, XVIb shows the highest mass peak at m/e 732, which as became apparent afterwards, results from the loss of acetic acid from the molecular ion. Based on this and other evidence, it was thought that the structure XVIIa which contains only four acetylated hydroxy groups was plausible. The synthesis of its dihydroderivative (XVIIb), containing the less acid-sensitive dihydro side chain was successfully accomplished from fusicoccin. The mass spectrum of XVIIb shows the molecular ion at m/e 734 but is clearly different from that of the dihydro-acetylated derivative of fusicoccin J. More substantial quantities of XVIb were accumulated and deacetylated with base to give fusicoccin J. The mass spectrum of fusicoccin J, and its dihydro derivative (XVIII) indicated that it contained one less hydroxyl group than fusicoccin D (Id) and suggests

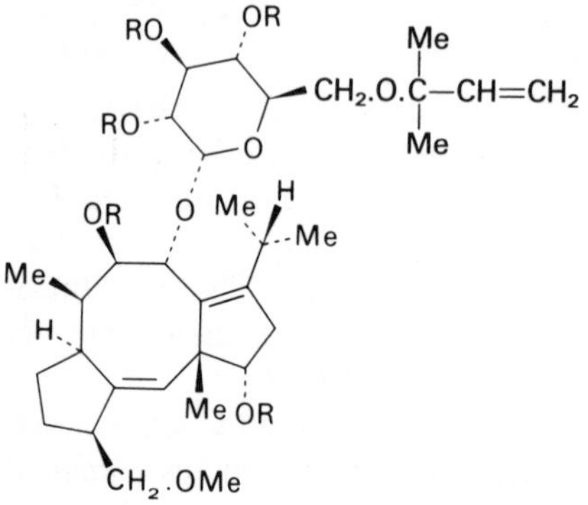

(XVI)

a: R = H
b: R = Ac

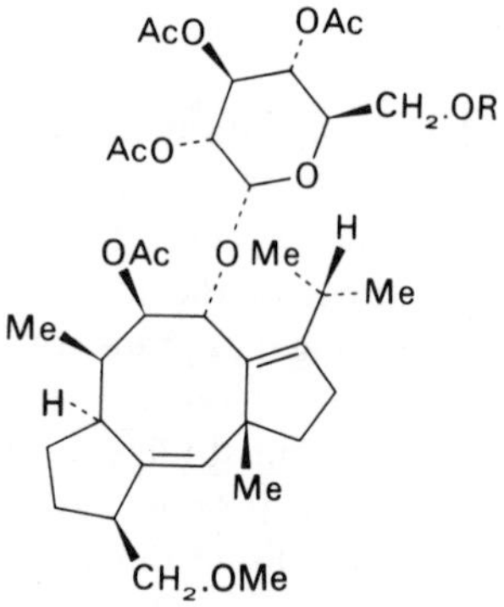

(XVII)

a: $R = -\overset{\displaystyle Me}{\underset{\displaystyle Me}{\overset{|}{\underset{|}{C}}}}-CH=CH_2$

b: $R = -\overset{\displaystyle Me}{\underset{\displaystyle Me}{\overset{|}{\underset{|}{C}}}}-CH_2.Me$

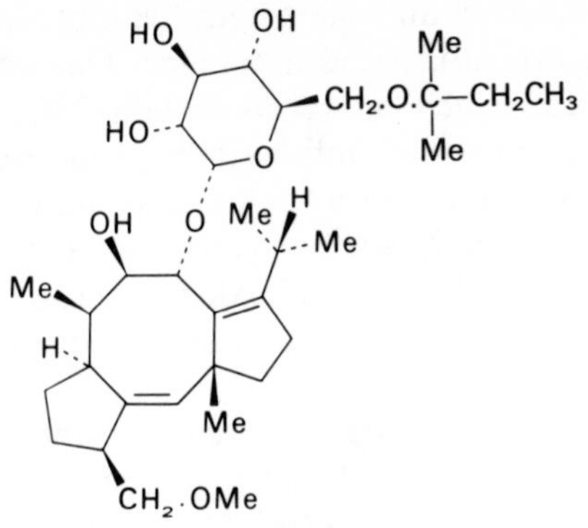

(XVIII)

structure XVIa as the most plausible one. This has been confirmed by direct correlation with fusicoccin as follows (Scheme 5.3).

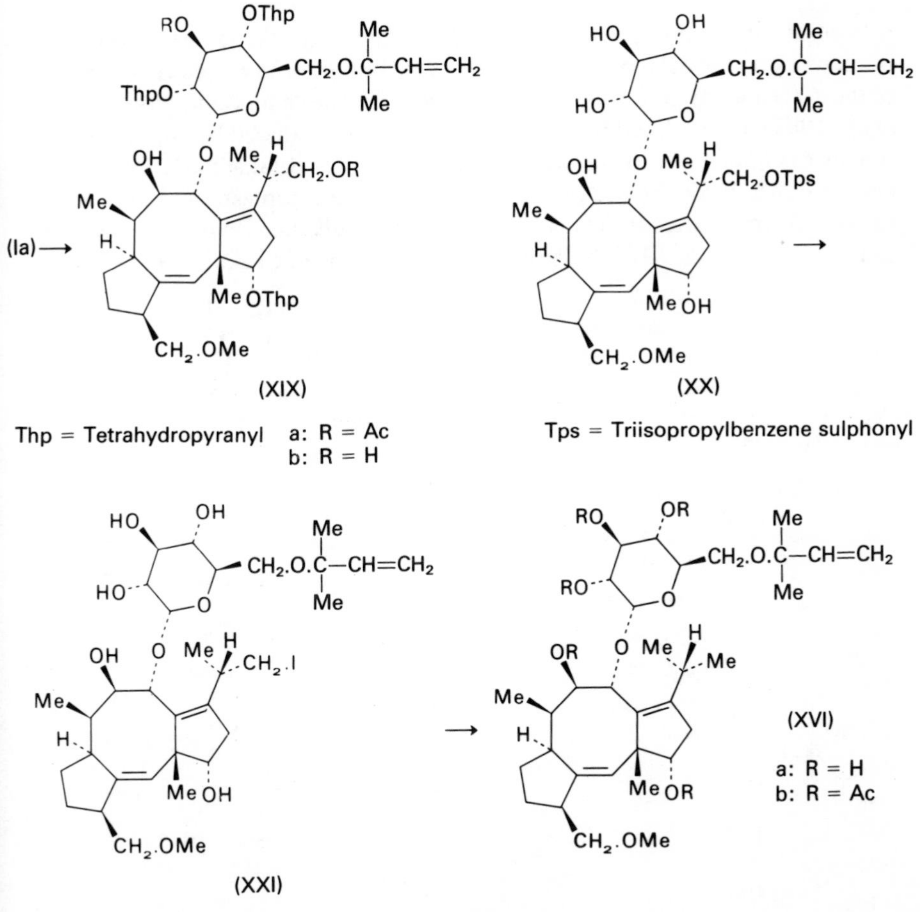

(Ia) →

(XIX)

Thp = Tetrahydropyranyl

a: R = Ac
b: R = H

(XX)

Tps = Triisopropylbenzene sulphonyl

(XXI)

(XVI)

a: R = H
b: R = Ac

Scheme 5.3

Fusicoccin was converted into the tritetrahydropyranyl ether (XIXa) with dihydropyran and hydrochloric acid in toluene. Deacetylation of XIXa with base generated XIXb, which on reaction with 2,4,6-triisopropylbenzene-sulphonyl chloride in pyridine, followed by acid treatment afforded the monosulphonate (XX). Conversion of XX into the monoiodide (XXI) was effected with sodium iodide in acetone containing ethylamine. Reduction of XXI with borohydride in dimethylsulphoxide gave fusicoccin J (XVIa) identi-cal with the natural isolate. This structure was also corroborated by Ballio *et al.* (1974).

More recently the Italian group have reported the isolation from culture extracts, in very low yield, of 16-*O*-demethyl fusicoccin J (XXVIa) (Ballio *et al.*, 1974) and 16-*O*-demethyl(-3-*epi*fusicoccin J (XXVIc) (Ballio *et al.*, 1975; Cerrini *et al.*, 1975).

BIOSYNTHESIS OF FUSICOCCINS

Several other groups of natural products have the same carbocyclic framework as the aglycone of the fusicoccins but differ in the stereochemistry of the A/B and/or B/C ring junctions. These are the ophiobolin group (Tsuda *et al.*, 1967), exemplified by ophiobolin C (XXII) produced by cultures of the fungus *Cochliobolus miyabeanus*; the ceroplastanes (Iitaka *et al.*, 1968; Rios and Quijano, 1969; Rios *et al.*, 1974), for example ceroplasteric acid (XXIII), isolated from the wax of the insect *Ceroplastes albolineatus*; and the cotylenins (Sassa, 1971; Sassa, 1972; Sassa *et al.*, 1975b; Sassa and Takahama, 1975), for

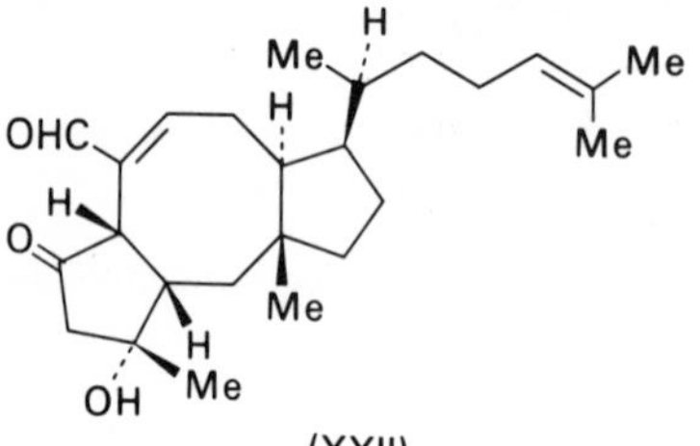

(XXII)

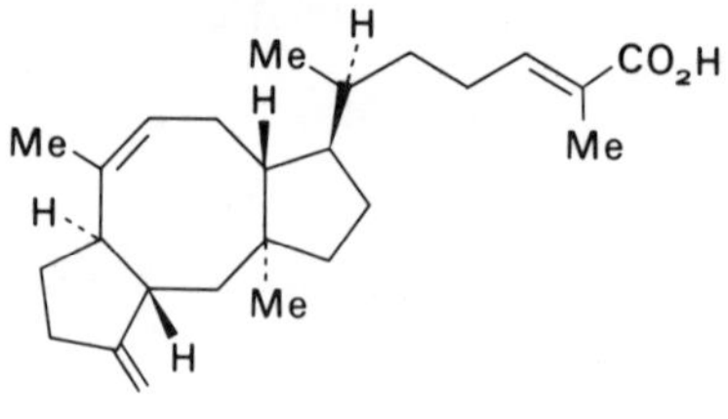

(XXIII)

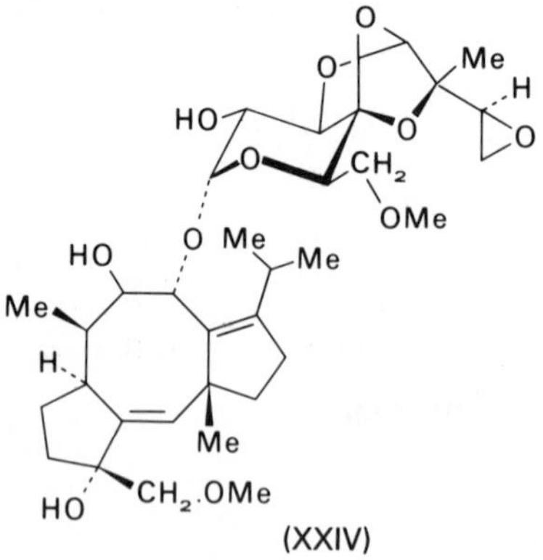

(XXIV)

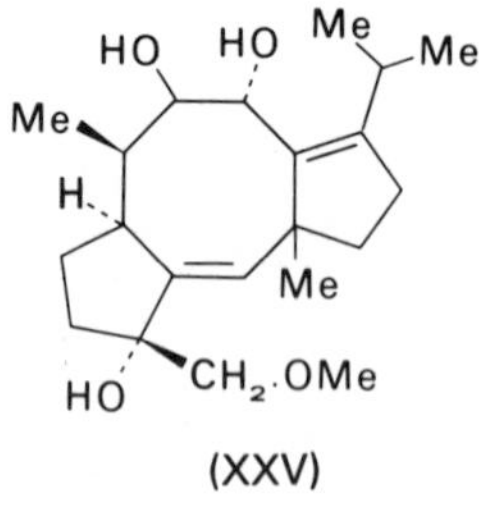

(XXV)

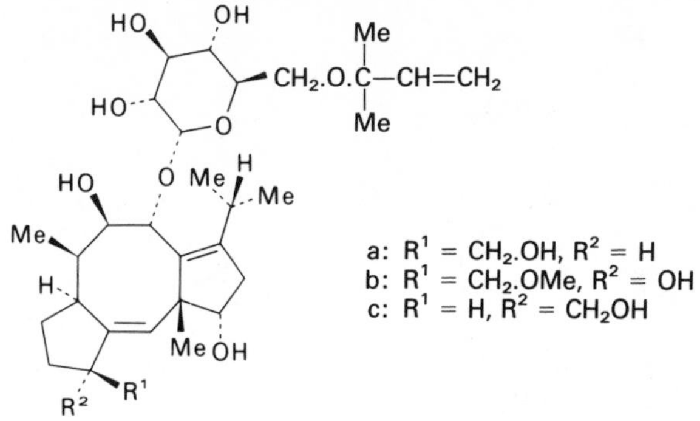

(XXVI)

a: $R^1 = CH_2.OH$, $R^2 = H$
b: $R^1 = CH_2.OMe$, $R^2 = OH$
c: $R^1 = H$, $R^2 = CH_2OH$

example cotylenin A (XXIV) produced by a fungus identified as a species of *Cladosporium*. The ophiobolins and ceroplastanes differ from the fusicoccins in that they are constructed from a polyprenyl pyrophosphate precursor containing five isoprenoid residues and are therefore sesterterpenoids. Although the aglycone moiety of the fusicoccins (and also that of the cotylenins) contains four isoprenoid residues, it was initially considered that Ia could be a rearranged sesterterpenoid being formed in the early stages by a biosynthetic process analogous to that of the ophiobolins (Scheme 5.4). Initial biosynthetic

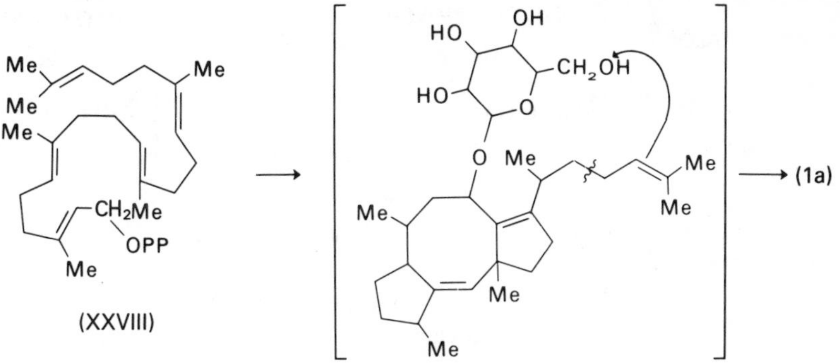

(XXVIII)

$\longrightarrow$ (1a)

Scheme 5.4

studies, in which [2-^{14}C]mevalonic acid was incorporated into the sugar C_5 fragment and the four isoprenoid residues of the aglycone to differing extents, disputed this and suggested that the sugar-appended C_5 unit was attached at a later stage in the biosynthesis (Barrow and Chain, 1969). The later isolation of fusicoccin H (VIa) which lacks the sugar C_5 residue provided further evidence for this notion. To confirm its intermediacy in the biosynthesis of Ia, fusicoccin H was labelled with ^{3}H at C8, by the procedure shown in Scheme 5.5 and fed to the fungus. The fusicoccin isolated showed a 2·3 per cent incorporation of label, 90 per cent of which was shown to be at C8 of Ia by the sequence shown in Scheme 5.6. The remaining 10 per cent was thought to be located at C6 as a result of enolization of the ketone under the reducing conditions. This

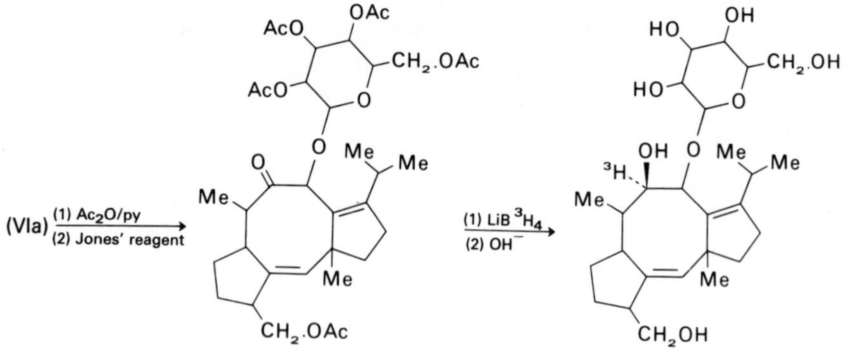

Scheme 5.5

observation demonstrated that fusicoccin H can act as precursor of Ia and provides convincing evidence that the fusicoccins are diterpenoids. The structural similarity of the cotylenins with the fusicoccins, and the recent characterization of the aglycone, cotylenol (XXV) (Sassa and Togoshi, 1973; Sassa *et al.*, 1975*a*) also establishes this family of compounds as diterpenoids.

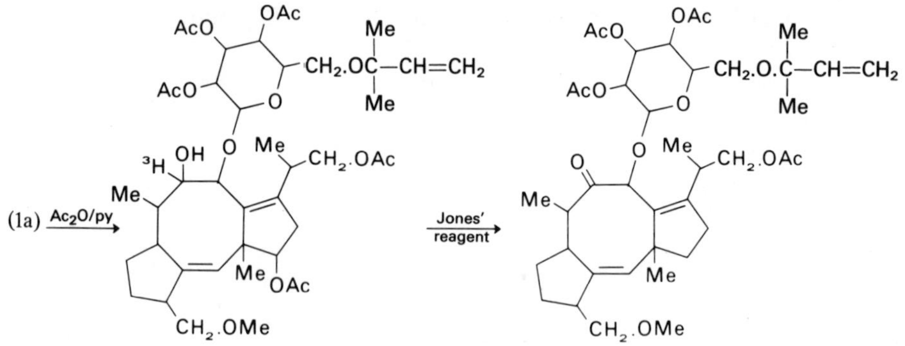

Scheme 5.6

In an analogous exercise, fusicoccin J (XVIa) was also labelled with ^{3}H at C8 and fed to the fungus under identical conditions. The isolated fusicoccin incorporated considerably more radioactivity (20·6 per cent incorporation) than observed for [8-^{3}H]VIa), and 89 per cent of the label was shown to be at C8 of Ia, confirming the specificity of incorporation of the label. Although no other fusicoccin isolates have been labelled and fed to the fungus it is probable that the biosynthesis proceeds by the route shown in Scheme 5.7.

The recently isolated cometabolite (XXVIb) (Radics *et al.*, 1975) could arise by the enzymatic hydroxylation of fusicoccin J at C3, representing a deviation from the main pathway to fusicoccin. The glucose residue would therefore be attached to the aglycone in the early stages of the biosynthesis and prenylated in the middle-order steps. Following the formation of fusicoccin J the final stages in the biosynthesis of (I) must involve the hydroxylation of C19

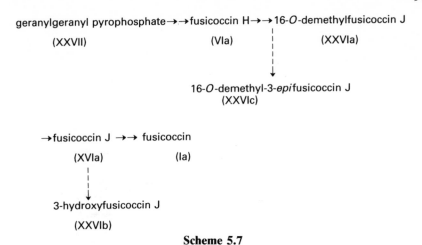

geranylgeranyl pyrophosphate→→fusicoccin H→→16-O-demethylfusicoccin J

(XXVII)   (VIa)   (XXVIa)

16-O-demethyl-3-epifusicoccin J
(XXVIc)

→fusicoccin J →→ fusicoccin

(XVIa)   (Ia)

3-hydroxyfusicoccin J

(XXVIb)

Scheme 5.7

and the acetylation of the primary hydroxy group so formed, as well as acetylation in the glucoside residue.

More recently, attention has been turned to the mechanism of cyclization of geranylgeranyl pyrophosphate (XXVII). In order to examine the folding of (XXVII) during the cyclization process, the incorporation of [1-^{13}C]- and [2-^{13}C]-acetate (Barrow et al., 1975b) and [3-^{13}C]mevalonic acid (Banerji et al., 1976) into fusicoccin was examined initially using the recently introduced ^{13}C nuclear magnetic resonance technique. In biosynthetic studies, this approach is finding widespread application particularly since it does not involve the often painstaking procedure of chemically degrading the labelled metabolite to prove the position(s) of labelling. However, in experiments using ^{13}C-labelled substrates it is necessary to feed much greater quantities of precursors than when employing tracer levels of radioactive substrates in order to incorporate sufficient ^{13}C into the metabolite to be detected spectroscopically. Since this isotope is also costly it is necessary to optimize incorporation efficiencies in order to avoid wastage. In the case of the [^{13}C]acetate-feeding experiments, the latter point did not present any problem since these precursors were incorporated efficiently. However, much time was spent developing suitable fermentation conditions before enough [3-^{13}C]mevalonic acid was successfully incorporated into Ia. Another prerequisite for the application of this technique is the assignment of the signals in the natural abundance, proton noise decoupled ^{13}C nuclear magnetic resonance spectrum of the metabolite. For these purposes the triacetate (Ik) was selected since this derivative is purified most conveniently. The assignment of the spectrum of Ik, which shows 37 signals, was made from chemical shifts, spectral comparisons with aglycone derivatives, especially IIb, signal multiplicities in the off-resonance spectra, incremental heteronuclear (^{13}C–^{1}H) decoupling, ^{13}C–T_1 measurements, and selectively induced nuclear Overhauser enhancement techniques (Barrow et al., 1975b; Radics et al., 1975). The assigned spectrum and the spectra of the ^{13}C-enriched specimens of Ik are presented in Figures 5.1–3. [1-^{13}C]Acetate selectively enhanced,

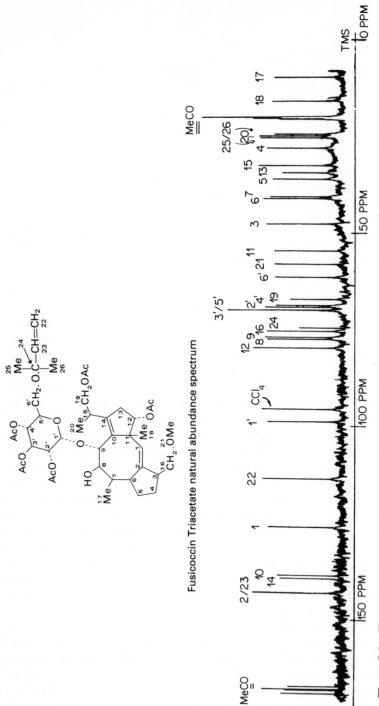

Figure 5.1 The assigned natural abundance proton noise decoupled ^{13}C nuclear magnetic resonance spectrum of fusicoccin triacetate

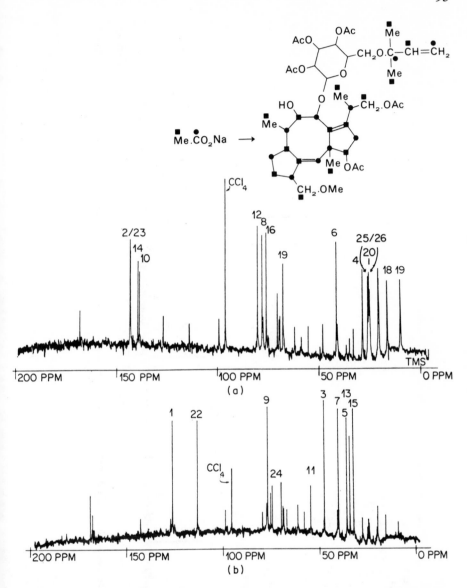

Figure 5.2   The proton noise decoupled ^{13}C nuclear magnetic resonance spectrum of fusicoccin triacetate following enrichment from (a) 2-^{13}C]acetate and (b) [1-^{13}C] acetate

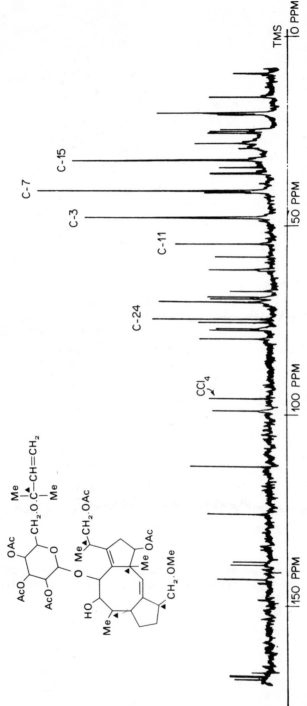

Figure 5.3 The proton noise decoupled ^{13}C nuclear magnetic resonance spectrum of fusicoccin triacetate following enrichment from [3-^{13}C]mevalonic acid

approximately five-fold, the signals due to C1, 3, 5, 7, 9, 11, 13, 15, 22, and 24 while [2-^{13}C]acetate enhanced the signals due to C2, 4, 6, 8, 10, 12, 14, 16, 17, 18, 19, 20, 23, 24, and 25. [3-^{13}C]Mevalonic acid lactone was incorporated with approximately four-fold signal enhancement, into C3, 7, 11, 15, and 24.

These labelling patterns are consistent with the formation of fusicoccin by the cyclization of XXVII in a manner resembling the cyclization of geranylfarnesyl pyrophosphate (XXVIII) generating ophiobolin F (XXX) (Canonica *et al.*, 1967a,b; Nozoe *et al.*, 1968; Nozoe and Morisaki, 1969) (Scheme 5.8). The biosynthesis of the ophiobolins has been studied extensively by Canonica and

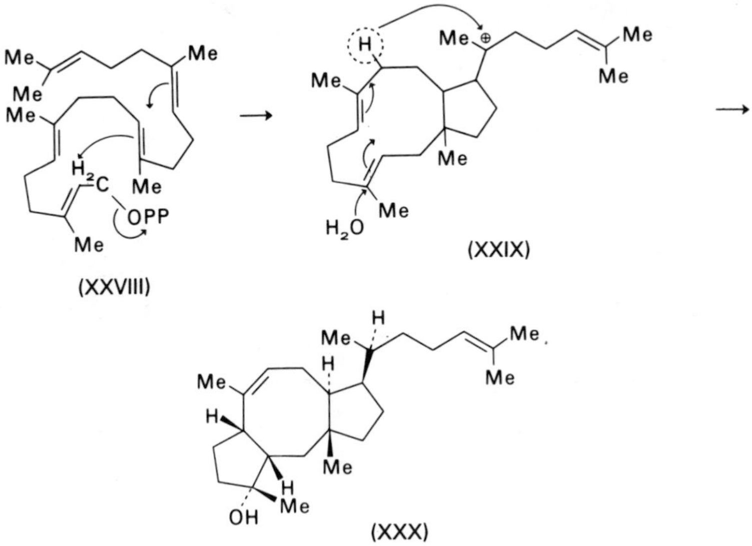

Scheme 5.8

coworkers. During the cyclization of XXVIII all the C2 mevalonoid hydrogens are retained (Canonica *et al.*, 1967b) and a *pro* 2R mevalonoid hydrogen undergoes an enzyme-mediated 1,5-shift from C8α to C15 of the ophiobolin precursor (Canonica *et al.*, 1967a). In addition, no *pro* 4R mevalonoid hydrogens are lost in the formation of ophiobolin C (Canonica *et al.*, 1968) and the hydroxy group at C3 was shown to arise from water in the medium rather than from molecular oxygen (Canonica *et al.*, 1967b; Nozoe *et al.*, 1967).

The absence of an oxygen function at C3—excepting the recently isolated minor isolate (XXVIb)—and the unsaturation pattern of the fusicoccins suggested that the further cyclization of the bicyclic carbonium ion (XXXI), or its biological equivalent analogous to XXIX, might proceed by an alternative route. This possibility was examined by feeding [2-^{14}C, (4R)-4-^{3}H$_1$]mevalonic acid (normalized ^{3}H:^{14}C = 5:5) to the fungus. In two independent experiments, fusicoccin and fusicoccin J (^{3}H:^{14}C = 3·92:5 and 3·76:5, respectively) retained four out of a possible five ^{3}H atoms, whilst fusicoccin H (^{3}H:^{14}C = 3·30:4) retained three ^{3}H atoms. If the cyclization of XXVII had followed the

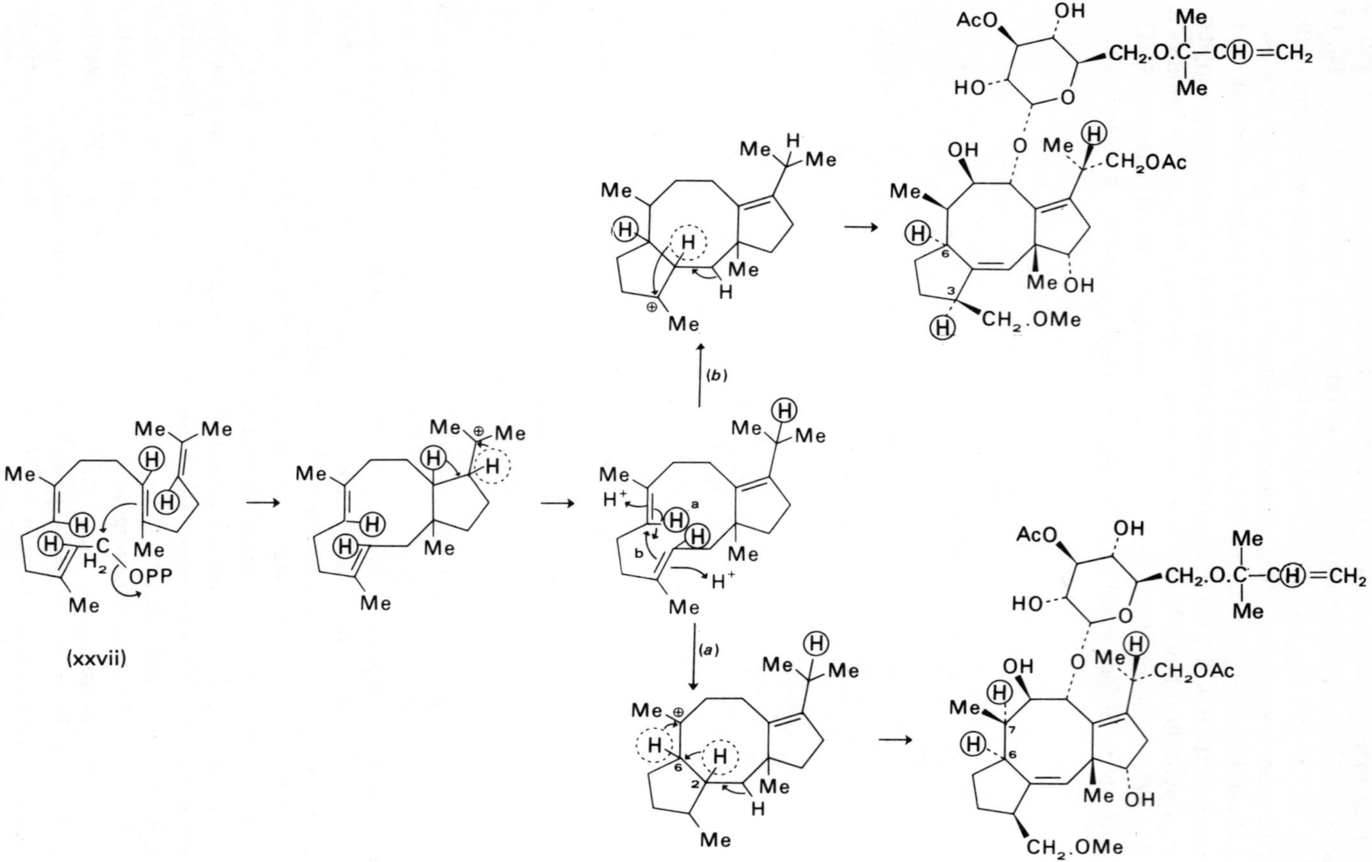

Scheme 5.9

process leading to the ophiobolins, only two ^{3}H atoms would have been retained, located at C15 and C23. The above observations can be explained by the further cyclization of XXXI in one of two ways (Scheme 5.9*a,b*), which differ in the direction of carbon–carbon bond formation between C2 and C6. In both pathways, the resulting carbonium ion would be quenched by a process initiated by the loss of a proton from C1. In route *a*, this would be followed by either two 1,2-hydride shifts or a 1,3-hydride shift, while route *b* necessitates only one 1,2-hydride shift.

PHYTOTOXICITY AND MODE OF ACTION OF FUSICOCCINS

When introduced into the xylem of almond and peach shoots, fusicoccin produces symptoms on the leaves resembling those that follow an infection of the fungal pathogen (Graniti, 1962), as described at the beginning of this article. Fusicoccin also affects markedly the water balance and transpiration of a wide range of plants (Graniti, 1974; Graniti and Turner, 1970). In tomato cuttings, transpiration and water uptake increase considerably, soon after the introduction of fusicoccin and prior to any sign of wilting or necrosis (Graniti, 1966*a,b*; Turner and Graniti, 1969). Fusicoccin induces wilt in tomato cuttings at concentrations as low as 10^{-7}–2×10^{-7} M ($0 \cdot 1$–$0 \cdot 2$ μg/ml or ppm) (Graniti, 1964). At higher concentrations (2 μg/ml), fusicoccin induces changes in the water balance and transpiration of treated plants which results in the disruption of water economy leading to rapid and irreversible alteration of the mechanisms which regulate tissue turgor (Graniti, 1966*b*; Ballio *et al.*, 1968*b*). This is a consequence of the increase in the rate of water loss and stomatal opening in both light and dark (Turner and Graniti, 1969; Graniti and Turner, 1970).

The mode of action is still not fully understood. Turner and Graniti (1969) have proposed a mechanistic explanation of the wilting syndrome based on the increase in stomatal aperture, induced by fusicoccin, which it has been argued is related to a greater permeability of the cells to K^+. The latter would be affected by energy derived from the increase in respiration. However, Chain *et al.*, (1971) were able to show that the wilt is not caused by interruption of vascular flow. They pointed out that any mechanistic explanation must centre on the phase of incipient wilt, since during this phase, flaccidity is not apparent even though water is being lost more rapidly than normal. They suggested that stomatal opening is a secondary effect regulated by water loss and is not the cause of wilting. More recently, Turner (1972*a,b*) has demonstrated that fusicoccin stimulates the accumulation of K^+ in the stomata guard cells as the stomata open and suggests that fusicoccin might be involved in the transport of these ions. Such leakage of K^+ out of the cells could lead to stomatal closure, causing the plant to wilt and die.

It is noteworthy that the ophiobolins are also phytotoxic but have a different mode of action from the fusicoccins. The ophiobolin-producing fungi (species of *Cochliobolus*) cause a disease in rice, which has been attributed to the inhibition, by the ophiobolin phytotoxins, of coleoptile and root elongation. In the tomato wilting assay, the ophiobolins are much less toxic than the fusicoc-cins. The cotylenins, which bear a closer structural resemblance to the fusicoc-cins have been shown to possess plant growth-promoting properties. These substances induce the growth of cotyledons of a number of vegetable seedlings at concentrations in the range 1–100 ppm.

Using the tomato plant assay it has been shown that isofusicoccin (Ib) is nearly as toxic as fusicoccin, whereas monodeacetyl- and dideacetyl-fusicoccins (Ic) and (Id) are, respectively, 12 and 100 times less active (Ballio *et al.*, 1970; Barrow *et al.*, 1969). In an attempt to throw further light on the structural basis of the phytotoxicity, Ballio *et al.* (1971) have shown that (*i*) hydrogenation or removal of the isopentenyl group, or partial or total deacyla-tion of fusicoccin, dihydrofusicoccin, and desisopentenylfusicoccin gives com-pounds with comparable, though reduced, activity, (*ii*) the glucose moiety is necessary for activity although the deacetylaglycone exerts an identical effect at $10\,\mu g/ml$, and (*iii*) acylation products of fusicoccin do not stimulate water uptake.

As a consequence of the mode of action studies, Turner (1970) has pointed out that fusicoccin could be put to commercial use. He has demonstrated that spraying a 10^{-5} M solution of fusicoccin on alfalfa grass (Lucerne) in the field, three hours before cutting, reduces the curing time (reduction of moisture content to 22 per cent by weight) from four to three days, thereby minimizing damage to this important hay-making crop. He also suggests that fusicoccin could be used to increase the carbon dioxide intake of hot-house plant leaves thereby hastening growth because of ability to induce openings of the stomata. These are possible areas for exploration and exploitation which have yet to materialize and will depend on toxicity trials which have so far not been reported.

ACKNOWLEDGEMENTS

The authors wish to thank both Sir Ernst Chain F.R.S. and Sir Derek Barton F.R.S., who have guided the fusicoccin programme at Imperial College, and the numerous coworkers cited in the text for making the presentation of this article possible.

REFERENCES

Ballio, A., Brufani, M., Casinovi, C. G., Cerrini, S., Fedeli, W., Pellicciari, R., Santurbano, B., and Vaciago, A. (1968*a*) *Experientia*, **24**, 631.

Ballio, A., Casinovi, C. G., D'Alessio, V., Grandolini, G., Randazzo, G., and Rossi, C. (1974) *Experientia*, **30**, 844.

Ballio, A., Casinovi, C. G., Framondino, M., Grandolini, G., Menichini, F., Randuzzo, G., and Rossi, C. (1972*a*) *Experientia*, **28**, 126.

Ballio, A., Casinovi, C. G., Framondino, M., Grandolini, G., Randazzo, G., and Rossi, C. (1972*b*) *Experientia*, **28**, 1150.

Ballio, A., Casinovi, C. G., Grandolini, G., Pomponi, M., Randazzo, G., and Rossi, C., (1975) *Gazz. Chim. Ital.*, **105**, 647.

Ballio, A., Casinovi, C. G., Randazzo, G., and Rossi, C. (1970a) *Experientia*, **26**, 349.

Ballio, A., Casinovi, C. G., Randazzo, G., and Rossi, C. (1970b) *Experientia*, **26**, 351.

Ballio, A., Chain, E. B., de Leo, P., Eerlanger, B. F., Mauri, M., and Tonolo, A. (1964) *Nature (London)*, **203**, 297.

Ballio, A., Graniti, A., Pocchiari, F., and Silano, V. (1968b) *Life Sciences*, **7**, 751.

Ballio, A., Pocchiari, F., Russi, S., and Silano, V. (1971) *Physiol. Plant. Path.*, **1**, 95.

Banerji, A., Jones, R. B., Mellows, G., Phillips, L., and Sim, K. Y. (1976) *J.C.S. Perkin I* **1976**, 2221.

Barrow, K. D., Barton, D. H. R., Chain, E. B., Bageenda-Kasujju, D., and Mellows, G. (1975a) *J.C.S. Perkin I*, **1975**, 877.

Barrow, K. D., Barton, D. H. R., Chain, E. B., Conlay, C., Smale, T. V., Thomas, R., and Weight, E. S. (1968a) *J.C.S. Chem. Comm.*, **1968**, 1195.

Barrow, K. D., Barton, D. H. R., Chain, E. B., Conlay, C., Smale, T. C., Thomas, R., and Waight, E. S. (1971a) *J. Chem. Soc., C*, **1971**, 1259.

Barrow, K. D., Barton, D. H. R., Chain, E. B., Ohnsorge, U. F. W., and Sharma, R. P. (1973) *J. Chem. Soc., C*, **1973**, 1590.

Barrow, K. D., Barton, D. H. R., Chain, E. B., Ohnsorge, U. F. W., and Thomas, R. (1968b) *J.C.S. Chem. Comm.*, **1968**, 1198.

Barrow, K. D., Barton, D. H. R., Chain, E. B., Ohnsorge, U. F. W., and Thomas, R. (1971b) *J. Chem. Soc., C*, **1971**, 1265.

Barrow, K. D., and Chain, E. B. (1969) *Biochem. J.*, **114**, 4P.

Barrow, K. D., Jones, R. B., Pemberton, P. W., and Phillips, L. (1975b) *J.C.S. Perkin I*, **1975**, 1405.

Cagnoli-Bellavita, N., Ceccherelli, P., Ribaldi, M., Baskevitch, Z., and Polonsky, J. (1967) *Gazz. Chim. Ital.*, **97**, 1344.

Canonica, L., Fiecchi, A., Galli-Kienle, M., Ranzi, B. M., and Scala, A. (1967a) *Tetrahedron Letters*, **1967**, 4657.

Canonica, L., Fiecchi, A., Galli-Kienle, M., Ranzi, B. M., Scala, A., Salvatori, T., and Pella, E. (1967b) *Tetrahedron Letters*, **1967**, 3371.

Canonica, L., Fiecchi, A., Galli-Kienle, M., Ranzi, B. M., and Scala, A. (1968) *Tetrahedron Letters*, **1968**, 275.

Chain, E. B., Mantle, P. G., and Milborow, B. V. (1971) *Physiol. Plant Path.*, **1**, 495.

Cerrini, S., Fedeli, W., and Gavuzzo, E. (1975) *Gazz. Chim. Ital.*, **105**, 651.

Graniti, A. (1962) *Phytopath. Medit.*, **1**, 182.

Graniti, A. (1964) in *Host-parasite relations in Plant Pathology*, (Iraly, Z., and Ubrizsy, G., eds.), Proceedings of a Symposium, Hungarian Acad. Sci. Budapest, p. 211.

Graniti, A. (1966a) *Phytopath. Medit.*, **5**, 146.

Graniti, A. (1966b) *Atti 1st Congr. Unione Fitopat. Medit.*, Bari-Napoli, p. 80.

Graniti, A., and de Leo, P. (1964) *Phytopath. Medit.*, **3**, 109.

Graniti, A., and Turner, N. C. (1970) *Phytopath. Medit.*, **9**, 160.

Grosclaude, C. (1956) *Ann. Epiphyt.*, **7**, 397.

Hauser, D., and Sigg, H. P. (1971) *Helv. Chim. Acta*, **54**, 1178.

Hough, E., Hursthouse, M. B., Neidle, S., and Rogers, D. (1968) *J.C.S. Chem. Comm.*, **1968**, 1197.

Iitaka, Y., Watanabe, I., Harrison, I. T., and Harrison, S. (1968) *J. Am. Chem. Soc.*, **90**, 1092.

Nozoe, S., and Morisaki, M. (1969) *J.C.S. Chem. Comm.*, **1969**, 1319.

Nozoe, S., Morisaki, M., Fukuskima, K., and Okuda, S. (1968) *Tetrahedron Letters*, **1968**, 4457.

Nozoe, S., Morisaki, M., Tsuda, K., and Okuda, S. (1967) *Tetrahedron Letters*, **1967**, 3365.

Radics, L., Kajitar-Peredy, M., Casinovi, C. G., Grandolini, G., and Rossi, C. (1975) *Org. Mag. Res.*, **7**, 137.

Rios, T., and Quijano, L. (1969) *Tetrahedron Letters*, **1969**, 1317.

Rios, T., Quijano, L., and Calderon, J. (1974) *J.C.S. Chem. Comm.*, **1974**, 728.
Sassa, T. (1971) *Agr. Biol. Chem.*, **35**, 1415.
Sassa, T. (1972) *Agr. Biol. Chem.*, **36**, 2037.
Sassa, T., and Takahama, A. (1975) *Agr. Biol. Chem.*, **39**, 2213.
Sassa, T., Takahama, A., and Shindo, T. (1975*a*) *Agr. Biol. Chem.*, **39**, 1729.
Sassa, T., and Togoshi, A. (1973) *Agr. Biol. Chem.*, **37**, 1505.
Sassa, T., Togashi, M., and Kitaguchi, T. (1975*b*) *Agr. Biol. Chem.*, **39**, 1735.
Tsuda, K., Nozoe, S., Morisaki, M., Hirai, K., Itai, A., Okuda, S., Canonica, L., Fiecchi,
    A., Galli-Kienle, M., and Scala, A. (1967) *Tetrahdron Letters*, **1967**, 3369.
Turner, N. C. (1970) *Agronomy J.*, **62**, 538.
Turner, N. C. (1972*a*) *Nature (London)*, **235**, 5337.
Turner, N. C. (1972*b*) *Am. J. Bot.*, **59**, 133.
Turner, N. C., and Graniti, A. (1969) *Nature (London)*, **223**, 1070.

DISCUSSION

Sir Ernst Chain

The question of mechanism of action of fusicoccin is interesting. The mode of action of this substance is essentially unknown. No other substance does this trick in such low concentrations. If botanists have not elucidated the mode of action, one reason is that there are very few botanists around! They are busy with other things which are not all intimately related with botany. I believe this substance will one day receive practical application, but more biological work must be done.

Dr. M. Carlile

Thank you Sir Ernst for pointing the way ahead to our botanical colleagues!

6

Mycoviruses: The Quest for Components in Filamentous Fungi with Antiviral Activity in Animals

G. T. Banks

Department of Biochemistry,
Imperial College of Science and Technology, London, U.K.

INTRODUCTION

The discovery in the late 1960s of viruses infecting filamentous fungi, particularly members of the fungi imperfecti, and the revelation that double-stranded RNA (ds-RNA) of viral origin was responsible for the antiviral and interferon-inducing properties of extracts of these organisms, caused an explosion of interest in this field. Evidence of this interest lies in the large number of relevant publications which has appeared in the scientific literature over the last 10 years. Some of the more recent developments concerning the biological and biochemical implications of fungal viruses, and the clinical and veterinary applications of viral ds-RNA, are described in subsequent chapters by Dr. K. W. Buck of Imperial College and by Dr. J. M. Dewdney of Beecham Research Laboratories, respectively. The purpose of the present article is to outline the events which led to the discovery of these fungal viruses and the interferon-stimulating properties of viral ds-RNA. It is hoped that this article will serve as an introduction to the subsequent chapters and also will illustrate the validity of one of the basic principles which has guided Sir Ernst Chain throughout his distinguished career, reference to which will be made later.

HISTORICAL DEVELOPMENT

Although viral infections of bacteria, higher plants, and animals are quite common, viral infections of fungi were unknown until 1962 when Hollings, at the Glasshouse Crops Research Institute, Littlehampton, Sussex showed that the die-back disease of the cultivated mushroom, *Agaricus bisporus*, was caused by a virus (Hollings, 1962; Hollings and Stone, 1969, 1971).

Two earlier observations were ultimately to lead to the discovery of the more wide-spread distribution of fungal viruses and the ability of viral ds-RNA to stimulate interferon production in animals. Powell *et al.* (1952) showed that culture filtrates of the mould *Penicillum stoloniferum* exhibited prophylactic and therapeutic activity against Semliki forest and MM viruses in mice. Subsequent work revealed that the crude material was active against a wide range of different viruses, both in tissue culture and in animals (Powell and Culbertson, 1953*ab*; Hull and Lavell, 1953, 1954; Cochran *et al.*, 1954; Johnson and Baker, 1958; Powell *et al.*, 1961, 1962; Furusawa *et al.*, 1963; Cochran and Payne, 1964). The term 'statolon' was applied to the active principle by Probst and Kleinschmidt (1961). Furthermore Shope (1953*a,b*) showed that culture filtrates and mycelial extracts of another mould, *P. funiculosum*, likewise exhibited therapuetic activity against swine influenza, Columbia SK encephalomyelitus, and Semliki forest viruses in mice. The activity was attributed by Shope to a substance, named 'helenine', which he was able to obtain in crude form from aqueous mycelial extracts by acetone precipitation.

In the late 1950s and 1960s, considerable effort was devoted to the search for antiviral drugs which might be used in the treatment of human and animal disease, but progress was slow. Viruses are intracellular parasites which associate closely with host metabolic processes; great difficulties were experienced in finding drugs capable of inhibiting viral replication without producing harmful side effects in the host. Consequently, considerable interest was shown in the original work of Powell and of Shope, and further studies were devoted to elucidating the nature of the active principles of statolon and helenine, and their role in inhibiting viral replication. Three groups of workers were primarily involved in these later studies. *i*) Kleinschmidt and his colleagues at Eli Lilly and Company in the USA, who devoted their efforts to investigating the structure and activity of statolon. *ii*) Hilleman and his colleagues at Merck, Sharpe, and Dohme, also in the USA, who concentrated their attention on helenine. *iii*) The group at Imperial College, London, who undertook in 1967 a study of the purification and properties of statolon under the direction of Sir Ernst Chain. This undertaking arose as a result of a suggestion made to Sir Ernst Chain by the late Dr. A. Isaacs. A grant was received from the Medical Research Council in order to facilitate these studies. The activities of these three research groups resulted in steady progress being made in the 1960s with respect to both statolon and helenine, leading to the ultimate discovery of the fungal viruses.

Lewis *et al.* (1960) at Merck, Sharpe, and Dohme obtained a helenine preparation from *P. funiculosum* mycelium by extraction with buffer, acetone precipitation, sedimentation by ultacentrifugation, and finally, chromatography on Ecteola cellulose. From tests carried out on the purified material, they concluded that it was almost certainly a ribonucleoprotein.

Kleinschmidt and Probst (1962) obtained a partially purified statolon preparation from five-day old culture filtrates of *P. stoloniferum* by a procedure which involved acetone precipitation, absorption onto Hyflo Supercell (a diatomaceous earth), elution with bicarbonate buffer, and removal of protein with butanol; an alternative procedure involved precipitation with isopropyl alcohol, treatment with sodium dodecyl sulphate, and further precipitation with ethanol and with lanthanum chloride. Both preparations contained polysaccharide, protein, and RNA. Kleinschmidt and Probst (1962) presented evidence which led them to conclude that statolon was a polyanionic polysaccharide. It is of interest to note that two of the reasons why they eliminated RNA as the active component were resistance to attack by ribonuclease and destruction of activity by periodate oxidation. However ds-RNA is resistant to ribonuclease, while it might be expected that periodate treatment would dissociate the RNA strands, resulting in loss of activity.

A major step forward was made by Kleinschmidt et al. (1964), who demonstrated that statolon exerted its antiviral effect in chick embryo cells by stimulating the production of interferon. Since only nucleic acids were known to induce interferon at that time (Isaacs and Lindenmann, 1957; Rotem et al. 1963), they attributed the presumed activity of their polyanionic polysaccharide to the structural similarities between it and RNA, both being polyanionic macromolecules. Rytel et al (1966) at Merck, Sharpe, and Dohme were also able to show that the antiviral effect of helenine in cell cultures and mice was due to its ability to induce interferon production.

The next major development was in 1967–68, when Hilleman and his colleagues published a series of excellent papers which demonstrated conclusively that only ds-RNA was capable of stimulating interferon production (Lampson et al., 1967; Field et al., 1967a,b, 1968; Tytell et al., 1967). They showed that ds-RNA was the active component of helenine and also that ds-RNA from other sources (for example, synthetic polynucleotides such as polyriboinosinic acid and polyribocytidilic acid, ds-RNA from Reovirus Type 3 virions, and the double-stranded replicative form of RNA from MS 2 coliphage) could induce interferon production.

At about this time, experimental work was being pursued actively by the group at Imperial College into the composition and properties of statolon. Initial investigations were concentrated on the need to purify the polyanionic polysaccharide thought to be responsible for interferon induction. Extensive use was made of the unique fermentation pilot plant facilities which exist at the College. Partially purified material was obtained from five-day old culture filtrates of *P. stoloniferum* produced in 400-l fermenters, by a procedure similar to that previously described involving acetone precipitation onto Hyflo Supercell (Kleinschmidt and Probst, 1962; Stark et al., 1963). Further purification of the crude material by ethanol fractionation and high-voltage electrophoresis produced some surprising results. As the polyanionic polysaccharide was progressively purified, it became progressively less active in stimulating interferon production. Furthermore, there appeared to be a correlation between the activity and phosphorus content of the various preparations. These observations, together with the findings of Hilleman and his colleagues which showed that ds-RNA was active in stimulating interferon production, suggested that RNA might, after all, be the active component of statolon. A purified RNA preparation, free of polysaccharide was, in fact, obtained from

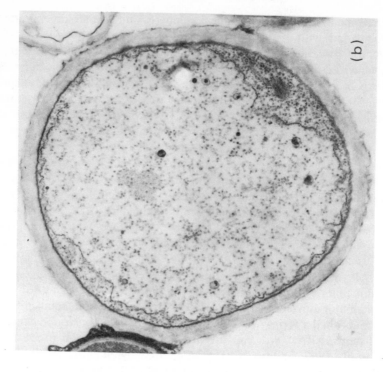

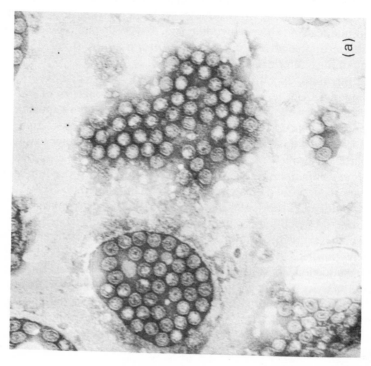

Figure 6.1 (a) Electron micrograph of purified *P. stoloniferum* virus (magnification ×146 000). (b) Electron micrograph of thin section through hyphal tip of *P. stoloniferum*, showing viral infection (magnification ×27 000)

two-day old mycelium by deproteinization with phenol/cresol/8-hydroxy quinoline after the method of Kirby (1965) and precipitation with ethanol/*m*-cresol, which induced interferon production. An incidental discovery was that a polyanionic polysaccharide, with similar composition and identical electrophoretic mobility to the polysaccharide previously designated statolon, could be isolated from soyabean meal, a component of the culture medium employed by both Kleinschmidt and his colleagues in the USA and the group at Imperial College. The presence of this polysaccharide could be demonstrated in the culture medium.

It was at this stage that Ellis and Kleinschmidt (1967) demonstrated the presence of virus-like particles at low concentrations in their statolon preparations by electron microscopy. These particles were polyhedral with a diameter of approximately 30 nm. Ellis and Kleinschmidt (1967) suggested that these particles might be associated with interferon-inducing activity since they were only present in active fractions. They also showed that the particles were present in thin sections of mycelia.

The cultures of *P. stoloniferum* were then examined by electron microscopy at Imperial College and the presence of virus-like particles was demonstrated in both two-day old mycelium and five-day old culture filtrates (Figure 6.1). It was evident that, in older cultures, the particles were liberated from the mycelium into the culture fluid by autolysis of the mycelium (see Figure 6.2).

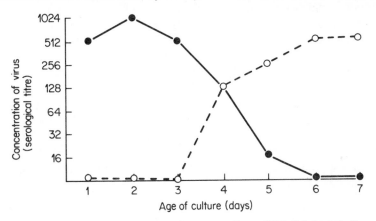

Figure 6.2 Release of virus from mycelium (●) of infected *P. stoloniferum* into culture fluid (○) during 7 days. Serological titres are reciprocals of maximum reacting dilutions of virus preparations in precipitin tube tests

In order to explore and exploit these new developments more rapidly, the Imperial College workers entered into collaboration with Hollings and his team at the Glasshouse Crops Research Institute who were the only group in the world with any experience of fungal viruses at that time. With the help of Hollings' group it was possible to obtain routinely partially purified virus preparations by a simple aqueous extraction procedure from two-day old mycelium. Such virus preparations could be further purified by rate–zonal density-gradient ultracentrifugation on sucrose columns. Both preparations were active in stimulating interferon production (Banks *et al.*, 1968). Furthermore, RNA preparations were obtained from partially purified virus using the phenol deproteinization techniques of Franklin (1966), the viral RNA being highly active in stimulating interferon production. Since the activity of the viral RNA could be destroyed by pancreatic ribonuclease at low ionic strength, but not at high ionic strength, it was concluded that ds-RNA was the active principle. The strain of *P. stoloniferum* employed for the studies both at Imperial College and at Eli Lilly and Company was ATCC 14586. Six other strains of *P. stoloniferum* were examined at Imperial College. None of these strains contained the virus and mycelial extracts of all six failed to exhibit interferon-inducing activity. Also, an isolate of Strain ATCC 14586, which remained free of any detectable virus infection after repeated serial subculture, was obtained by heat treatment of spores at 70°C; mycelial extracts and culture filtrates of this virus-free isolate failed to stimulate interferon production. Therefore heat treatment eliminated both the virus infection and the ability of the mould to produce an interferon-inducing substance. These observations constituted further proof, if any was needed, that the active component of statolon was of viral origin. Many of these findings were confirmed independently by Kleinschmidt *et al.* (1968). A strain of *P. funiculosum*, which was not identical to that employed by Hilleman and his colleagues, was obtained from Beecham Research Laboratories, and it was found that it too contained a polyhedral virus capable of stimulating interferon production. It thus seemed likely that helenine ds-RNA was of viral origin although, to the author's knowledge, this possibility has never been confirmed.

These observations, apart from indicating that viral ds-RNA was the active principle of both statolon and helenine, opened up the possibility that virus infections of filamentous fungi might be more wide-spread than had previously been imagined. An examination of other fungi was undertaken for possible viral content, in particular those fungi which had been reported to produce anti-viral compounds were investigated. Attention was, in fact, concentrated on three fungi, all members of the fungi imperfecti.

(*i*) *P. chrysogenum.* Strain No. Q.176, which had previously been reported by Sutherland and Bessel (1968, 1969) to produce an anti-viral compound.
(*ii*) *P. cyaneofulvum* Strain No. IMI 58138, reported to produce an anti-viral agent (Syeklocha 1962, 1964, 1967; Cooke and Stevenson, 1965*a,b*; David-West *et al.*, 1968*a,b*).
(*iii*) *Aspergillus foetidus* Strain No. IMI 41871. This organism has a high level of galactosamine in its cell wall, and in this respect, is similar to the virus-infected strain of *P. stoloniferum* (Buck *et al.*, 1969).

The Imperial College team, and collaborators, were able to demonstrate the presence of virus-like particles of similar morphologies (polyhedral particles 30–40 nm diameter) in mycelial extracts of all of the above fungi. In each case, ds-RNA was obtained from partially purified virus preparations and shown to be active in stimulating interferon production. (Banks *et al.*, 1969*a*,*b*; 1970). In the case of the two *Penicillium* species, it was considered that viral ds-RNA was almost certainly responsible for their reported antiviral properties. The viruses obtained from the three micro-organisms were shown to be unrelated serologically to each other and to the *P. stoloniferum* virus. Seven different penicillin-producing strains of *P. chrysogenum* were examined (Banks *et al.*, 1969*a*), which were closely related to each other and derived from strain NRRL 1951 by mutation and strain selection procedures; all contained virus-like particles. This result is of considerable interest because all modern high-yielding industrial strains are derived from these strains. Since the virus had presumably survived treatment with various mutagenic agents, it seemed likely that many of the current industrial strains were similarly infected. The presence of virus might be expected to influence host metabolism and hence the biosynthesis of penicillin. However, no reports have appeared in the scientific literature concerning the effect of the virus upon penicillin production, to the author's knowledge. This lack of published information is almost certainly due partly to the need to maintain industrial secrecy and partly due to the difficulty in eliminating and initiating virus infection.

Thus it will be seen that the research carried out independetly at Eli Lilly and Company, Merck, Sharpe, and Dohme, and Imperial College, on these two fungal products, statolon and helenine, converged and led to the discovery of the more wide-spread distribution of fungal viruses and to the inescapable conclusion that ds-RNA of viral origin is the active principle stimulating interferon production in both cases.

Collaboration was established between Imperial College and Beecham Research Laboratories, with financial support from the Medical Research Council. The experience and facilities offered by a firm like Beechams was considered to be essential for the rapid exploration and exploitation of the possible clinical and veterinary applications of fungal viruses and viral ds-RNA. Subsequent work at Imperial College was primarily devoted to the elucidation of the biological and biochemical properties of the viruses from *P. stoloniferum*, *P. chrysogenum*, *P. cyaneofulvum*, and *A. foetidus* with a view to gaining a greater understanding of the host-virus relationship. It was subsequently shown that *P. stoloniferum* contains not one but two distinct serologically unrelated viruses (Buck and Kempson-Jones 1970, 1973, 1974; Bozarth *et al.*, 1971). Similarly, two distinct viruses were found in both *A. foetidus* and the closely related *A. niger* strain IMI 146891. (Ratti and Buck 1972; Buck *et al.*, 1973; Buck and Ratti, 1975). In the case of the *A. foetidus* and *A. niger* viruses, it was found that the two viruses infecting each individual host strain are not serologically related to each other but are related to the corresponding viruses in the other host. At Beecham Research Laboratories, attention was focused on the *P. chrysogenum* virus, since it appeared to offer the best prospects for large-scale production. These subsequent developments are discussed in later chapters by Dr. Buck and by Dr. Dewdney.

PRODUCTION AND ISOLATION OF THE VIRUSES AND VIRAL ds-RNA

It was found that very similar procedures could be adopted for the isolation of viruses and viral ds-RNA P. *stoloniferum*, P. *chrysogenum*, P. *cyaneofulvum*, and A. *foetidus*. While small quantities of virus could be obtained from fermentations carried out on the shaken-flask scale, the larger quantities required for chemical/biochemical evaluation of the viral ds-RNA could only be obtained from pilot plant-scale fermentations. Procedures were therefore established for the routine isolation of virus from 60-l fermentations (Banks *et al.*, 1971). In all cases, virus was isolated from the fungal mycelium, the fermentations being terminated when maximal growth of the host organism was recorded. Isolation of virus from the mycelium was preferred to the alternative of isolating it from culture filtrates after autolysis. In the latter case the impurities present in the filtrates would have necessitated a more complex extraction procedure.

a. Shaken-flask scale

The fungus was grown in submerged culture in shaken flasks at 27°C in the appropriate medium (Banks *et al.*, 1968; 1969*a,b*; 1970). After 24 or 48 hours (time of maximal mycelial dry weight), 2–5 g wet weight of mycelium were collected by filtration and washed with distilled water. The mycelium was then thoroughly ground with carborundum powder and the virus extracted with 20 times this weight of 0·03 M phosphate buffer (pH 7·6). Debris were removed by low-speed centrifugation and the virus sedimented by ultracentrifugation at 78 000g for 90 minutes. The virus was then resuspended in 1–2 ml of the same buffer and debris again removed by low-speed centrifugation.

Further purification of the viruses could be effected by density-gradient ultracentrifugation. The actual techniques employed varied somewhat for the different viruses. For P. *stoloniferum*, purification was best accomplished on linear sucrose gradients (10–50 per cent) by rate–zonal ultracentrifugation at 69 000 *g* for 2 hours. In the case of P. *chrysogenum*, isopycnic ultracentrifugation on potassium tartrate columns (10–50 per cent) at 69 000 *g* for 18 hours gave the best results, while with P. *cyaneofulvum* and A. *foetidus*, optimal results were achieved by a similar technique, but using caesium chloride columns.

Viral RNA was obtained from purified, or occasionally crude, viral preparations by the phenol–sodium dodecyl sulphate procedure of Franklin (1966).

b. Pilot plant-scale

Fungal cultures were grown in submerged culture, again at 27°C in the appropriate medium, in conventionally designed stirred, baffled, sparger-aerated fermenters of 100 l capacity with a working liquid volume of 60 l. The fermentations were terminated when maximal fungal growth was recorded

(0·5–1·0 per cent mycelial dry weight after 24-48 hours) by rapidly chilling the fermenter contents to 4°C. The mycelium was collected by filtration using a plate and frame filter press, washed *in situ* with chilled distilled water, suspended in three times its weight of chilled 0·03 M phosphate buffer (pH 7·6), and disrupted by one passage through an APV Manton–Gaulin Homogenizer Type 18.M–8.BA operating at a pressure of 8000 psig. with a flow rate of 800 ml/min. The mycelial syspension and homogenate were maintained under chilled conditions throughout; a temperature rise of 10–15°C occurred during homogenization but the virus was only exposed to these higher temperatures for a very short period. Microscopic examination revealed that cell breakage was greater than 90 per cent in all cases. The homogenate was then diluted with the same chilled buffer to the original volume of the culture fluid. Cell debris was removed by passing the diluted homogenate through a Sharples Super Centrifuge Model AS–6 developing a centrifugal force of 13 200 g at a flow rate of approximately 1 l/min.

The method employed for concentration and purification of the virus particles was developed from that of Charney *et al.* (1961) for poliomyelitis virus on a laboratory scale. Yeast RNA (BDH) 0·02 per cent, dissolved in a minimum quantity of buffer was added to the chilled supernatant containing the virus. The pH of the supernatant was lowered slowly with 10 per cent acetic acid in order to form the insoluble yeast RNA-virus complex. The optimum pH for complex formation depended on the virus concerned; pH 4·0 was optimal for the *P. stoloniferum* virus, while pH 5·0 gave maximal recoveries for the other three viruses. After pH adjustment, the suspension was maintained overnight (12–18 hours) in an unagitated, cylindrical stainless steel vessel to facilitate complete precipitation. The precipitate was collected by passage of the suspension through the Sharples Centrifuge at a flow rate of 1 l/min. The net weight of the complex, derived from 60-l culture, was 100–300 g.

Further processing of the virus was carried out on the laboratory scale. The yeast RNA-virus complex was washed with 0·03 M phosphate buffer at pH 4·0 or 5·0 (depending upon the particular virus) and resuspended in approximately 600 ml of the phosphate buffer (pH 8·5) to dissociate the complex. After resuspension the fluid was adjusted to pH 7·6 with dilute sodium hydroxide solution. Debris was removed by low-speed centrifugation and the virus particles sedimented by ultracentrifugation at 35 000 g for 16 hours. The virus was then suspended in 10–50 ml of buffer (pH 7·6) and debris again removed by low-speed centrifugation. The resltant crude virus could be further purified by density-gradient ultracentrifugation, as previously described, and viral RNA obtained by the method of Franklin (1966).

The average yields of virus obtained from a 60-l fermenter, after purification by density-gradient ultracentrifugation, are shown in Table 6.1. The average final mycelial dry weights are also shown, together with the approximate RNA content of the purified viruses, for each host organism.

All purified viral preparations isolated exhibited an ultraviolet spectrum characteristic of ribonucleoprotein and were shown to be over 95 per cent pure

Table 6.1   Virus yields from 60-l fermenters

	Average final mycelial dry weight (per cent w/v)	Average weight of purified virus from 60-l fermentation (mg)	Approximate RNA content of virus (per cent w/w)
P. stoloniferum	0·9	450	16
P. chrysogenum	0·7	450	16
P. cyaneofulvum	0·5	60	16
A. foetidus	0·8	200	12

Data from Banks et al. (1971).
Reproduced by permission of The Institution of Chemical Engineers.

by centrifugation in a Beckman Model E analytical ultracentrifuge and examination with Schlieren optics.

More recently, an alternative procedure to that of Charney et al. (1961) for purification of the fungal viruses has been successfully introduced and routinely employed on the pilot-plant scale. The new technique is based upon that of Yamamoto et al. (1970) and involves precipitation of the extracted virus with 6–10 per cent polyethylene glycol in the presence of 0·5 M sodium chloride. The precipitated virus can then be recovered by centrifugation and final purification effected as previously described.

THE DOUBLE STRANDED NATURE OF VIRAL RNA

Viral RNA, obtained by the procedures described in the preceding section, was shown to be double-stranded by its characteristic behaviour on treatment with ribonuclease and on heating.

ds-RNA is stable to ribonuclease at high ionic strength but is susceptible to it at low ionic strength, when strand separation occurs. Viral RNA was dissolved in standard saline–citrate solution (SSC, consisting of 0·15 M sodium chloride, 0·015 M sodium citrate pH 7·0) and 0·1 SSC (10 × diluted SSC) and treated with Boehringer pancreatic ribonuclease at 23°C. Evidence of the double-stranded nature of viral RNA is given by the pronounced hyperchromic effect—increase in optical density at 260 nm due to the hydrolytic action of the enzyme—in 0·1 SSC but not in SSC. A typical set of results, obtained with the RNA from the P. cyaneofulvum virus, is illustrated in Figure 6.3a.

It can be seen that, in this particular case, there was a 29 per cent increase in optical density in 0·1 SSC after two hours incubation; the original RNA could not then be detected in the digest by polyacrylamide gel electrophoresis or analytical ultracentrifugation. In contrast, there was no detectable hyperchromic effect in SSC.

Heat denaturation of viral RNA was studied similarly by measuring the increase in optical density at 260 nm of RNA solutions in SSC and 0·1 SSC as a

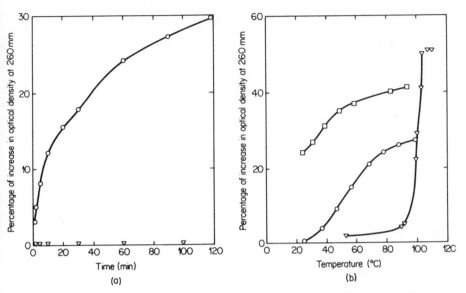

Figure 6.3 (a) Action of ribonuclease on viral RNA. ▽, viral RNA in SSC; ○, viral RNA in 0·1 SSC. (b) Thermal denaturation of RNA. ▽, viral RNA in SSC; ○, yeast RNA in SSC; □, viral RNA in 0·1 SSC, previously heated to 96°C and rapidly cooled.

function of temperature. A characteristic feature of ds-RNA subjected to steadily increasing temperatures is that it exhibits a sudden and dramatic increase in optical density over a very narrow temperature range due to strand separation. With single-stranded RNA (ss-RNA), however, denaturation occurs over a much wider range of temperatures. The double-stranded nature of the viral RNA is illustrated in Figure 6.3b, in which 'melting curves' for RNA from *P. cyaneofulvum* virus are shown. It can be seen that for viral ds-RNA in SSC, there is a sudden increase in optical density over the temperature range 95–105°C, the thermal transition mid-point being 101°C. For purposes of comparison, similar results obtained with yeast ss-RNA and viral RNA previously heated to 96°C in 0·1 SSC to separate the RNA strands are also shown in Figure 6.3b. In both these cases, denaturation occurs over a much wider temperature range. Similar results have been obtained with RNA preparations from the other fungal viruses.

INTERFERON-INDUCING AND ANTIVIRAL ACTIVITIES OF ds-RNA FROM FUNGAL VIRUSES

The interferon-stimulating properties of virus and viral RNA preparations were studied by injecting the preparations into groups of mice. Pooled lots of sera were analysed for interferon activity on monolayers of mouse embryo cells by the plaque-reduction method (Wagner, 1961). Treated and untreated cells were challenged with bovine vesicular stomatitis virus; 50 per cent end points were determined by interpolating between the probits of the percentage reduction values obtained from serial dilutions of the sera (Lindenmann and Gifford, 1963). A typical set of results, obtained with virus and viral RNA preparations obtained from *P. cyaneofulvum*, is shown in Table 6.2.

Table 6.2 Interferon-stimulating activity of viral RNA preparations from *P. cyaneofulvam* Strain CM1 58138

Viral RNA preparation	Weight of RNA injected per mouse (μg)	Interferon titre (PPD 50) of pooled sera from 15 mice
Purified intact viral preparation in SSC	83	78
Viral RNA in SSC	67	1064
Viral RNA in SSC treated with ribonuclease ($0 \cdot 2$ μg/ml) for 2 hr at 25°C	67	1016
Viral RNA in $0 \cdot 1$ SCC treated with ribonuclease ($0 \cdot 2$ μg/ml) for 2 hr at 25°C	72	<5

Data from Banks *et al.* (1969*b*).
Reproduced by permission of MacMillan (Journals) Ltd.

It can be seen that untreated viral RNA in SSC and viral RNA in SSC treated with ribonuclease both actively stimulated interferon production. However, the viral RNA in $0 \cdot 1$ SSC treated with ribonuclease did not. This result clearly demonstrates the active nature of viral ds-RNA. The lower interferon-stimulating activity exhibited by intact virus particles is associated with the 'protective' effect exerted by the protein coat of these particles. This result is consistent with the findings of Tytell *et al.* (1967) for reovirus and its RNA.

Table 6.3 Antiviral activity induced in mice by virus particles and viral RNA from *A. foetidus*

	Dose of challenge virus (mouse LD50)	Mortality* of mice pretreated with		Mortality* of control mice
		Aspergillus viral RNA	*Aspergillus* virus particles	
Encephalo-myocarditis virus	6·3	0/10	0/10	8/10
	63	3/10	0/10	10/10
	630	5/10	5/10	10/10
	6300	9/10	9/10	10/10
Semliki forest virus	50	1/10	3/10	10/10
	500	4/10	7/10	10/10
	5000	10/10	9/10	10/10

*11 days after administration of the challenge virus.
10 μg of the *Aspergillus* viral RNA, either in its free state or as virus particles, was injected intraperitoneally into 18 g mice 24 hr before administration of the challenge virus.
Data from Banks *et al.* (1970), with permission.

Assessment of the antiviral activities of intact viral particles and viral RNA preparations *in vivo* was undertaken both at Imperial College and at Beecham Research Laboratories. Typical results, obtained at Beecham Research Laboratories with preparations from *A. foetidus*, are shown in Table 6.3.

Single doses of 10 μg viral RNA, either in its free state or as intact particles, were injected into mice, and after 24 hours these mice were challenged with varying dilutions of encephalomyelocarditis or Semliki forest virus suspension administered intraperitoneally. The mortality rates were compared with those of untreated mice. The results clearly demonstrate that both free ds-RNA and the intact virus induce protection against the challenge viruses. Similar results have also been obtained with virus and viral RNA preparations from the other fungi.

INFECTIVITY OF THE FUNGAL VIRUSES

The polyhedral particles found in these filamentous fungi have been described throughout as virus-like particles or virus particles. At the time of the discovery of these particles in the fungi concerned, there was no conclusive evidence that they were true virus particles, since they had not been shown to be infective. Apart from infectivity, the particles possessed all the properties normally associated with viruses: characteristic morphology and staining properties when examined by electron microscopy; specific serological reactions; ultraviolet absorption spectra typical of viral nucleoproteins; and sedimentation patterns typical of small isometric viruses during density-gradient and analytical ultracentrifugation.

The importance of demonstrating infectivity was realized and the efforts at Imperial College were concentrated on the *P. stoloniferum* virus, since this was the first to be discovered and more information was available concerning the properties of the virus and of its host. In order to demonstrate infectivity, a virus-free, susceptible strain of the fungus was obviously required. In the case of *P. stoloniferum*, six virus-free-strains were available (Banks *et al.*, 1968), although it was not known whether they were susceptible to infection. The 'heat-cured' virus-free strain obtained from Strain ATCC 14586 (the infected strain) was also available. The fact that the heat-cured strain was related to the infected strain, and therefore more likely to be susceptible to viral infection, rendered it superficially attractive as a potential acceptor strain during infection; however, certain doubts were attached to this strain. Firstly, the strain might not have been fully cured, that is it might still have contained virus at a very low concentration which had escaped detection and which might have re-established itself during further subculture. Secondly, the heat treatment to which the strain had been subjected might not have resulted in 'curing' in the true sense, but simply in the selection of a virus-resistant variant. In view of these considerations, it was decided to use the 'wild-type' virus-free strains for infectivity studies. Early attempts at infection involved treatment of

114

mechanically damaged mycelium (to permit entry of virus through the ruptured cell wall) with viral suspensions. Such techniques, which had proved successful with the mushroom viruses (Hollings, 1962), were ineffective.

The Imperial College team was, at this time, strengthened by the addition of Dr. P. Lhoas, a fungal geneticist. Dr. Lhoas was able to demonstrate infectivity of the *P. stoloniferum* virus by two separate routes, namely heterokaryosis (Lhoas, 1971a) and by infection of naked protoplasts with virus suspensions (Lhoas, 1971b).

a. Infection by heterokaryosis

The donor strain was the normal infected strain ATCC 14586 with green conidia; the recipient strain was a white-conidiated mutant of the virus-free strain ATCC 10111, obtained by artificial mutation with n-methyl n-nitro nitrosoguanidine (NTG). The procedure for infection is illustrated diagrammatically in Figure 6.4.

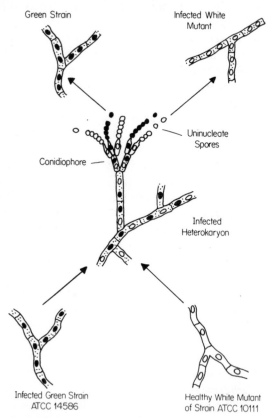

Figure 6.4 Diagrammatic representation of method employed for infection of *P. stoloniferum* by heterokaryosis

A mixture of conidia from the two parent strains were seeded onto an agar plate, and allowed to germinate and form mycelia. Heterokaryons were formed by hyphal anastomosis. Heterokaryotic conidiophores produced conidia of both the green and white types and could be distinguished from conidiophores of the two parent strains by careful stereomicroscopic examination. By equally careful manipulation, conidia of both types were taken from a single heterokaryotic conidiophore and plated onto agar medium to obtain discrete colonies. The white-conidiated isolates were sub-cultured in shaken flasks and examined for virus content by electron microscopy and polyacrylamide gel electrophoresis. A high proportion of these isolates were found to contain virus, that is the virus of the original green parent strain had been transmitted to the white mutant via heterokaryosis.

Infection of virus-free strains of a fawn-conidiated mutant of *P. stoloniferum* Strain CMI 91966 and *A. niger* (Lhoas, 1970) *via* heterokaryosis was also successfully accomplished.

b. Infection of protoplasts

Two recipient strains were employed: the white-conidiated mutant of Strain ATCC 10111 and the fawn-conidiated mutant of Strain CMI 91966, mentioned above. Both strains were grown in submerged culture in shaken flasks, the mycelium collected by filtration, washed with an isotonic medium, osmotically stabilized with a 1 M ammonium chloride, and then suspended in isotonic medium containing helicase (a crude mixed enzyme preparation from the gut of the snail, *Helix pomatia*). Under these conditions, cell-wall lysis occurred and naked protoplasts were formed. Cell debris was removed by filtration through 20 μm nylon mesh, the protoplasts collected by centrifugation, and washed with isotonic medium to remove residual enzyme. The protoplast suspension was mixed with an equal volume of viral suspension (10^9 particles/ml) obtained from the green-conidiated strain ATCC 14586 and incubated for 30 minutes to facilitate infection. The protoplasts were again collected by centrifugation, washed with isotonic medium to remove free virus particles, and finally suspended in regenerating medium, osmotically stabilized with 1 M sucrose. The protoplasts were then plated onto regenerating agar medium to obtain discrete colonies. In the cases of both the white and fawn-conidiated mutant strains, a high proportion of the treated isolates were found to contain virus when examined by electron microscopy and polyacrylamide gel electrophoresis.

The results of these infection studies have left no room for doubt that the polyhedral particles observed in these fungi are indeed virus particles. A further feature to emerge from these studies is that the newly infected fungal strains are no different, in terms of morphological characteristics or growth rates, from the corresponding uninfected strains, that is the presence of the virus has no profound outward effect on either the morphology or the growth of the host.

116

ACKNOWLEDGEMENTS

It is hoped that this account of the discovery of the fungal viruses, and the events which led to their discovery, will illustrate the degree of collaboration required between biologists, biochemists, chemists and chemical engineers. In this context, the author wishes to emphasize the 'team' nature of the work carried out at Imperial College and to acknowledge the contributions made by other members of the team, including Mrs. J. E. Darbyshire (preliminary microbiological studies), Dr. K. W. Buck, Dr. G. F. Kempson-Jones, Dr. G. Ratti, and Dr. M. Szekely (biochemical/chemical studies of the viruses and viral RNA), Dr. F. Himmelweit (interferon assays and virological investigations), Dr. D. Border (electron microscopy), Dr. P. Lhoas (infection studies), Mr. A. Fleming, and the staff of the Fermentation Pilot Plant (large-scale preparation of virus and viral RNA). Acknowledgements are also due to collaborators, principally Dr. M. Hollings and Dr. O. Hollings (née Stone) at the Glasshouse Crops Research Institute, and Dr. J. Dewdney, Dr. D. N. Planterose, and others at Beecham Research Laboratories.

It is almost unnecessary to state that the work conducted at Imperial College owes much to the vision, energy, and enthusiasm of Sir Ernst Chain, who initiated these studies and directed them throughout. Sir Ernst has always passionately advocated not only the necessity for close collaboration between scientists of different disciplines but also the realization of the importance of the biological approach to biochemistry. His beliefs are summarized in the following extract from his Inaugural Lecture at Imperial College in May, 1964.

'The importance of the biological approach to biochemical research. Many great biochemical discoveries had at their origin a biological observation which subsequently, through the application of suitable biochemical techniques, could be explained in chemical terms. The sequence of events in these cases was always: biology first, chemistry second—not *vice versa*. The importance of the biological approach for biochemical research cannot be over-emphasized. Close contact and collaboration in a harmonious team between the biochemist and the biologist in the different regions of the biological sciences—and this includes, it should not be forgotten, clinical medicine—has been a characteristic feature of much successful biochemical research in the past and will increasingly become such in the future.'

The events and activities which culminated in the discovery of these fungal viruses and the role of viral ds-RNA in stimulating the production of interferon in animal tissues represent one of many examples which confirm the validity of Sir Ernst's views.

REFERENCES

Banks, G. T., Buck, K. W., Chain, E. B., Himmelweit, F., Marks, J. E., Tyler, J. M., Hollings, M., Last, F. T., and Stone, O. M. (1968) *Nature (London)*, **218**, 542.

Banks, G. T., Buck, K. W., Chain, E. B., Darbyshire, J. E., and Himmelweit, F. (1969a) *Nature (London)*, **222**, 82.

Banks, G. T., Buck, K. W., Chain, E. B., Darbyshire, J. E., and Himmelweit, F. (1969b) *Nature (London)*, **223**, 155.

Banks, G. T., Buck, K. W., Chain, E. B., Darbyshire, J. E., Himmelweit, F., Ratti, G., Sharpe, T. J., and Planterose, D. N. (1970) *Nature (London)*, **227**, 505.

Banks, G. T., Buck, K. W., and Fleming, A. (1971) *Chem. Eng.*, No. 251, July 1971.

Bozarth, R. F., Wood, H. A., and Mandelbrot, A. (1971) *Virology*, **45**, 516.

Buck, K. W., Chain, E. B., and Darbyshire, J. E. (1969), *Nature (London)*, **223**, 1273.

Buck, K. W., Girvan, R. F., and Ratti, G. (1973) *Biochem. Soc. Trans.*, **1**, 1138.

Buck, K. W., and Kempson-Jones, G. F. (1970), *Nature (London)*, **225**, 945.

Buck, K. W., and Kempson-Jones, G. F. (1973), *J. Gen. Virol.*, **18**, 223.

Buck, K. W., and Kempson-Jones, G. F. (1974) *J. Gen. Virol.*, **22**, 441.

Buck, K. W., and Ratti, G. (1975) *J. Gen. Virol.*, **27**, 211.

Charney, J., Machlowitz, R., Tytell, A. A., Sagin, J. F., and Spicer, D. S. (1961) *Virology*, **15**, 269.

Cochran, K. W., Brown, G. C., and Francis, T. (1954) *Proc. Soc. Exp. Biol. Med.*, **85**, 104.

Cochran, K. W., and Payne, F. E. (1964) *Proc. Soc. Exp. Biol. Med.*, **115**, 471.

Cooke, P. M., and Stevenson, J. W. (1965a) *Can. J. Microbiol.*, **11**, 913.

Cooke, P. M., and Stevenson, J. W. (1965b) *Can. J. Microbiol.*, **11**, 921.

David-West, T. S., Cooke, P. M., and Stevenson J. W. (1968a) *Can. J. Microbiol.*, **14**, 189.

David-West, T. S., Cooke, P. M., and Stevenson, J. W. (1968b) *Can. J. Microbiol.*, **14**, 197.

Ellis, L. F., and Kleinschmidt, W. J. (1967), *Nature (London)*, **215**, 649.

Field, A. K., Lampson, G. P., Tytell, A. A., Neimes, M. M., and Hilleman, M. R. (1967b) *Proc. Nat. Acad. Sci. U.S.A.*, **58**, 2102.

Field, A. K., Tytell, A. A., Lampson, G. P., and Hilleman, M. R. (1967a) *Proc. Nat. Acad. Sci. U.S.A.*, **58**, 1004

Field, A. K., Tytell, A. A., Lampson, G. P., and Hilleman, M. R. (1968) *Proc. Nat. Acad. Sci. U.S.A.*, **61**, 340.

Franklin, R. M. (1966) *Proc. Nat. Acad. Sci. U.S.A.*, **55**, 1504.

Furusawa, E., Cutting, W., and Furst, A. (1963), *Proc. Soc. Exp. Biol. Med.*, **112**, 617.

Hollings, M. (1962), *Nature (London)*, **196**, 962.

Hollings, M., and Stone, O. M. (1969) *Sci. Prog. (Oxford)*, **57**, 371.

Hollings, M., and Stone, O. M. (1971) *Ann. Rev. Phytopathol.*, **9**, 93.

Hull, R. N., and Lavell, J. M. (1953) *Proc. Soc. Exp. Biol. Med.*, **83**, 787.

Hull, R. N., and Lavell, J. M. (1954) *Ann. New York Acad. Sci.*, **58**, 1188.

Isaacs, A., and Lindenmann, J. (1957) *Proc. Roy. Soc., Series B*, **147**, 258.

Johnson, I. S., and Baker, L. A. (1958) *Antibiot. Chemotherapy*, **8**, 113.

Kirby, K. S. (1965) *Biochem. J.*, **96**, 266.

Kleinschmidt, W. J., and Probst, G. W., (1962) *Antiobiot. Chemotherapy*, **12**, 298.

Kleinschmidt, W. J., Cline, J. C., and Murphy, E. B., (1964) *Proc. Nat. Acad. Sci.*, **52**, 741.

Kleinschmidt, W. J., and Murphy, E. B. (1965) *Virology*, **27**, 484.

Kleinschmidt, W. J., Ellis, L. F., Van Frank, R. M., and Murphy, E. B. (1968), *Nature (London)*, **220**, 176.

Lampson, G. P., Tytell, A. A., Field, A. K., Neimes, M. M., and Hilleman, M. R. (1967) *Proc. Nat. Acad. Sci.*, **58**, 782.

Lewis, U. J., Rickes, E. L., Williams, D. E., McClelland, L., and Brink, N. G., (1960) *J. Am. Chem. Soc.*, **82**, 5178.

Lhoas, P. (1970) *Aspergillus News Letter*, **11**, 8.

Lhoas, P. (1971a) *Nature*, **230**, 248.

118

Lhoas, P. (1971b) J. Gen. Virol., 13, 365.
Lindenmann, J., and Gifford, G. E. (1963) Virology, 19, 302.
Powell, H. M., Culbertson, C. G., McGuire, J. M., Hoehn, M. M., and Baker, L. A. (1952) Antibiot. Chemotherapy, 2, 432.
Powell, H. M., and Culbertson, C. G. (1953a) Proc. Soc. Exp. Biol. Med., 83, 161.
Powell, H. M., and Culbertson, C. G. (1953b) In Antibiotics Annual 1953–1954 (Welch, A., and Marti-Ibanez, F. ed.) Medical Encyclopedia Inc. New York. p. 147.
Powell, H. M., Walcher, D. N., and Mast, C. (1961) Proc. Soc. Exp. Biol. Med., 107, 55.
Powell, H. M., Walcher, D. N., and Mast, C. (1962) Antibiot. Chemotherapy, 12, 337.
Probst, G. W., and Kleinschmidt, W. J. (1961) Fed. Proc., 20, 441.
Ratti, G., and Buck, K. W. (1972) J. Gen. Virol., 14, 165.
Rotem, Z., Cox, R. A., and Isaacs, A. (1963) Nature (London), 197, 564.
Rytel, M. W., Shope, R. E., and Kilbourne, E. D. (1966) J. Exp. Med., 123, 577.
Shope, R. E. (1953a) J. Exp. Med., 97, 601.
Shope, R. E. (1953b) J. Exp. Med., 97, 627.
Stark, W. M., Kleinschmidt, W. J., and Probst, G. W. (1963) U.S. Pat. 3 108 047.
Sutherland, E. S., and Bessel, C. J. (1968) Belgian Pat. 691 881.
Sutherland, E. S., and Bessel, C. J. (1969) British Pat. 1 170 929.
Syeklocha, D. (1962) M.Sc. Thesis, McGill University, Montreal.
Syeklocha, D. (1964) Ph.D. Thesis, McGill University, Montreal.
Syeklocha, D., Cooke, P. M., and Stevenson, J. W. (1967) Canad. J. Microbiol., 13, 1481.
Tytell, A. A., Lampson, G. P., Field, A. K., and Hilleman, M. R. (1967) Proc. Nat. Acad. Sci. U.S.A., 58, 1719.
Wagner, R. R. (1961) Virology, 13, 323.
Yamamoto, K. R., Alberts, B. M., Benzinger, R., Lawhorne, L., and Treiber, G. (1970) Virology, 40, 734.

DISCUSSION

Dr. S. Ochoa

Is it correct that you actually infect the fungi with the virus?

Mr. G. Banks

Yes, this is exactly what Dr. Lhoas has demonstrated and the viruses were repeatedly subcultured. Yields can be very high.

Dr. J. Dewdney

We haven't got high yields from artificially infected strains, but from the natural strains we have yields in kilogram quantities.

Mr. G. Banks

If there is one sure way of making Sir Ernst happy, it is to produce something in kilogram quantities!

Sir Ernst Chain

Is Professor Pirt here? Do you remember, when you worked in Rome we had a phenomenon, in transferring *P. chrysogenum* to a different culture medium? We got good growths for about 18 hours and then suddenly lysis. We thought there must be something like a virus; suddenly that phenomenon disappeared, and unfortunately, we could never repeat the observation.

Professor S. Pirt

It was in 1952, and coincided with the use of glucose and lactose in the defined medium. So in theory there should have been induction of β-galactosidase. Instead, the organism collapsed. This follow-up 20 years later is a fascinating illustration of the complexity which you can have changing from one organism to another.

Dr. S. Ochoa

Do fungi produce anti-viral substances?

Mr. G. Banks

This has not been directly confirmed in artificially infected strains.

Sir Ernst Chain

The point was the emergence of a new biological phenomenon. Originally we thought interferon was a polysaccharide. We never realized that there were really two organisms present and that there might be a virus present in complete symbiosis with the fungus.

7
Biochemical and Biological Implications of Double-stranded RNA Mycoviruses

K. W. Buck

Department of Biochemistry,
Imperial College of Science and Technology, London, U.K.

INTRODUCTION

Since the discovery of viruses associated with a die-back disease of the cultivated mushroom, *Agaricus bisporus*, (Hollings, 1962) and the discovery of virus particles associated with the antiviral activity of statolon, a product obtained from the mould *Penicillium stoloniferum* (Ellis and Kleinschmidt, 1967; see the previous chapter by G. T. Banks), many different fungal viruses (mycoviruses) have been described. The purpose of the present article is not to present a comprehensive coverage of this rapidly developing field, which has been reviewed by Hollings and Stone (1969; 1971), Bozarth (1972), and Lemke and Nash (1974), but to attempt to draw some conclusions from the data on fungal viruses which have accumulated, and to discuss their biological and biochemical implications.

VIRUSES ARE WIDESPREAD IN THE FUNGAL KINGDOM

Virus particles have been discovered in just over 100 fungal species from more than 60 genera spread among the five subdivisions of the Eumycota (Table 7.1). It is likely that this figure will be increased substantially in the future, since Bozarth (1972) estimated that 10–15 per cent of randomly sampled fungal isolates contains virus particles, as detected by electron microscopy, and he considered that viruses could be found in any species with diligent searching. Ainsworth (1968) estimated that there are about 50 000 well-defined fungal species (in addition to a large undescribed population), but the number of distinct fungal viruses will depend on how often a particular virus occurs in different fungal species and on the number of viruses which can infect a particular species, that is on the host range of the viruses.

The known incidence of viruses in fungi is compared with that in other phyla in Table 7.2. The apparent uneven distribution of viruses within these phyla is

Table 7.1 Distribution of morphological virus types[a] among subdivisions of the Eumycota[b]

Virus morphology	Probable genome type	Number of viruses					
		Ascomycotina	Basidiomycotina	Deuteromycotina	Zygomycotina	Mastigomycotina	Total
Small isometric (25–50 nm diameter)	ds-RNA	10	25	33	—	1	69
Large isometric (100–200 nm diameter)	ds-DNA	—	1	—	1	1	3
Bacilliform	ss-RNA	1	1	—	—	—	2
Filamentous	ss-RNA	—	4	—	—	—	4
Rods	ss-RNA	1	1	2	—	—	4
Herpes-like	ds-DNA	—	—	—	—	1	1
T-phage-type with head and tail	ds-DNA	1	—	5[c]	—	—	6
Polymorphic with membrane envelope	ss-RNA	1	—	—	—	—	1
Total		14	32	40	1	3	90

[a] Based on electron microscopy. For lists of infected fungal species see Bozarth (1972), Lemke and Nash (1974), Moffit and Lister (1975), Yamashita *et al.* (1975). Viruses of unspecified morphology from 30 fungal species, reported by Bozarth (1972), are not included in this table.

[b] Fungal classification as described by Ainsworth (1973). No viruses have been reported in the division Myxomycota, with the possible exception of isometric particles detected in *Dermocystidium marinum* (=*Labyrinthomyxa marina*?), an organism of problematic taxonomic position (Perkins, 1974).

[c] Viruses from *Penicillium* cultures, which multiply in bacteria (Tikchonenko *et al.*, 1974). While it is clear that these viruses multiply in bacteria, confirmatory evidence that they multiply in fungi is awaited with interest.

Table 7.2 Incidence of viruses in different phyla

	Phylum	Number of species infected[a]
Prokaryotes	Bacteria and blue-green algae	+++
Eukaryotes	Fungi	+++
	Algae	+
	Pteridophytes	+
	Gymnosperms	+
	Angiosperms	+++
	Protozoa	+
	Nematodes	(+)
	Arthropods	+++
	Molluscs	+
	Vertebrates	+++

Viruses have not been reported from lower plants such as diatoms, bryophytes, and cycads, nor from many phyla of lower animals such as the sponges, coelenterates, platyhelminths, rotifers, polyzoa, brachiopods, annelids, and echinoderms.
[a] Number of species with which viruses are known to be associated: +, 1–10 species; +++, >100 species. Table adapted from Gibbs and Harrison (1976). Reproduced by permission of Edward Arnold (Publishers) Ltd.

probably merely a reflection of the rather uneven concentration of activity of virologists. The most widely studied viruses are those which cause disease in man, domesticated animals, and plants, those which may be of value in controlling unwanted organisms, and those which are of interest to the biochemist as model systems. The absence of reports of viruses from some phyla of lower plants and animals probably reflects the absence of diligent searches for viruses in these phyla.

MANY FUNGAL VIRUSES HAVE GENOMES OF DOUBLE-STRANDED RNA

A number of different morphological types of virus particles has been found in fungi (Table 7.1), but by far the most common are the small isometric particles (Group A), an example of which is shown in Figure 7.1. Less than 20 of these isometric viruses have been isolated and purified, but in every one of these cases the virus nucleic acid has been found to be double-stranded RNA (ds-RNA) (Table 7.3). Using a serological test for ds-RNA, Moffitt and Lister (1975) found ds-RNA in mycelial extracts of more than 20 per cent of about 70 fungal isolates which they screened, suggesting the widespread occurrence of ds-RNA viruses in fungi, although it should be remembered that small amounts of ds-RNA may be isolated from cells infected with single-stranded RNA (ss-RNA) or DNA viruses (Ralph, 1969). That this figure is actually higher than the estimate of Bozarth (1972) of virus particles in 10–15 per cent of randomly sampled fungi observed by electron microscopy may be due to (*i*)

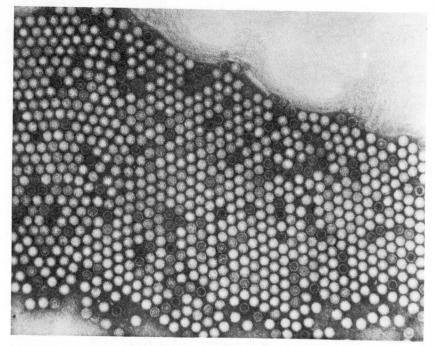

Figure 7.1 Electron micrograph magnification of virus particles, isolated from *Colletotrichum lindemuthianum*, negatively stained with phosphotungstate (magnification × 90 000). (Courtesy of Dr. C. J. Rawlinson)

random variation because the number of isolates tested was comparatively small, (*ii*) the greater sensitivity of the ds-RNA assay compared with the electron microscopic assay, or (*iii*) the occurrence of 'free' ds-RNA in some fungi. ds-RNA, was detected in *Endothia parasitica* in quantities where virus particles would have been detected easily by electron microscopy. However, two independent groups have failed to detect virus particles in this fungus (Moffit and Lister, 1975). In the following discussions only those mycoviruses whose genomes have been proved to be ds-RNA will be considered; these are listed in Table 7.3.

ds-RNA MYCOVIRUSES DIFFER FROM OTHER KNOWN ds-RNA VIRUSES

Viruses with ds-RNA genomes are widely distributed in nature, being found in animals, plants, and bacteria, as well as in fungi (Table 7.3; Wood, 1973; Joklik, 1974). All the ds-RNA viruses discovered so far have two properties in common: their genomes consist of multiple segments of ds-RNA rather than a single molecule and the virus particles possess an RNA polymerase. Many RNA viruses of eukaryotes are now known to have multi-partite genomes, for example, influenza virus, brome mosaic virus, and alfalfa mosaic virus (Jaspars,

Table 7.3   Three families of ds-RNA viruses

1. Reoviridae*
   (a) *Reovirus genus*, viruses of vertebrates, including human reovirus, avian reovirus.
   (b) *Orbivirus genus*, viruses of vertebrates, which are transmitted by, and also multiply in, insects; possess large ring-like capsomers; about 50 members including blue tongue virus of sheep, African horse sickness virus.
   (c) *Cytoplasmic polyhedrosis virus genus*, viruses form polyhedral inclusion bodies in mid-gut of about 80 species of insects.
   (d) *Plant virus genus* (or *genera*), viruses infect plants and are transmitted by leafhopper vectors in which they also multiply, e.g. clover wound tumour virus, rice dwarf virus, Fiji disease virus.
   (e) *Rotavirus genus*, viruses have a wheel-like appearance and are a major cause of acute gastroenteritis in children and domestic animals.

2. ds-RNA mycoviruses
   Aspergillus foetidus viruses S and F (Ratti and Buck, 1972)
   A. niger viruses S and F (Buck *et al.*, 1973a)
   Colletotrichum lindemuthianum virus (Rawlinson *et al.*, 1975)
   Gaeumannomyces graminis viruses (Rawlinson *et al.*, 1973)
   Mushroom viruses 1 and 4 (Hollings, 1975)
   Penicillium brevicompactum virus (Wood *et al.*, 1971)
   P. chrysogenum virus (Buck *et al.*, 1971)
   P. cyaneofulvum virus (Banks *et al.*, 1969)
   P. stoloniferum viruses S and F (Bozarth *et al.*, 1971)
   Periconia circinata virus (Dunkle, 1974)
   Saccharomyces cerevisiae virus (Herring and Bevan, 1974)
   Ustilago maydis virus (Wood and Bozarth, 1973)

3. Cystoviridae
   Bacteriophage φ6, from *Pseudomonas phaseolytica* (Vidaver *et al.*, 1973).

* For further details see Joklik (1974), and Fenner (1975, 1976).

1974). This property is considered to promote rapid recombinations in mixed infections with different strains of a virus, since new 'strains' are easily formed by selecting components from a pool without any requirement for recombination enzymes, and so provides an evolutionary advantage for such a virus. It may also provide a convenient way of producing monocistronic viral messenger RNA (mRNA), which seems to be preferred by the eukaryotic cell. The presence of a particle RNA polymerase is considered essential for the infectivity of a ds-RNA virus, since ds-RNA cannot be translated as such, but must first be transcribed into mRNA. Since no cellular enzyme has been described which will transcribe viral ds-RNA, the virus must take its own transcriptase into the host cell.

There appears to be, however, a number of differences between ds-RNA mycoviruses, ds-RNA viruses of animals and higher plants (*Reoviridae*, Fenner, 1975, 1976), and phage φ6 (*Cystoviridae*, Fenner, 1976), the only known ds-RNA virus which infects a bacterium (Vidaver *et al.*, 1973). In the following sections, in which properties of ds-RNA mycoviruses are described, comparisons with the ds-RNA viruses of other phyla will be made where appropriate.

CAPSIDS OF ds-RNA MYCOVIRUSES ARE BUILT UP FROM ONE MAJOR SPECIES OF POLYPEPTIDE

ds-RNA mycoviruses consist of small polyhedral particles with diameters in the range 25 to 40 nm and with particle molecular weights ranging from 6×10^6 to 13×10^6. The capsids are single-layered and are built up from one major species of polypeptide, the molecular weight of which may range from 42 000 to 130 000 (Table 7.4). In the few cases examined, the capsid has been found to be built up of either 120 or 60 molecules of the major polypeptide. Although no detailed morphological studies by electron microscopy or X-ray diffraction have been carried out these data are consistent with icosahedral structures built up of 60 structural units, with each unit consisting of either one or two polypeptide chains, depending on whether the capsid contains 60 or 120 polypeptide chains, respectively.

Table 7.4 Molecular weights and numbers of major polypeptide subunits in ds-RNA mycoviruses

Virus	Polypeptide molecular weight	Number/ viral particle*	Reference
Penicillium stoloniferum virus S	42 000	120	a
Penicillium stoloniferum virus F	47 000		a
Colletotrichum lindemuthianum virus	52 000		b
Mushroom virus 4	64 000		c
Gaeumannomyces graminis virus	70 000		d
Saccharomyces cerevisiae virus	75 000		e
Aspergillus foetidus virus S	83 000	120	f
Aspergillus foetidus virus F	87 000	120	f
Penicillium chrysogenum virus	130 000	60	g
Penicillium cyaneofulvum virus	130 000	60	g

* Absence of a value indicates that no data is available. References: *a* Buck and Kempson-Jones (1974); *b* Rawlinson *et al.* (1975); *c* Hollings (1975); *d* Rawlinson *et al.* (1973); *e* Herring, personal communication; *f* Buck and Ratti (1975); *g* Buck and Girvan (1977).

Small amounts of minor polypeptide components are often detected in the particles of ds-RNA mycoviruses. These may either be the RNA polymerase molecules, or arise by proteolytic cleavage of the major coat protein or RNA polymerase either *in vivo* or during isolation of the virus. The virus RNA polymerase molecules have been identified in only two cases. *P. stoloniferum* virus S particles contain one molecule of single-chain RNA polymerase of molecular weight 55 500, whereas *P. stoloniferum* virus F particles contain one or two molecules of RNA polymerase of molecular weight 59 000 (Buck and Kempson-Jones, 1974). The RNA polymerase molecules are presumably bound to the RNA in the interior of the virus particle; empty particles lacking RNA do not contain the RNA polymerase molecules. *A. foetidus* virus F contains two minor polypeptides (molecular weight 125 000 and 100 000), each present in the amount of one molecule per particle, but it is not known whether one or both of these polypeptides is required for RNA polymerase activity (Buck and Ratti, 1975a,b).

In contrast to the ds-RNA mycoviruses, viruses of the *Reoviridae* family have much larger polyhedral particles (60–80 nm in diameter) with complex capsids consisting of two layers and composed of several polypeptide species. The capsid polypeptides of reovirus, the best studied member of the *Reoviridae*, and two ds-RNA mycoviruses are compared in Table 7.5. The RNA polymerase of reovirus lies in the inner shell, or core, but it has not been demonstrated on which of the core polypeptides the catalytic sites are situated. Reovirus cores possess 12 hollow projections or spikes, comprised of polypeptide $\lambda 2$, which are located as if on the 12 five-fold vertices of an icosahedron and which act as exit channels for the mRNA synthesized by the polymerase; removal of the spikes abolishes polymerase activity (White and Zweerink, 1976).

Bacteriophage $\phi 6$ differs from both the ds-RNA mycoviruses and the *Reoviridae*, in that although its inner capsid is polyhedral (diameter 60 nm) it is enclosed in a lipoprotein envelope, which is essential for its infectivity (Vidaver *et al.*, 1973).

Table 7.5 Comparison of the capsid polypeptides of reovirus and two ds-RNA mycoviruses

Virus	Polypeptide	Molecular weight	Number per particle	Location/ function
Reovirus*	$\lambda 1$	153 000	110	core
	$\lambda 2$	148 000	90	core (spikes)
	$\lambda 3$	143 000	<20	core
	P_{135}	135 000	<20	unknown
	$\mu 1$	79 000	20	core
	$\mu 3$	72 000	<20	unknown
	P_{73}	73 000	550	outer shell
	$\sigma 1$	54 000	200	core
	$\sigma 2$	52 000	30	outer shell
	$\sigma 4$	43 000	900	outer shell
Penicillium stoloniferum virus S	S1	56 000	1	RNA polymerase
	S2	42 000	120	structural
Aspergillus foetidus virus F	$\phi 1$	125 000	1 ⎫	RNA polymerase
	$\phi 2$	100 000	1 ⎭	
	$\phi 3$	87 000	120	structural

* Data compiled from Smith *et al.* (1969), Both *et al.* (1975), and Shatkin and Both (1976). Molecular weights and polypeptide nomenclature are those given by Shatkin and Both (1976).

RNA COMPONENTS OF ds-RNA MYCOVIRUSES ARE ENCAPSIDATED SEPARATELY

The genomes of ds-RNA mycoviruses contain from two to six segments of ds-RNA with molecular weights varying from $0\cdot06 \times 10^6$ to $2\cdot9 \times 10^6$ (Figure

7.2) and total molecular weight from $2 \cdot 0 \times 10^6$ to $8 \cdot 5 \times 10^6$. With few exceptions, it has been found that each ds-RNA component is encapsidated separately, producing a series of particles each of which contains only one molecule of RNA. ds-RNA mycoviruses are therefore multi-component systems. An

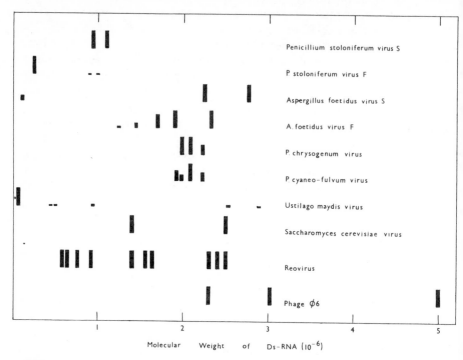

Figure 7.2 Molecular weights and relative molar proportions of ds-RNA components of ds-RNA mycoviruses, reovirus, and bacteriophage $\phi 6$. RNA proportions are expressed relative to the component in greatest amount, which is taken arbitrarily as unity in each case

example is provided by *A. foetidus* virus F (Figure 7.3). An exception is found in *A. foetidus* virus S, in which the small RNA component (Figure 7.2) occurs only in particles containing separately each of the two larger RNA species (Buck and Ratti, 1975a, b); this small RNA may have a special function in the control of transcription. Preparations of ds-RNA mycoviruses often contain intermediates of ds-RNA replication, which add further to their heterogeneity.

Separate encapsidation of genome segments would appear to be a disadvantage for a virus which must infect from outside the cell, since each of the several components must be taken up together by the host in order to ensure infection. This, however, would not be a drawback in the case of viruses which are transmitted by insects, in which case large quantities of virus may be injected into the host. However ds-RNA mycoviruses may never need to infect from without and probably always remain intracellular. In such cases, separate

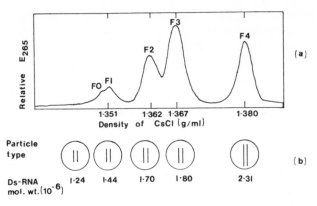

Figure 7.3 Separate encapsidation of the five ds-RNA components of *A. foetidus* virus F. (*a*) Isopycnic centrifugation of *A. foetidus* virus F particles in a caesium chloride density gradient. The preparation was centrifuged at 40 000 rev/min for 18 hours in a Beckman Model E analytical ultracentrifuge and then scanned at 265 nm. (*b*) Diagrammatic representation of the five particle types. Each particle type has the same capsid, but a different ds-RNA component and hence a different density

encapsidation of RNA species may be an advantage in that it allows considerable variation in the proportion of different RNA components, which could be important in the control of gene expression either by selective gene amplication or suppression. Moreover separate encapsidation eliminates the need for selection of each RNA component, which would be required if all RNA components were encapsidated in one particle.

The genomes of members of the *Reoviridae* contain 10–12 RNA segments with molecular weights varying from 0.2×10^6 to 2.8×10^6, and total genome molecular weight from 12×10^6 to 15×10^6. In contrast to the ds-RNA mycoviruses, all 10 ds-RNA components of reovirus (Figure 7.2), and those of other members of the *Reoviridae*, are enclosed together in single virus particles. The three RNA components of phase $\phi6$ (Figure 7.2) are apparently also all enclosed within one particle. These viruses infect from outside the cell, and it is clear in the case of the *Reoviridae*, with their large numbers of RNA components, that encapsidation of all the genome segments in single particles is necessary to ensure an efficient infection process.

IN MIXED INFECTIONS WITH TWO SEROLOGICALLY UNRELATED ds-RNA MYCOVIRUSES THERE IS NO GENOMIC MASKING

Mixed infections with two serologically unrelated viruses appear to be quite common in fungi, for example *P. stoloniferum* viruses S and F (Buck and Kempson-Jones, 1970; Bozarth *et al.*, 1971), *A. foetidus* viruses S and F (Buck and Ratti, 1975a), A. niger viruses S and F (Buck et al., 1973a). However no phenotypic mixing (mixing of polypeptides in the virus capsids) or genomic masking (encapsidation of the RNA components of one virus by the capsid of the other) has been observed in any case. Originally it was thought that one RNA component may have been common to both A. niger viruses (Buck et al., 1973a), but this was later disproved when it was found that the two viruses had an RNA component of identical molecular weight, but quite different base composition (Buck, unpublished results). Phenotype mixing and genomic masking usually occur readily in vivo between related viruses, and genomic masking, but not phenotypic mixing, has been reported between structurally dissimilar unrelated bacterial, animal, and plant viruses (Dodds and Hamilton, 1976). In the cases of the ds-RNA mycoviruses referred to above, the ds-RNA components of the two viruses are in the same size range, so that genomic masking is not prevented by gross differences in genome size. In a study of the replication of P. stoloniferum viruses in vivo using fluorescent antibody techniques Adler and Mackenzie (1972) found that both viruses occur together in the cytoplasm; hence the absence of genomic masking is not due to compartmentalization of the two viruses. It is likely that the answer lies in the high specificity of viral RNA–RNA polymerase interactions, for example phage $Q\beta$ RNA polymerase binds strongly to $Q\beta$ RNA, but not to RNA of other viruses (Kuppers and Sumper, 1975). The first stage in encapsidation of a ds-RNA molecule in a mycovirus is probably the binding of the viral RNA polymerase to the ds-RNA; this complex may then accept only homologous polypeptide subunits in order to build up the virus capsid. Studies of the assembly of these viruses in vitro would be well worth while.

RNA POLYMERASE OF P. STOLONIFERUM VIRUS S PARTICLES CATALYSES THE REPLICATION OF ds-RNA

Two types of RNA polymerase activity are associated with reovirus infections. Transcriptase activity is latent in virions and is activated by removal of outer shell polypeptides by proteinase action. This activity catalyses the formation of multiple copies of mRNA molecules, which are copied from each of the 10 ds-RNA genome segments and are released from the particles (Skehel and Joklik, 1969). The second type of activity is associated with subviral particles, isolated from infected cells during the replication cycle, which contain the 10 viral mRNA segments. This polymerase catalyses the synthesis of the 10 ds-RNA genome segments using these 10 ss-RNA molecules as templates. In this case, the ds-RNA products remain associated with the subviral particles, which are believed to be precursors of mature virions (Zweerink, 1974).

Preparations of P. stoloniferum virus S contain a number of different particle types, readily separated by isopycnic centrifugation in caesium chloride density gradients, namely L1 and L2 particles each containing one molecule of ds-RNA of molecular weight 0.94×10^6 (RNA-S1) and 1.11×10^6 (RNA-S2), respectively, M1 and M2 particles, each containing one molecule of ss-RNA of molecular weight 0.47×10^6 and 0.56×10^6, respectively, (probably the viral mRNA molecules), and a range of H particles, containing one molecule of ds-RNA (either RNA–S1 or RNA–S2) together with differing amounts of ss-RNA with sedimentation coefficients of from 0 to 15 S (Buck and Kempson-Jones, 1973). When it was discovered that the products of RNA polymerase activity in this virus are ds-RNA molecules of the same molecular weight as RNA–S1 and RNA–S2 and remain within the viral particles (Chater and Morgan, 1974), it was expected that the activity would lay in the M particles, by analogy with the reovirus system. However, it was found that in the *in vitro* RNA polymerase assay system the activity is associated with H particles, not with M or L particles. In H particles, the reaction occurs with the formation of one new molecule of ds-RNA (or two complementary single strands of RNA) per virus particle and the production of product (P) particles, which contains two molecules of ds-RNA (or its equivalent). The RNA polymerase is therefore a replicase, which catalyses the synthesis of the two complementary strands of ds-RNA within a single virus particle (Buck, 1975). In contrast, ds-RNA synthesis in the reovirus system is asynchronous and requires both the types of subviral particle and RNA polymerase activity described above.

Fungal colonies usually contain 'cells' (or hyphal compartments) of different ages and ds-RNA mycoviruses replicate both during and after the growth of their hosts (see the following section). Mycovirus preparations may therefore be expected to contain intermediates of replication in addition to mature virions. The range of H particles found in *P. stoloniferum* virus S preparations (Buck and Kempson-Jones, 1973; Buck, 1975) corresponds to the different stages of the ds-RNA replication process. Whether the newly synthesized RNA is present in virus particles as one molecule of ds-RNA or as two complementary ss-RNAs which anneal to form ds-RNA on extraction, is not certain, but the latter interpretation is favoured, because RNA molecules partially double stranded, which would be expected in H particles if the former interpretation were correct, have not been detected.

The lack of RNA polymerase activity *in vitro* in L and M particles does not necessarily imply a similar absence of activity *in vivo*. Indeed, L particles are probably the precursors of H particles *in vivo* and isolated L particles contain the same amount of S1 RNA polymerase molecule as H particles. The absence of RNA polymerase activity *in vitro* in L particles indicates merely that RNA synthesis cannot be initiated in the *in vitro* assay system; RNA synthesis occurs in this system only in those particles (H particles) in which RNA synthesis has been initiated *in vivo*. It is probable, therefore, that initiation of RNA synthesis in L particles requires specific host-initiation factors, not present in the *in vitro* assay system. One possible candidate for a host-initiation factor was thought to be *S*-adenosyl methionine, since in the case of *Bombyx mori* cytoplasmic polyhedrosis virus (Furuichi, 1974; Furuichi and Miura, 1975), initiation of transcription *in vitro* is coupled to the *S*-terminal methylation of the nascent

RNA in the presence of the methyl donor which enhances the rate of transcription over 50-fold. However in the case of *P. stoloniferum* virus S is was found that *S*-adenosyl methionine is unable to initiate RNA synthesis in M or L particles, or to stimulate ds-RNA synthesis in H particles.

Although RNA synthesis is not initiated *in vitro* in L particles, it is clear that in H particles, once synthesis of one RNA strand has been completed, initiation of synthesis of the second strand must occur *in vitro* since the final product particles contain both complementary strands of RNA newly synthesized. In this context, it is noteworthy that transciption of phage $Q\beta$ RNA by $Q\beta$ RNA polymerase requires two host protein factors, F1 and F2 (in addition to the host subunits of the polymerase itself), whereas transcription of $Q\beta$ complementary minus strand does not require F1 and F2 (Shapiro *et al.*, 1968). The absence of RNA polymerase activity *in vitro* in *P. stoloniferum* virus S M particles may also be due to the absence of host-initiation factors, but it could be due to lack of ability of ss-RNA to act as a template for the RNA polymerase. However, the presence of S1 RNA polymerase molecules in these particles implies at least that the polymerase binds to the viral ss-RNA. Recently, Herring and Bevan (1976) have obtained evidence for a ss-RNA → ds-RNA polymerase activity in a viral particle fraction obtained from log phase cells of the yeast *Saccharomyces cerevisiae*.

IN *P. STOLONIFERUM* VIRUS S ONE POLYPEPTIDE MUST FUNCTION BOTH AS REPLICASE AND TRANSCRIPTASE

Since *P. stoloniferum* virus S can code only for one single-chain RNA polymerase, it is clear that the enzyme must function *in vivo* as both a replicase and a transcriptase. The two processes are related to the extent that transcription involves repeated copying of the negative strand of ds-RNA to form mRNA molecules, whereas replication involves copying of òne strand of ds-RNA, followed by the copying of the complementary strand. How the same polypeptide achieves these two functions is not known, but is is possible that a 'free' ds-RNA–RNA polymerase complex might function as a transciptase and be converted ihto a replicase when encapsidated in virus particles. Alternatively, both types of activity may reside in the virus particles and be controlled by the conformation of the virus particles, which in turn may depend on interaction with host factors. For transcription the particles would have to adopt a conformation which would allow release of the mRNA molecules and subsequent re-initiation of transcription, whereas in replication the RNA transcripts are retained in the particles, at least in the *in vitro* reaction; hence the particles may need to be programmed for transcription or replication early in the RNA polymerase reaction. This second possibility of two particle conformations seems more likely in view of the recent finding that the major RNA polymerase activity of *A. foetidus* virus S particles is a transcriptase, which catalyses the formation of complete transcripts from the viral ds-RNA genome, and these are released from the viral particles; apparently re-initiation of RNA synthesis occurs readily *in vitro* with this system (Ratti and Buck, unpublished results). A minor product of this reaction is ds-RNA. This may have been formed by a replicase reaction similar to the one described for *P. stoloniferum* virus S, since small quantities of particles containing one molecule of ds-RNA, one molecule of ss-RNA (S3 particles), and particles containing two molecules of ds-DNA (S4 particles) have been found in *A. foetidus* virus S preparations (Buck and Ratti, 1975*a*).

The RNA polymerase of phage ϕ6 catalyses the synthesis of ds-RNA but the small amount of synthesis, coupled with the base analysis of the products, suggests that the reaction consists merely of 'filling-in' of short ss-RNA tails on pre-existing ds-RNA molecules (Van Etten *et al.*, 1973). Hence the activity may be similar to the ss $\rightarrow$ ds-RNA polymerase activity of reovirus subviral particles, the activity observed being essentially the completion of the reaction.

HOW DO ds-RNA MYCOVIRUSES REPLICATE *IN VIVO*?

The finding of replicase activity in ds-RNA mycovirus particles and the isolation of particles, which are apparently intermediates of this reaction, from virus-infected cells (H particles from *P. stoloniferum*, S3 and S4 particles from *A. foetidus*) led Buck and Ratti (1975*b*) to propose a model for the replication of these viruses *in vivo*. A modification of this model for a two-component system is shown in Fig. 7.4. In this system, A and B particles contain ds-RNA molecules which code for RNA polymerase and capsid structural polypeptides, respectively. It is envisaged that at any time a fraction of these particles will be active in transcription with release of mRNA molecules, whereas another fraction may be involved in ds-RNA replication, by a mechanism similar to the

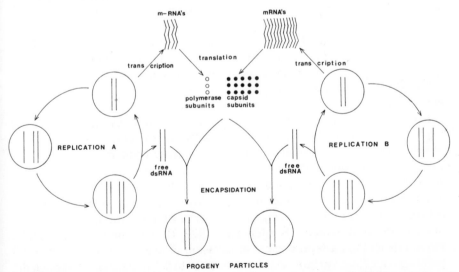

Figure 7.4   A model for the replication cycle of a two component ds-RNA mycovirus

one discussed for *P. stoloniferum* virus S. After replication the newly formed molecule of ds-RNA (or its equivalent) may be released from its particle and encapsidated to form a progeny particle. The course of the viral replication cycle, according to this model, would depend on the relative rates of ds-RNA replication and transcription/translation; these relative rates may vary with the course of the cycle and the physiological state of the host cell. The implications of this model with respect to the biology of the virus will be discussed in the next two sections.

The main difference between this model and the replication cycle of reovirus, is that replication of ds-RNA can occur without the need for prior formation of mRNAs. The recent finding of ss-RNA → ds-RNA polymerase activity in viral particles from *Saccharomyces cerevisiae* (Herring and Bevan, 1976) suggests that these particles may replicate by an assymmetric mechanism, possibly similar to that of reovirus. However, it should be noted that the two replication mechanisms are not mutually exclusive. It could well be that ds-RNA mycoviruses have a choice of two different ways of replicating their ds-RNA; factors governing the choice could be the host cell and its physiological state. On the other hand, not all ds-RNA mycoviruses may replicate in the same way. The scheme in Figure 7.4 is presented purely as a working model. If it stimulates good experiments to prove or disprove it, it will have achieved its purpose.

MANY ds-RNA MYCOVIRUSES DO NOT HARM THEIR HOSTS

Unlike members of the *Reoviridae* and phage $\phi 6$, which are virulent viruses causing cytopathogenic effects in their hosts, many ds-RNA mycoviruses are avirulent, do not cause cell lysis, and indeed appear to have little effect on the growth rate of their hosts. Still *et al.* (1975) observed no apparent differences in host RNA, DNA, or protein synthesis between virus-free and virus-infected strains of *P. stoloniferum*. The absence of any overt symptoms in the host was the main reason for the belated discovery of most of these viruses. ds-RNA mycoviruses appear to have no direct effect on the production of secondary metabolites by fungi, for example penicillin by *P. chrysogenum* (Lemke *et al.*, 1973), or on the pathogenicity of phytopathogenic fungi, such as *Gaeumanno-myces graminis* (Rawlinson *et al.*, 1973) or *Periconia circinata* (Dunkle, 1974).

In order to observe the intracellular accumulation of virus particles in fungal hyphae as a function of the age of the host 'cells' and to examine possible effects of virus infection on host-cell degeneration, Border compared virus-free and virus-infected strains of *P. stoloniferum* by electron microscopy. The problems associated with the asynchronous replication of these fungi were overcome by examining thin sections of a *single* fungal hypha, growing in an agar surface culture starting from the growing tip and working back towards the older cells in the centre of the colony (Border *et al.*, 1972; Border, unpublished results). Using this method a reproducible progression of events was observed. Viral particles were found to be absent from the apex to 0·1 mm behind, although the cytoplasm was densely packed with ribosomes (Figure 7.5a). Viral particles

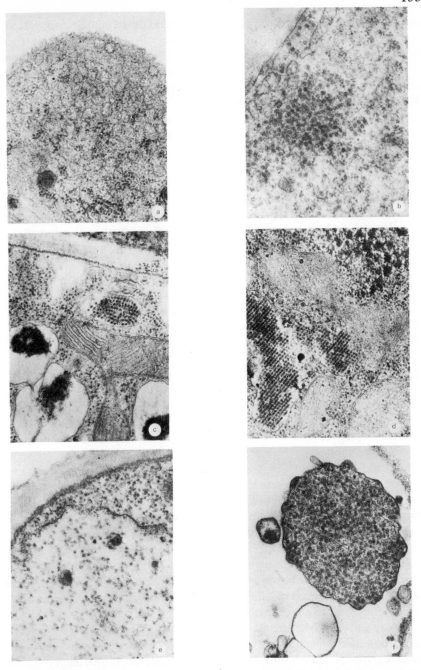

Figure 7.5 Thin sections of *P. stoloniferum*, Strain ATCC 14586, hyphae stained with uranyl acetate (magnification × 32 000). (*a*) Hyphal tip: the particles seen in this area are ribosomes and appear similarly in both virus-infected and virus-free strains; (*b*) 1 mm from tip; (*c*) 2·5 mm from tip; (*d*) 4 mm from tip; (*e*) 6 mm from tip; (*f*) centre of colony, 10 mm from top. (Courtesy of Dr. D. J. Border)

were first detected between 0·1 and 2 mm behind the hyphal tip and were seen in aggregates of up to several hundred which were free in the cytoplasm (Figure 7.5b). In the region 2 to 3 mm from the tip, aggregates of viral particles were bounded by a single membrane (Figure 7.5c) in addition to the many particles still free in the cytoplasm. Further back (3–5 mm), a lumen developed between the aggregates of viral particles and their surrounding membrane forming small vacuoles (Figure 7.5d). From 5 mm inwards, the vacuoles containing viral particles appear to have fused producing one large vacuole which fills almost the entire cell (Figure 7.5e). In cells at the centre of the colony, which are almost completely autolysed, the plasmalemma frequently appears to withdraw from the cell wall and form an envelope surrounding the viral particles (Figure 7.5f). Apart from the viral particles, no differences in cell ultrastructure were observed between virus-infected and virus-free strains; in both cases cell degeneration was observed in the older parts of the hyphae starting at about 3 mm from the hyphal tip. Similar results have been obtained with *P. chrysogenum* and *P. funiculosum*.

Although fungal hyphae increase in length only at their apices, protoplasm in a much longer portion of the hypha must increase in volume in order to supply the advancing tip. The width of this peripheral growth zone varies considerably with the fungus and to some extent with nutrient concentration. In *Pencillium* and *Aspergillus* species the width is usually in the range 0·5 to 1·5 mm, (Trinci, 1971). Behind the peripheral growth zone the septa are plugged; hence these hyphal compartments do not contribute to apical hyphal extension (Trinci, 1971, 1973). It is clear from results obtained by Border that, in the *Penicillium* species studied, viruses are found free in the cytoplasm in the peripheral growth zone, but some particles become enclosed in vesicles and later in vacuoles in the plugged hyphal compartments. The discovery of viruses in the peripheral growth zone implies that they are actively multiplying in this region—otherwise they would be gradually diluted out by hyphal growth. Presumably the viral particles are carried from one hyphal compartment to the next by cytoplasmic streaming. It is clear, therefore, that the virus is transmitted in the vegetative growth of the host (vertical transmission). Moreover, viruses are commonly carried in the conidia of species in the Deuteromycotina (Hooper *et al.*, 1972; Sansing *et al.*, 1973) and in the basidiospores of species in the Basidiomycotina (Schisler *et al.*, 1967)—although not apparently in the ascopores of *Gaeumannomyces graminis* Rawlinson *et al.*, 1973). Hence cell lysis and viral release, followed by re-infection of other cells from without, are not requirements for continued reproduction of these viruses.

Detroy and co-workers (Still *et al.*, 1975; Detroy and Still, 1975) studied the replication of *P. stoloniferum* virus F. The overall rate of virus and ds-RNA doubling appear to be similar to that of the host, but the virus and ds-RNA synthesis have an initial lag period so that their concentration in the exponential phase of growth is relatively low. On the other hand, virus and ds-RNA synthesis continue after host growth has slowed down so that during the latter phase viral yield increases four-fold while biomass increases only 1·4 times.

Also viral multiplication can occur in resting mycelium, presumably by utilizing the products of catabolism of host macromolecules. There is no evidence for the production of free ds-RNA and the results do not help to distinguish between the symmetric or asymmetric mode of the ds-RNA replication. If replication does occur symmetrically, as suggested in Figure 7.4, the results imply co-ordinated replication and transciption/translation so that each ds-RNA molecule is encapsidated as soon as it is released.

In the absence of any direct cytopathogenic effect, the only effect of the virus on its host may be expected to result from competition for nucleotide and amino acid precursors, and competition of viral mRNAs for host ribosomes. By effectively limiting the majority of viral and ds-RNA synthesis to the end of the growth period and to non-growing mycelium, the viral multiplication will have a minimal effect on the growth of the host. Yields of virus in fungi commonly range from less than 10 μg to 4 mg/g dry weight of fungus, probably only about 10 to 20 per cent of this is produced during exponential fungal growth and the remainder takes place afterwards. In the case of *P. stoloniferum*, yields can reach 4 mg/g dry weight of mycelium, of which not more than 1 mg/g dry weight or 0·1 per cent of the dry weight is synthesized during exponential growth. It is clear therefore that the amount of virus synthesized during the main growth of the host is insufficient to have any marked effect by direct competition on fungal growth.

The enclosure of the virus particles in vesicles in the older hyphal compartments probably helps to control the overall level of virus particles in the fungus. It has been shown (Border, personal communication) by electron microscopy that if growth in the form of a branch starts again from an older hyphal compartment although the virus-containing vesicles enter this branch they are apparently not transported into its active growth zone. However, free particles are transported and a progression of events similar to that found in a leading hypha (Figure 7.5) is soon established. This may imply that only viral particles free in the cytoplasm undergo multiplication; those enclosed in vesicles or vacuoles may be effectively isolated from the rest of the cell, so that the number of free multiplying particles in each hyphal compartment may remain relatively constant.

In a study of the replication of *P. chrysogenum* virus in liquid culture, Wood (1975) obtained different results to those described above for *P. stoloniferum* virus F. In rapidly growing cultures, ds-RNA increases in parallel with fungal growth but only small numbers of particles are produced. However, when the host growth slows prior to the onset of complete viral particle formation, there is a decrease in the rate of ds-RNA synthesis. As the assembly of viral particles occurs there is a second burst of ds-RNA synthesis. The production of free ds-RNA is in accord with the model proposed for mycovirus ds-RNA replication (Figure 7.4) since an asymmetric replication, such as in reovirus, would not produce any free ds-RNA. However, it should be noted that measurement of free ds-RNA is difficult with a labile virus such as *P. chrysogenum* virus since some particles may be disrupted during the relatively harsh methods required to disrupt the fungal hyphae. Wood noted that maximal yields of virus are obtained just prior to conidiation and suggested that events leading to sporulation control the viral replicative events. While it is likely that conditions which favour conidiation also favour virus production, it is unlikely that virus production is controlled by the conidiation process since very high yields of this virus may be obtained in a medium (Banks *et al.*, 1969) in which conidiation does not occur.

SOME ds-RNA MYCOVIRUSES MAY BENEFIT THEIR HOSTS

a. Killer systems of *Saccharomyces cerevisiae* and *Ustilago maydis*

Killer, neutral, and sensitive strains may all contain ds-RNA virus particles, factor), which is able to kill cells of sensitive yeast strains (Woods and Bevan, 1968). A third type of strain, termed neutral, does not produce killer factor and is resistant to its action. Both killer and neutral phenotypes are inherited cytoplasmically, but a number of nuclear genes affects the maintenance and expression of killer and neutral determinants (Bevan and Somers, 1969; Wickner, 1974; Leibowitz and Wickner, 1976).

Killer, neutral, and sensitive strains may all contain ds-RNA virus particles, but they differ in their RNA components. Killer strains always have two molecules of ds-RNA with molecular weights of $2 \cdot 5 \times 10^6$ and $1 \cdot 4 \times 10^6$, whereas sensitive strains, with few exceptions, have only the larger of the two ds-RNA molecules (Herring and Bevan, 1974, 1975), or lack ds-RNA altogether. Under a variety of conditions where sensitive clones have been segregated from killer parents, it was found that loss of killer function (and conferment of sensitivity) is always accompanied by loss of the smaller ds-RNA molecules. This suggests that the smaller ds-RNA may code for both killer toxin and an immunity factor.

In common with other ds-RNA mycoviruses, the two species of ds-RNA molecules are encapsidated separately giving rise to two types of particles. Molecular weight and serological studies have shown that both types of particle have the same capsid (Herring and Bevan, 1975). Since particles containing the larger ds-RNA are able to replicate alone in sensitive cells, it is likely that this RNA can code for both capsid polypeptide and RNA polymerase, thus it may be dicistronic. Its molecular weight of $2 \cdot 5 \times 10^6$ is sufficient to code for a polypeptide of molecular weight 140 000. Since the capsid polypeptide has a molecular weight of 74 500 (Herring, personal communication), it is clear that this RNA could code for at least one further polypeptide. The particle containing the smaller RNA would thus be replicated as a 'satellite' of the particle containing the larger RNA molecule. Replication of the smaller RNA also requires at least one nuclear maintenance gene M, which is not required by the larger RNA (Bevan *et al.*, 1973); the biochemical function of gene M is not yet known.

Killer strains of the corn smut pathogen, *U. maydis*, have also been discovered, and the ability to produce killer and immunity factors, which are inherited cytoplasmically, is associated with the presence of ds-RNA virus particles (Wood and Bozarth, 1973). In this case, however, resistance to killer toxin can also be conferred by nuclear genes. Three killer specificities have been found in *U. maydis*; each killer is insensitive to its own killer toxin, but sensitive to the others. Koltin and Day (1975) have suggested that the inhibitory action of *U. maydis* killer proteins could be employed for the biological control of cereal smuts. This would involve introduction of nucleic acid which codes for killer protein into the cells of cereals. If this nucleic acid could be transcribed and translated in the cytoplasm of the plant cells the plant would produce the killer protein and hence be protected from the fungal pathogen.

The killer proteins of *U. maydis* are specific for *U. maydis* strains and related species in the *Ustilaginales* (Koltin and Day, 1975). Similarly, the *S. cerevisiae* killer factor acts on the same or closely related species (Woods and Bevan, 1968). Thus, the ability to produce killer proteins may confer an advantage over sensitive strains in the same ecological niche. Darwin (1859) proposed 'As species of the same genus have usually, though by no means invariably, some similarity in habits and constitution, and always in structure, the struggle will generally be more severe between species of the same genus, when they come into competition with each other, than between species of distinct genera'. Fungal killer proteins are analogous to bacteriocins, a term which has been applied to both plasmid-determined bacteriocidal proteins of low molecular weight and to defective bacteriophages (Hardy, 1975), and to the killer toxins of *Paramecium aurelia*. Production of the latter is dependent on defective phages harboured by bacterial endosymbionts of the *Paramecium* (Preer *et al.*, 1974). In all cases, the protein toxins are specific for species or strains related to those which produce them. Although the benefits of killer toxin production seem obvious, proof that they improve the survival of their producers in a natural environment is still lacking.

b. Are all ds-RNA mycoviruses associated with the production of killer toxins?

When different strains of the same species of many fungi are mixed, heterokaryon formation is often prevented by vegetative incompatability, which may be of three main types; (*i*) hyphae anastomose, but mixing of the protoplasm leads either to rapid degeneration and death of the fused cells, or to unilateral elimination of the nuclei of one strain (heterogenic incompatability) (Esser and Blaich, 1973); (*ii*) the hyphae do not fuse and instead may grow over each other (fusion incompatability); and (*iii*) one strain may secrete a substance, inhibitory or even lethal to the other strain, which may prevent hyphae from meeting and/or cause necrosis of the hyphal tips (Caten and Jinks, 1966). Although the biochemical bases of reactions of type (*iii*) are largely unknown they could include reactions similar to the yeast and *U. maydis* killer-protein type; whether in general this type of response is associated with the presence of ds-RNA mycoviruses is not known. Philliskirk and Young (1975) established that species from seven genera of yeasts produce toxins active against *S. cerevisiae*, but possible correlations with ds-RNA mycoviruses have not been studied.

If a ds-RNA mycovirus is able to code for the production of killer proteins, its genome must contain information other than that required for the structure and replication of the virus. In order to see whether this is possible for some of the *Penicillium* and *Aspergillus* viruses, the coding capacities of their ds-RNA components and known viral proteins are compared in Table 7.6. There is a number of possibilities.

(*i*) All the RNA components are required to code for virus structural proteins and RNA polymerase molecules. This appears to be the case for *P. stoloniferum* virus S, in which each RNA component is probably monocistronic.

Table 7.6 Coding capacities of ds-RNA components of mycoviruses

Virus	Molecular weight of ds-RNA component $(\times 10^{-6})$	RNA coding capacity[†]	Molecular weight of known virus polypeptides	Function
P. stoloniferum	1·00	61 000	56 000	RNA polymerase
virus S	0·94	52 000	42 000	structural
P. stoloniferum	0·99	55 000	59 000	RNA polymerase
virus F	0·89	49 000	47 000	structural
	0·24	13 000		
A. foetidus	2·76	153 000	83 000	structural
virus S	2·24	124 000	78 000*	?
	0·1	6 000		
A. foetidus	2·31	128 000	125 000⎫	
virus F	1·87	104 000	100 000⎭	RNA polymerase
	1·70	94 000	87 000	structural
	1·44	80 000		
	1·24	69 000		
P. chrysogenum	2·21	123 000	130 000	structural
virus	2·08	116 000		
	1·98	110 000		
P. cyaneofulvum	2·21	123 000	130 000	structural
virus	2·08	116 000		
	1·98	110 000		
	1·93	108 000		
S. cerevisiae virus	2·5	140 000	75 000	structural
(from killer strain)	1·4	80 000	?	toxin

* Probably derived from the major structural polypeptide by proteinase action.
† Expressed in daltons of polypeptide, assuming that a ds-RNA can code for a polypeptide of 1/18 of its molecular weight.

(*ii*) The multiple RNA components may be merely conformational isomers of the same molecule and may not actually differ in their molecular weight. This was suggested by Burnett *et al.* (1975) as a possibility for the three RNA components of *P. chrysogenum* virus, but it seems unlikely since one RNA molecule of this virus is required to code for the capsid protein and at least one further RNA molecule would be required to code for RNA polymerase. Conformational isomers seem equally unlikely in other viruses, for example the difference in base composition of the two larger RNA species of *A. foetidus* virus S (Buck and Ratti, 1975*a*), precludes such a relationship.

(*iii*) Some RNA components may be defective due to deletion mutations of others; such RNAs might be replicated as satellites. A ds-RNA replication by doubling as suggested in Figure 7.4 would allow maintenance of such satellite RNAs without the need for their transcription and translation. Moreover, accumulation of defective particles may be favoured in fungi, since cell lysis and re-infection from without are not required for the continued replication of these viruses. The smallest RNA component of *P. stoloniferum* virus F, and some small ds-RNAs found in mutant strains of yeast (Vodkin *et al.*, 1974) may fall into this category. Defective particles containing pieces of the viral genome are common in animal viruses and arise from clonally purified viral preparations (Fenner, 1974). Deletion mutations in the ds-RNA genome segments of wound tumour virus were observed after maintenance in sweet clover for periods of up to 24 years without passage through the insect vector; such deletions are often accompanied by loss of vector transmissibility (Reddy and Black, 1974).

(*iv*) Some RNA components may code for non-structural proteins essential for viral replication, as in the case of reovirus (Zweerlink *et al.*, 1971).

(*v*) Some ds-RNA components may be directly involved in control of viral multiplication. The smallest RNA component of *A. foetidus* virus S may possibly be involved in control of transcription in this virus.

(*vi*) RNA components may code for proteins such as killer toxins, which are not essential for viral multiplication. This appears to be the case for *S. cerevisiae* and *U. maydis*, and may well be widespread in fungi.

All of the viruses in Table 7.6, except *P. stoloniferum* virus S, could contain information other than that required to code for capsid and structural proteins of the virus, but the available evidence does not allow all of the other possibilities to be distinguished. Moreover, since few infected isolates of each fungal species have been examined, the possibility of further ds-RNA components being associated with these viruses in other isolates cannot be excluded.

In summary, it is clear that the problem of whether all mycoviruses are associated with the production of killer toxins cannot be solved at present, but the available evidence, sparse as it is, indicates that it is a possibility worth further consideration. A general survey of the occurrence of the killer phenomenon in fungi, in conjunction with a study of the biological and biochemical functions of mycovirus ds-RNA components, is urgently required.

SOME ds-RNA MYCOVIRUSES CAUSE DISEASE

During the 1950s an epidemic disorder in cultivated mushroom, *Agaricus bisporus*, was observed in several countries with considerable loss of yield. Hollings (1962) showed that the disease is caused by viral infection and at least five different types of virus particles have been isolated from diseased mushrooms; four polyhedral particles have been identified with diameters of 25 nm, 29, 34, and 50 nm (mushroom viruses 1, 2, 4, and 5, respectively) and a bacilliform particle 19×50 nm (mushroom virus 3). The bacilliform particle contains ss-RNA (Lapierre, 1975), and of the polyhedral particles at least viruses 1 and 4 contain ds-RNA (Hollings, 1975). The main route of transmission of these particles appears to be by hyphal anastomosis, but the particles are also transmitted in the basidiospores. Infectivity and pathogenicity of these viruses have been confirmed (Hollings, 1962; Dieleman-van Zaayen and Temmink, 1968), but the precise role of individual particles in determining the course of the disease is not yet known.

One of the interesting aspects of this die-back disease in mushrooms is that it arose apparently spontaneously in the USA in 1949, and in England a few years later. Symptoms of this type had not been observed by mushroom growers over a period of more than 20 years previously (Sinden and Hauser, 1950). One possibility is that the disease may have arisen by a mutation in an avirulent virus already infecting some mushroom races; latent viral infections have been reported in mushrooms (Hollings, 1975; Passmore and Frost, 1974). It is noteworthy that a mutation in a ds-RNA, carrying killer and immunity functions, could lead either to non-production or non-functioning of killer proteins (that is to neutral strains), or to loss of immunity rendering a cell sensitive to its own killer protein. The latter effect is, of course, equivalent to the generation of a virulent virus from an avirulent one. Killer mutants of *S. cerevisiae*, which are immunity-minus and hence sensitive to their own toxin, have been produced (Vodkin *et al.*, 1974) and these 'suicide' strains grow very poorly on low-pH media when the toxin is active.

Another possibility is that the virulence of the mushroom viruses (and other mycoviruses) could be controlled by the presence of defective interfering particles. The possibility of such particles occurring in ds-RNA mycovirus preparations has been discussed already. In animal virus systems, defective particles interfere with the intracellular replication of non-defective homologous virus and may play a role in the self-limiting of acute viral infections, and the establishment of persistent and slow viral infections (Huang, 1973). The production of defective, interfering particles is dependent on many factors and alteration of environmental conditions could upset the balance between defective and non-defective particles and consequently affect the virulence of the virus. What controls the virulence of the mushroom viruses is not known at present, but it is clear that studies of individual mushroom viruses, and of the biological and biochemical functions of their ds-RNA components, should help to answer some of these questions.

A completely different phenomenon has been observed in the potential of *P. chrysogenum* virus (Lemke *et al.*, 1973; Lemke, 1975), and two other *Penicillium* viruses, not yet proved to contain ds-RNA (Borré *et al.*, 1971), to produce lytic plaques when the fungi are grown in surface cultures. By a series of infection experiments using heterokaryosis with genetically marked strains it was proved that plaque formation in *P. chrysogenum* occurs as a result of viral infection. Plaque formation with these viruses is completely different to bacteriophage plaque formation, taking several weeks to develop and not involving any re-infection from without of neighbouring cells. Moreover, plaque formation apparently occurs only when the fungi are grown in an unbuffered medium with a high lactose content and in mutant, but not wild-type, *P. chrysogenum* strains. It has been shown that wild type *P. chrysogenum* carries a gene for resistance to lysis, which can be mutated to sensitivity; in diploids, resistance is dominant over sensitivity. This evidence suggests that the mutant *P. chrysogenum* strains may be defective in cell-wall synthesis. Moreover, growth in a high lactose medium may enhance this effect since a number of sugars is known to inhibit some of the enzyme systems required for cell-wall production, which involves a delicate balance between synthetic and hydrolytic enzyme systems (Bartnicki-Garcia, 1973). Increased vesicle formation or vacuolation of fungal cells, as a result of viral infection, may result in an increase in hyphal turgor pressure (Bracker, 1967) or, if cell walls are defective, in cell lysis. Hence this type of lytic effect could reflect defective wall synthesis by the host fungus rather than the virulence of the infecting virus.

Although reports of virulent ds-RNA mycoviruses are scarce, this could be due partly to artificial selection by the virologists studying mycoviruses. For example, many viruses have been found in fungi obtained from culture collections, in which case the fungal strains have been selected *inter alia* for their stability and good growth characteristics. The discovery of diseased fungi in their natural environment may require a special search in many cases; thus while a diseased mushroom is comparatively easily observed, a diseased *Penicillium* or *Gaeumannomyces* species may be more difficult to detect. On the other hand, attempts to implicate viral infections in various cytoplasmically inherited disorders, such as vegetative death in *A. glaucus* (Hollings and Stone, 1971) or senescence in *Podospora anserina* (Hollings, 1975), have not been successful. Although some new diseases of fungi caused by viruses doubtless remain to be discovered there is little doubt that very many ds-RNA mycoviruses are avirulent.

HOW ARE ds-RNA MYCOVIRUSES TRANSMITTED IN NATURE?

In previous sections, it has been shown that ds-RNA mycoviruses can be transmitted vertically in the vegetative growth of the fungus or in spores. It is also well-documented that viruses can be transferred between compatible strains of fungus by heterokaryosis (Lhoas, 1971a; Lemke, 1975) and that spread of viruses in mushroom crops is largely by heterokaryosis (Hollings and Stone, 1969). Although many attempts have been made, infection of fungal hyphae with extracellular virus has not been reported; presumably the fungal cell wall prevents virus uptake. Infection of naked protoplasts—which does not occur in nature—with extracellular virus has been achieved (Lhoas, 1971b). The claim to have infected matching pairs of the yeast, S. cerevisiae with viruses from A. niger (Lhoas, 1972) should probably be discounted in view of the discovery of viruses of the same size and shape in the yeast strains used for infection (Buck et al., 1973b; Morgan and Smith, 1974). Moreover, the electrophoretic mobility of the claimed newly infecting virus is the same as that of authentic yeast virus, but different from those of either of the two A. niger viruses (Buck, unpublished results). However, the possibility that the mating of yeasts in the presence of A. niger viruses in some way stimulates increased production of yeast virus particles should be considered.

If the main method of horizontal spread of ds-RNA mycoviruses is through heterokaryosis, then such spread is likely to be limited to compatible strains of the same species. Systems of vegetative incompatibility—previously discussed in connection with the production of killer toxins—by limiting anastomosis and/or heterokaryon formation, in addition to promoting inbreeding and the formation of new races, will reduce the transfer of cytoplasmic elements, such as plasmids or viruses, which may be harmful to the host (Caten, 1972). On the other hand, many ds-RNA mycoviruses are not harmful to their hosts; in fact it has been suggested that some may be beneficial. In addition, they may actually promote incompatability via killer toxin production, although the importance of this in natural conditions is hard to assess; for example, yeast killer toxin has a rather narrow pH range of activity and its maximal production is by stationary-phase cells (Woods and Bevan, 1968).

From the above considerations it may be expected that the natural host range of ds-RNA mycoviruses will be very limited. Of the viruses studied so far, few serological relationships have been reported. For example, A. foetidus viruses S and F are serologically related to A. niger viruses S and F, respectively, (Buck and Ratti, 1975a) and P. chrysogenum, P. brevicompactum, and P. cyaneoful-vium viruses are serologically related (Wood and Bozarth, 1972; Buck and Girvan, 1977). Although the fungi in which the serologically related viruses occur are from the same genus in each case, it is unlikely that the species concerned will anastomose or form heterokaryons.

One explanation is that the viruses arose early in the phylogeny of the fungal species concerned, before they diverged, and have remained with them during subsequent evolution. It has also been reported that a virus found in Diplocar-pon rosae, the causative agent of rose black spot, is serologically related to P. stoloniferum virus S (Bozarth et al., 1972). In this case the fungi are much further apart taxonomically and it seems less likely that the virus could have arisen from a common ancestor since that would imply a widespread occurrence of this virus in many fungi. Another possibility is that horizontal transmission of the virus, other than by heterokaryosis, could have occurred. However, in view of the importance of this result, a detailed comparison of the two viruses is required in order to determine how closely related they are. Hollings (1975) has pointed out the necessity to distinguish between genuine reactions based on the capsid protein and those which may arise from the common presence of ds-RNA. It has been shown that antisera to rice black-streaked dwarf virus and maize rough dwarf virus (members of the *Reoviridae*) contain antibodies to ds-RNA (Ikegami and Francki, 1973).

FUTURE PROSPECTS

It is clear that ds-RNA mycoviruses form a new family of ds-RNA viruses quite distinct from the *Reoviridae* and *Cystoviridae*. Even from the small number of ds-RNA mycoviruses studied it is evident that there is considerable diversity among them and the family will be required to be split up into several genera. Before such a classification can be carried out, however, a study of the biological and biochemical function of each ds-RNA component of a given virus will be required, particularly in view of the possibility of viruses carrying one or more species of 'defective' RNA.

ds-RNA mycoviruses are currently of great interest to biochemists in view of their apparently novel method of replication and as a comparison with the *Reoviridae* and *Cystoviridae*. Their comparatively simple capsids and RNA polymerases make these viruses ideal for studying the relationships between ds-RNA replication and transcription. Moreover, these properties, together with the ease with which the viruses can be cultivated—gram quantities of some of the viruses can be obtained easily—offer real hope for the isolation of template-free RNA polymerase specific for ds-RNA. If this can be achieved the way is open for studying RNA polymerase–ds-RNA interactions, particularly for establishing the specificity of binding and determining the structures of binding-site, and the *in vitro* assembly of these viruses. Isolation of virus mRNA molecules combined with *in vitro* protein synthesis offers a convenient and direct method of examining the functions of each ds-RNA component of the genome, particularly in view of the absence of a convenient method for infection of fungi with extracellular virus and the difficulty of separating completely individual component viral particles.

A study of the occurrence of the killer phenomenon in fungi and possible correlations with virus ds-RNA components should determine whether the *raison d'être* of many ds-RNA mycoviruses is in the production of killer factors and the establishment of a symbiotic relationship with their hosts. The role of host genes in the replication of killer ds-RNAs is of particular interest in this context. Further incentive in this area is provided by the possibility of exploiting the killer phenomenon for the control of fungal pathogens.

The molecular basis of the pathogenicity of some ds-RNA mycoviruses, the latent nature of others, and the possible role of killer factors or defective

146

particles in this area are problems requiring urgent attention. Such studies should increase knowledge of the interaction of viruses with eukaryotic cells.

Finally virus-infected fungi offer a convenient source of ds-RNA for use as an antiviral agent with clinical and veterinary applications. This aspect will be covered in the next chapter by J. M. Dewdney.

ACKNOWLEDGEMENTS

The work on fungal viruses at Imperial College owes much to the encouragement of Sir Ernst Chain, whose enthusiasm for science and whose sense of urgency which has instilled into his manifold activities are exemplified by one of his favourite remarks 'yesterday was too late'. I am also indebted to Dr. M. Hollings who first introduced me to some of the intricacies of the isolation and purification of viruses. I wish to thank Drs. G. Ratti, D. Border, M. Carlile and P. Lhoas, other colleagues at Imperial College, and Dr. C. Rawlinson of Rothamsted Experimental Station for many stimulating discussions, Dr. A. Herring for making available a manuscript and for discussing his results on yeast viruses prior to publication, Dr. C. Rawlinson for providing an electron micrograph for Figure 7.1, Dr. B. D. Harrison, and Edward Arnold Ltd. for permission to publish Table 7.2, Dr. D. Border for providing electron micrographs for Figure 7.5 and making available some of his unpublished work, and Mr. G. Banks, who for several years has provided fungal mycelium in kilogram quantities from the Pilot Plant at Imperial College. Mycovirus research at Imperial College was supported initially by the Medical Research Council and is supported currently by the Science Research Council.

REFERENCES

Adler, J. P., and Mackenzie, D. W. (1972) *Abstr. Ann. Mtg. Am. Soc. Microbiol.*, **1972**, 68.

Ainsworth, G. C. (1968) in *The Fungi*, Vol. 3 (Ainsworth, G. C., and Sussman, A. S., eds.), Academic Press, New York and London, pp. 505–514.

Ainsworth, G. C. (1973) in *The Fungi*, Vol. 4A (Ainsworth, G. C., Sparrow, F., and Sussman, A. S. eds.), Academic Press, New York and London, pp. 1–7.

Banks, G. T., Buck, K. W., Chain, E. B., Darbyshire, J. E., and Himmelweit, F. (1969) *Nature (London)*, **222**, 89.

Bartnicki-Garcia, S. (1973) in *23rd Symposium of the Society for General Microbiology* (Ashworth, J. M., and Smith, J. E., eds.), Cambridge University Press, London, pp. 245–267.

Bevan, E. A., Herring, A., and Mitchell, D. J. (1973) *Nature (London)*, **245**, 81.

Bevan, E. A., and Somers, J. M. (1969) *Genet. Res.*, **14**, 71.

Border, D. J., Buck, K. W., Chain, E. B., Kempson-Jones, G. F., Lhoas, P., and Ratti, G. (1972) *Biochem. J.*, **127**, 4P.

Borré, E., Morgantini, L. E., Ortali, V., and Tonolo, A. (1971) *Nature (London)*, **229**, 568.

Both, G. W., Lavi, S., and Shatkin, A. J. (1975) *Cell*, **4**, 173.

Bozarth, R. F. (1972) *Environ. Hth. Perspec.*, **2**, 23.

Bozarth, R. F., Wood, H. A., and Goenaga, A. (1972) *Phytopathology*, **62**, 493.

Bozarth, R. F., Wood, H. A., and Mandelbrot, A. (1971) *Virology*, **45**, 516.

Bracker, C. E. (1967) *Ann. Rev. Phytopathol.*, **5**, 343.
Buck, K. W. (1975) *Nucleic Acids Res.*, **2**, 1889.
Buck, K. W., Chain, E. B., and Himmelweit, F. (1971) *J. Gen. Virol.*, **12**, 131.
Buck, K. W., and Girvan, R. F. (1977) *J. Gen. Virol.*, **34**, 145.
Buck, K. W., Girvan, R. F., and Ratti, G. (1973*a*) *Biochem. Soc. Trans.*, **1**, 1138.
Buck, K. W., and Kempson-Jones, G. F. (1970) *Nature (London)*, **225**, 945.
Buck, K. W., and Kempson-Jones, G. F. (1973) *J. Gen. Virol.*, **18**, 223.
Buck, K. W., and Kempson-Jones, G. F. (1974) *J. Gen. Virol.*, **22**, 441.
Buck, K. W., Lhoas, P., Border, D. J., and Street, B. K. (1973*b*) *Biochem. Soc. Trans.*, **1**, 1141.
Buck, K. W. and Ratti, G. (1975*a*) *J. Gen. Virol.*, **27**, 211.
Buck, K. W., and Ratti, G. (1975*b*) *Biochem. Soc. Trans.*, **3**, 542.
Burnett, J. P., Frank, B. H., and Douthart, R. J. (1975) *Nucleic Acids Res.*, **2**, 759.
Caten, C. E. (1972) *J. Gen. Microbiol.*, **72**, 221.
Caten, C. E., and Jinks, J. L. (1966) *Trans. British Mycol. Soc.*, **49**, 81.
Chater, K. F., and Morgan, D. H. (1974) *J. Gen. Virol.*, **24**, 307.
Darwin, C. (1859) *On the Origin of Species*, John Murray, London.
Detroy, R. W., and Still, P. E. (1975) *J. Gen. Microbiol.*, **92**, 167.
Dieleman-van Zaayen, A., and Temmink, J. H. M. (1968) *Neth. J. Plant Pathol.*, **74**, 48.
Dodds, J. A., and Hamilton, R. I. (1976) *Adv. Virus Res.*, **20**, 33.
Dunkle, L. D. (1974) *Physiol. Plant Pathol.*, **4**, 107.
Ellis, L. F., and Kleinschmidt, W. J. (1967) *Nature (London)*, **215**, 649.
Esser, K., and Blaich, R. (1973) *Adv. Genet.*, **17**, 107.
Fenner, F. (1974) *The Biology of Animal Viruses*, 2nd edn., Academic Press, New York and London.
Fenner, F. (1975) *J. Gen. Virol.*, **26**, 215.
Fenner, F. (1976) *J. Gen. Virol.*, **31**, 463.
Furuichi, Y. (1974) *Nucleic Acids Res.*, **1**, 809.
Furuichi, Y. and Miura, K. (1975) *Nature (London)*, **253**, 374.
Gibbs, A. J., and Harrison, B. D. (1976) *Plant Virology: The Principles*, Edward Arnold, London.
Hardy, K. G. (1975) *Bacteriol. Rev.*, **39**, 464.
Herring, A. J., and Bevan, E. A. (1974) *J. Gen. Virol.*, **22**, 387.
Herring, A. J., and Bevan, E. A. (1975) in *Molecular Biology of Nucleocytoplasmic Relationships* (Puiseux-Dao, S., ed.), Elsevier Scientific Publishing Company, Amsterdam, pp. 149–154.
Herring, A. J., and Bevan, E. A. (1976) in *Mitochondrial Genetics, Biogenesis and Bioenergetics*, De Gruyter and Co., Berlin, in press.
Hollings, M. (1962) *Nature (London)*, **196**, 962.
Hollings, M. (1975) in *Proceedings of the First Intersectional Cogress of IAMS*, Vol. 3 (Hasegawa, T., ed.), Science Council of Japan, pp. 323–339.
Hollings, M., and Stone, O. M. (1969) *Sci. Progr.*, **57**, 371.
Hollings, M., and Stone, O. M. (1971) *Ann. Rev. Phytopathol*, **9**, 93.
Hooper, G. R., Wood, H. A., Myers, R., and Bozarth, R. F. (1972) *Phytopathology*, **62**, 823.
Huang, A. S. (1973) *Ann. Rev. Microbiol.*, **27**, 101.
Ikegami, M., and Francki, R. I. B. (1973) *Virilogy*, **56**, 404.
Jaspars, E. M. J. (1974) *Adv. Virus Res.*, **19**, 37.
Joklik, W. K. (1974). in *Comprehensive Virology*, Vol. 2 (Fraenkel-Conrat, H., and Wagner, R. R., eds.), Plenum Press, New York and London, pp. 231–334.
Koltin, Y., and Day, P. R. (1975) *Appl. Microbiol.*, **30**, 694.
Kuppers, B., and Sumper, M. (1975) *Proc. Nat. Acad. Sci., U.S.A.*, **72**, 2640.
Lapierre, P. (1975) in *Proceedings of the First Intersectional Congress of IAMS*, Vol. 3 (Hasegawa, T., ed.), Science Council of Japan, pp. 359–361.

148

Leibowitz, M. J., and Wickner, R. B. (1976) *Proc. Nat. Acad. Sci., U.S.A.,* **73,** 2061.
Lemke, P. A. (1975) in *Proceedings of the First Intersectional Congress of IAMS,* Vol. 3 (Hasegawa, T., ed.), Science Council of Japan, pp. 380–395.
Lemke, P. A., and Nash, C. H. (1974) *Bacteriol. Rev.,* **38,** 29.
Lemke, P. A., Nash, C. H., and Pieper, S. W. (1973) *J. Gen. Microbiol.,* **76,** 265.
Lhoas, P. (1971*a*) *Nature (London),* **230,** 248.
Lhoas, P. (1971*b*). *J. Gen. Virol.,* **13,** 365.
Lhoas, P. (1972) *Nature, New Biol.,* **236,** 86.
Moffitt, E. M., and Lister, R. M. (1975) *Phytopathology,* **65,** 851.
Morgan, D. H., and Smith, B. A. (1974) *Report John Innes Institute 1973,* pp. 122–123.
Passmore, E. L., and Frost, R. R. (1974) *Phytopathol. Z.,* **80,** 85.
Perkins, F. O. (1974) in *Veroeff. Inst. Meeresforsch. Bremerhaven,* Suppl. 5 (Gaertner, A., ed.), F. Leuwer, Bremen, pp. 45–63.
Philliskirk, G., and Young, T. W. (1975) *Antonie Van Leeuwenhoek,* **41,** 147.
Preer, J. R., Preer, L. B., and Jurand, A. J. (1974) *Bacteriol. Rev.,* **38,** 113.
Ralph, R. K. (1969) *Adv. Virus Res.,* **15,** 61.
Ratti, G., and Buck, K. W. (1972) *J. Gen. Virol.,* **14,** 165.
Rawlinson, C. J., Carpenter, J. M., and Muthyalu, G. (1975) *Trans. Brit. Mycol. Soc.,* **65,** 305.
Rawlinson, C. J., Hornby, D., Pearson, V., and Carpenter, J. M. (1973) *Ann. Appl. Biol.,* **74,** 197.
Reddy, D. V. R., and Black, L. M. (1974) *Virology,* **61,** 458.
Sansing, G. A., Detroy, R. W., Freer, S. N., and Hesseltine, C. W. (1973) *Appl. Microbiol.,* **26,** 914.
Schisler, L. C., Sinden, J. W., and Sigel, E. M. (1967) *Phytopathology,* **57,** 519.
Shapiro, L., Franze de Fernandez, M. T., and August, J. T. (1968) *Nature (London),* **220,** 478.
Shatkin, A. J., and Both, G. W. (1976) *Cell,* **7,** 305.
Sinden, J. W., and Hauser, E. (1950) *Mushroon Sci.,* **1,** 96.
Skehel, J. J., and Joklik, W. K. (1969) *Virology,* **39,** 822.
Smith, R. E., Zweerink, H. J., and Joklik, W. K. (1969) *Virilogy,* **39,** 791.
Still, P. E., Detroy, R. W., and Hesseltine, C. W. (1975) *J. Gen. Virol.,* **27,** 275.
Trinci, A. P. J. (1971) *J, Gen. Microbiol.,* **67,** 325.
Trinci, A. P. J. (1973) *Arch. Mikrobiol.,* **91,** 355.
Tikchonenko, T. I., Velikodvorskaya, G. A., Bobkova, A. F., Bartoshevich, Y. E., Lebed, E. P., Chaplygina, N. M., and Maksimova, T. S. (1974) *Nature (London),* **249,** 454.
Van Etten, J. L., Vidaver, A. K., Koski, R. K., and Semancik, J. S. (1973) *J. Viriol.,* **12,** 464.
Vidaver, A. K., Koski, R. K., and Van Etten, J. L. (1973) *J. Viriol.,* **20,** 61.
Vodkin, M., Katterman, F., and Fink, G. R. (1974) *J. Bacteriol.,* **117,** 681.
White, C. K., and Zweerink, H. J. (1976) *Virology,* **70,** 171.
Wickner, R. B. (1974) *Genetics,* **76,** 423.
Wood, H. A. (1973) *J. Gen. Virol.,* **20,** 61.
Wood, H. A. (1975) in *Proceedings of the First Intersectional Congress of IAMS,* Vol. 3 (Hasegawa, T., ed.), Science Council of Japan, pp. 362–379.
Wood, H. A., and Bozarth, R. F. (1972) *Virilogy,* **47,** 604.
Wood, H. A., and Bozarth, R. F. (1973) *Phytopathology,* **63,** 1111.
Wood, H. A., Bozarth, R. F., and Mislivec, P. B. (1971) *Virology,* **44,** 592.
Woods, D. R., and Bevan, E. A. (1968) *J. Gen. Microbiol.,* **51,** 115.
Yamashita, S., Doi, Y., and Yora, B. (1975) in *Proceedings of the First Intersectional Congress of IAMS,* Vol. 3 (Hasegawa, T., ed.), Science Council of Japan, p. 340.
Zweerink, H. J. (1974) *Nature (London),* **247,** 313.
Zweerink, H. J., McDowell, M. J., and Joklik, W. K. (1971) *Virology,* **45,** 716.

8

Clinical and Veterinary Applications of Double-stranded Ribonucleic Acid from Fungal Viruses

J. M. Dewdney

Beecham Pharmaceuticals Research Division,
Betchworth, Surrey, U.K.

INTRODUCTION

Viral infections of bacteria, higher plants, and animals are commonplace. In many instances, the viruses possess frank pathogenicity which results in morbidity and mortality in the infected host. It has been a matter of some interest to both mycologists and virologists that viral infections of fungi seem to be rare. Until recent years the only well-documented example of viral disease of a fungus, with associated pathology, was that of the mushroom, for which the disease die-back was proved to be of viral aetiology (Hollings, 1962; Hollings and Stone, 1969, 1971).

This situation changed dramatically, however, in the late 1960s with the discovery of virus particles in a large number of fungal species, including the Fungi imperfecti, to which group *Penicillium* belongs—see reviews by Hollings and Stone (1969, 1971) Chain (1972), Pallett (1975), and references given in Table 8.1. No one could have predicted in the early days of the discovery and development of this mould as a producer of penicillin G, in which pioneer work Sir Ernst played such an important role, that the mould held yet another secret. When this secret, its cryptic fungal virus infection, was finally to be revealed it was Sir Ernst who again played a significant role.

This review takes as its subject, the biological consequences and implications of the discovery of viruses which infect fungi and the extent to which it has proved possible to exploit them both in clinical and in veterinary medicine.

The search for substances of value in the control of viral disease in mammalian species has proved largely unrewarding, although some drugs are available as antiviral agents. Of these drugs the thiosemicarbazones with activity against viruses of the pox group, the amantadines with activity against some strains of influenza, and the antimetabolite drugs, such as iododeoxyuridine and cytosine arabinoside, deserve mention. However, progress in antiviral chemotherapy has been slow. Viruses are by definition intracellular

Table 8.1   ds-RNA fungal virus interferon inducers

Species	References
P. stoloniferum (statolon)	Powell et al., 1952; Kleinschmidt and Probst, 1962; Ellis and Kleinschmidt, 1967; Banks et al., 1968; Kleinschmidt et al., 1968; Buck and Kempson-Jones, 1970; Border et al., 1972; Bozarth et al., 1971.
P. funiculosum (helenine)	Shope, 1953a,b: Lewis et al., 1959; Rytell et al., 1966; Lampson et al., 1967; Banks et al., 1968.
P. chrysogenum*	Banks et al., 1969a; Sutherland and Bessell, 1969; Cox et al., 1970; Lemke and Ness, 1970; Buck et al., 1971; Border et al., 1972; Bessell et al., personal communication.
P. cyaneofulvum	Banks et al., 1969b; Border et al., 1972.
P. cyclopium	Naficy and Carner, 1963.
P. brevicompactum	Wood et al., 1971.
Stemphylium botyrosum	Cole and Planterose, 1968.
A. foetidus	Banks et al., 1970; Border et al., 1972.
A. niger	Banks et al., 1970.
Cortinellus shiitake	Tsunoda and Ishida, 1970

* ds-RNA isolated and studied at Beecham Research Laboratories referred to as BRL 5907.

parasites which associate themselves intimately with host-cell metabolic processes. To inhibit their metabolism, while at the same time avoiding any serious injury to the host, has to date proved too difficult a task, for it demands an exceptional degree of selectivity in drug action.

The ability, therefore, of culture filtrates of *Penicillium stoloniferum* to protect animals from viral infections as first described by Powell *et al.* (1952) was subjected to serious examination, and was followed shortly afterwards by a similar discovery in relation to *P. funiculosum* (Shope, 1953a,b). It was from these observations that the whole area to be described in this review was to develop.

Chemical characterization of the active principle of *P. stoloniferum* led initially to the belief that antiviral activity resided in a polyanionic polysaccharide termed 'statolon' (Kleinschmidt and Probst, 1962). Further examination, however, revealed the presence, in both *P. stoloniferum* cultures and in statolon, of virus-like particles (Ellis and Kleinschmidt, 1967). Sir Ernst Chain and his group (Banks *et al.*, 1968), and Kleinschmidt *et al.* (1968) were able to show conclusively that the interferon-inducing property and antiviral activity (Planterose *et al.*, 1970) were functions of the double-stranded ribonucleic acid (ds-RNA) components in the virus particles. In similar fashion, the active component of *P. funiculosum* (helenine) was characterized initially as a ribonucleoprotein (Lewis *et al.*, 1959) and was shown subsequently also to contain a ds-RNA of fungal virus origin (Lampson *et al.*, 1967; Banks *et al.*, 1968). Studies in the author's laboratories had also identified a fungal culture filtrate with pronounced, though capricious, antiviral properties, and this material has now also been characterized as a ds-RNA derived from a virus associated with *Stemphylium botyrosum* (Cole and Planterose, 1968).

Meanwhile, research under the leadership of Sir Ernst Chain at Imperial College and also by workers in the Glaxo laboratories had demonstrated the presence of viral particles in yet other fungal cultures—strains of *P. chrysogenum* (Banks *et al.*, 1969*a*; Sutherland and Bessel, 1969). These particles were shown to contain ds-RNA (Lemke and Ness, 1970; Cox *et al.*, 1970; Buck *et al.*, 1971). It was to produce and evaluate this material that Beecham Research Laboratories entered into an extensive collaborative programme with Imperial College and the Medical Research Council.

It had been suggested by several groups evaluating culture filtrates as antiviral agents that the mode of action of these materials is through modulation of the host's response to virus rather than as a consequence of a direct effect upon the virus. Investigations have shown that at least one mechanism by which antiviral protection is obtained is through the induction of interferon, a host-determined protein substance described first by Isaacs and Lindenmann (1957) which can protect cells from viral infection (Shope, 1953*a,b*; Kleinschmidt *et al.*, 1964; Rytel *et al.*, 1966). Here then were substances deserving of the title interferon-inducers, and it seemed at that time that this property would prove the most amenable to clinical exploitation. Whether this is so is a matter for discussion and this review will raise questions concerning other biological properties subsequently described which may in the longer term prove more exciting. Reference should be made to publications by, for example, Brown (1971) and Kleinschmidt (1972) for general reviews of interferon inducers.

CHARACTERIZATION AND PRODUCTION

It was rapidly realized that the fungi are susceptible to viral infections with, in some instances, several antigenically distinct viruses being present in a single culture. This led workers to question the nature of these apparent infections—reviewed by Buck at this Symposium—and, in particular, the nature of the viral particles.

It is well-documented that all fungal viruses known so far to possess antiviral properties contain ds-RNA. The subunit structure of the ds-RNA which has been isolated from cultures of *P. chrysogenum* is as shown in Figure 8.1 and assigned the number BRL 5907. It comprises three molecular weight species, identified on polyacrylamide gels, each consisting of two polynucleotide chains made up of a ribose-phosphate backbone and the purine bases (adenine and guanine) and pyrimidine bases, (cytosine and uracil) in equimolar amounts. Hydrogen bonds link guanine with cytosine and adenine with uracil to form a helical structure with a molecular weight of approximately two million daltons.

The promising clinical applications of the biological properties of BRL 5907 and the need to improve upon them by chemical modification of the molecule,

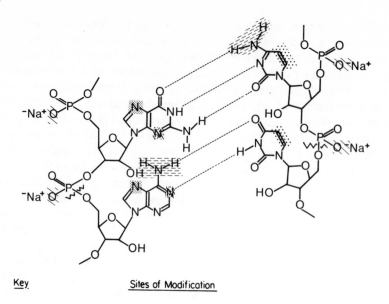

Key   Sites of Modification

Position 7 modification of purines		Alkylation
5-6 double bond modification of pyrimidines		Reactions with bisulphite
Primary amino modification		Reaction with formaldehyde
Basic tertiary nitrogens		Reactions with peroxy acids or n-chloroperbenzoic acid
Ionic bonding at phosphate groups		Reaction with poly-bases such as polyquarternary ammonium salts
Phosphate-ribose 5'-hydroxyl ester linkage		Ribonuclease digestion

Figure 8.1   Subunit Structure of BRL 5907 of *P. chrysogenum* virus. Sites of modification and nature of modification

encouraged the Beecham research group to embark upon the preparation of purified material in large quantities. A strain of *P. chrysogenum* yielding a high viral content was selected. Fermentation, extraction, and purification programmes led to the development of an acceptable production process capable of significant scale-up. In this system, a five-day fermentation proved optimal. Viral particles were then separated from the mycelial mass by centrifugation and disruption. The naked nucleic acid was then isolated and purified by precipitation, separation in 2-methoxyethanol, and membrane filtration. By this process, kilogram quantities of BRL 5907 were produced and characterized. It proved to be a remarkably standard product with only a marginal spread of molecular weight and a higher T_m value than many of the semisynthetic polyribonucleotides, such as poly I : C or poly A : U. Production of viral ds-RNA on this scale is in itself a significant achievement and one that has proved to be of great value in providing adequate quantities of pure ds-RNA for subsequent work.

Thus, the skills in fermentation technology acquired by the Beecham group of workers in the 1950s, again in collaboration with Sir Ernst Chain and with his enthusiastic encouragement, were to be exploited in the production, not of a metabolite, penicillin G but of another product, in this case a ds-RNA-containing virus, from the same *Penicillium* strains.

ANTIVIRAL PROPERTIES

Full evaluation of the purified ds-RNA proved that it is a potent antiviral agent *in vitro* and *in vivo*. Work at Beechams Pharmaceutical Research Division showed that chick embryo fibroblasts could be protected in culture from infection by Semliki forest virus using a dose of ds-RNA which represented no more than a few molecules per cell. Mice could be protected from a range of viruses using doses as low as 1 μg; efficacy was also demonstrated in other animal species. It proved, for example, possible to influence the course of viral infection in the respiratory tract of a primate, the vervet monkey, by the application of BRL 5907 to the nasal mucosa, thus providing some optimism for the use of BRL 5907 to protect man from infections of the upper respiratory tract. Before a clinical programme was initiated, however, a detailed study of the kinetics of the antiviral effect was carried out in mice.

Studies in mice indicate that optimal protection can only be achieved by administering the ds-RNA some hours before viral infection; treatment delayed until a few hours after infection is notably less effective. BRL 5907, on this basis, seems to be essentially a prophylactic agent. It is still a matter of debate whether such an agent would be of clinical value in the common run of self-limiting viral infections of the upper respiratory tract, such as colds and influenza. The decisive point would seem to be the extent to which viral multiplication continues after the first symptoms or clear prodromal effects of infection are apparent. While it is true that interferon protects cells prophylactically only and cannot therefore protect the already infected cell, nor can interferon destroy its contained virus, in the multicellular host interferon may well be able to protect the host by preventing the spread of infection to as yet unprotected, susceptible cells. Provided therefore that viral infectivity is a continuing phenomenon after the symptoms are first noticed, an interferon inducer would be expected to be effective. On the basis of studies of virus shedding and isolations from the human respiratory tract following infection with, for example, rhinovirus it appears that viral multiplication does continue (Panusarn *et al.*, 1974). This is true also in experimental infections as shown in the case of influenza infection in ferrets and respiratory tract infections in primates (Boyd and Planterose, personal communication).

Even if the prophylactic properties of ds-RNA as an antiviral agent were not a significant problem would not hyporesponsiveness undermine the potential value of it for clinical use? It is known that cells cannot be stimulated repeatedly to produce interferon and a state of hyporesponsiveness rapidly develops in animals repeatedly injected with an inducer (Ho *et al.*, 1968; de Clerq and Merigan, 1970). In mice, for example, as shown in Figure 8.2, each daily administration of BRL 5907 results in a lower titre of serum interferon; by only the third injection no serum interferon can be detected (Sharpe *et al.*, 1971). These results would seem to impose a severe limitation on the usefulness of ds-RNA, or any other interferon inducer, as an antiviral agent.

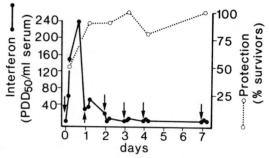

Figure 8.2 Effects of repeat dosing on the interferon response and antiviral efficacy of BRL 5907 in mice. ds-RNA (BRL 5907) (0·5 mg/kg) was administered at times indicated by arrow. ●——●, serum interferon levels expressed as the dilution of serum required to depress the plaque count by 50 per cent. ○‐‐‐○, percentage of animals surviving challenge with 100 LD$_{50}$ doses of encephalomyocarditis virus. Reproduced from Sharpe *et al.* (1971), by permission of Cambridge University Press

A significant discovery was made, however, in the author's laboratories by Planterose and his colleagues. Throughout all their antiviral research the authors had evaluated materials in terms of the antiviral effects—protection from viral infection—rather than on the basis of the levels of serum interferon obtained. However, as shown in Figure 8.2, these two measurements do not always run in parallel. Repeated injections of inducer leads, as expected from the literature, to a much diminished and finally immeasurable quantity of serum interferon, but antiviral protection remains unimpaired, or is even modestly enhanced (Sharpe *et al.*, 1971). In similar experiments, it was shown that repeated aerosol administration of BRL 5907 to mice subsequently infected with influenza virus does not lead to any diminution of antiviral efficacy (Planterose, 1975).

It is clear that these results would have a significant bearing upon the future clinical exploitation of BRL 5907, indicating that repeated administration of drug may well give rise to significant antiviral protection even if interferon induction cannot be demonstrated. The results, however, require explanation in cellular terms. A number of possible mechanisms can be put forward. It is possible that the antiviral state may be maintained, but not induced, by very small amounts of interferon or that interferon primes host cells to increased interferon uptake so that, while still fully protected, less interferon is circulating in serum. These mechanisms cannot be ruled out but it seems to be more likely that the total antiviral potential of polyribonucleotides is the sum, not only of interferon induction but also of less well-defined effects upon cells of the reticuloendothelial and lymphoid systems. BRL 5907 and other polyribonucleotides whether of natural or semisynthetic origin exhibit an impressive spectrum of biological effects when injected into experimental animals. Antiviral properties may therefore represent the composite of several of these effects and one of the tasks for the future is to try to separate and characterize not only the precise biology of these effects but also the chemical and physical determinants of the polyribonucleotide structure responsible for them.

Full exploitation of ds-RNA will demand an understanding of the cellular and biochemical events which follow administration of the material. Some of these activities may be clinically useful and lead to the development of ds-RNA as, for example, an adjuvant or an antitumor agent. Other activities lead to frank and overt toxicity which will need to be minimized by perhaps topical administration of the drug. Still other activities of the molecule might lead to complex interactions with host-cell metabolism. It is still too early to predict whether events favourable or detrimental to the health of the host will ensue. Many of these topics are referred to later in this review.

Meanwhile, the author has, in collaboration with a number of scientists, investigated the antiviral properties of BRL 5907 in clinical situations. Studies were initiated in farm animals and the main experimental findings are summarized in Table 8.2. The studies carried out in collaboration with Sellers *et al.* (1973) afforded direct information on the ability of BRL 5907 to protect farm animals against natural exposure to a virus of real commercial importance, foot and mouth disease virus. In pigs, the results were encouraging. The vesicular lesions characteristic of this disease either failed to develop or developed later and to a lesser extent (Figure 8.3) in those animals which received BRL 5907 over a 10-day period. It was found that although overt disease is prevented,

Table 8.2 Antiviral studies with BRL 5907: Veterinary primate and clinical investigations

Species	Virus and route of administration	Dose, route, and schedule BRL 5907	Result	References
Cattle	Foot and mouth disease virus natural exposure	5 mg/kg day^{-1} s.c. from 2 days before infection to 7 days after	reduction in numbers delay in appearance of lesions	Sellers *et al.*, 1973
Pig	Aujeszky's disease intranasal	0·1 mg/kg day^{-1} s.c. from 1 day before infection to 7 days after	non-significant increase in survival time	McFerran, J. D., personal communication
Pig	Transmissible gastroenteritis by mouth	Intranasal administration 0·1 mg/kg day^{-1} i.p. from 1 day before infection to 7 days after	no effect no effect	Leiper, J. and Knight, D., personal communication
Pig	Foot and mouth disease virus natural exposure	0·1 mg/kg day^{-1} i.p. or s.c. from 2 days before infection to 7 days after	spread of lesions prevented	Sellers *et al.*, 1973 Sellers and Herniman, 1974
Chicken	Marek's disease virus by intraperitoneal injection	0·5 mg/kg day^{-1} days −1, 0, +1	no effecy on mortality	Knight, D. and Payne, L., personal communication
Vervet monkeys	Equine rhinovirus Parainfluenza SV5 virus Adenovirus SV17 Adenovirus SV17 by intranasal spray	2 mg/dose; by intranasal route, 2 doses given 1 day before infection and 1 dose given daily for 9 days after infection	some reduction in viraemia with rhinovirus delay in virus excretion in all systems reduced virus shedding of parainfluenza	Boyd, M. and Planterose, D., personal communication
Man	Rhinovirus by intranasal instillation	5 mg/day by intranasal drops in 5 divided doses 1 day before infection to 2 days after infection	reduced and delayed clinical symptoms slightly reduced virus shedding	Tyrrell, D., Reed, S., and Aoki, F., personal communication

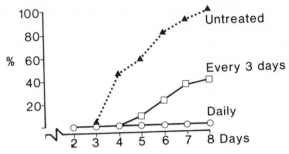

Figure 8.3. Effect of treatment with ds-RNA (BRL 5907) on the development of lesions caused by foot and mouth disease virus in pigs. Percentage of sites developing lesions following natural exposure to foot and mouth disease virus. ds-RNA was given daily or every third day at 0·1 mg/kg, s.c. starting day −1. Data from Sellers *et al.* (1973), redrawn by Planterose (1975). Reproduced by permission of Academic Press

antibody to the virus is stimulated suggesting that viral multiplication at the site of primary infection, the nasopharynx, is not prevented, but disease dissemination to other parts of the body was limited. Efficacy was demonstrated also in calves, but a 50-fold greater dose is required. It is likely that this is a reflection of the rapid inactivation of BRL 5907 by ribonucleases in cattle serum.

The susceptibility of polyribonucleotides to ribonucleases is an important determinant of activity in any species. Bovine serum rapidly degrades BRL 5907, but a modified polyribonucleotide prepared in the Beecham laboratories and designated BRL 10739 is significantly less susceptible to the action of these enzymes (Heyes *et al.*, 1974). This material, discussed further below, has been shown to afford some protection to calves infected experimentally with a herpes group virus, infectious bovine rhinotracheitis. The intravenous administration of 0·05 mg/kg of BRL 10739 24 hours prior to intranasal infection delays virus shedding, although the response is not dramatic (Knight, personal communication).

Other studies in domesticated animals have failed to demonstrate significant activity, although several virus types have been used in the different animal species (Table 8.2). While it is unlikely that optimal schedules have been used, it is nonetheless clear from these studies that the order of efficacy of polyribonucleotides in mice will not be equalled in these farm animals, although a useful degree of antiviral effect may be achieved.

Clinical studies in man also are in hand currently with BRL 5907 (Table 8.2). The toxicity and pharmacodynamic effects of BRL 5907 sprayed intranasally in uninfected human volunteers has been studied (D. Tyrrell *et al.*, personal communication). In multiple doses of 0·10 to 0·20 mg/kg day^{-1} for five days, there was a relationship between the development of cold-type symptoms and drug therapy, although in no case were the symptoms sufficient to interrupt the dosage. In this study, only one of the five volunteers produced measurable interferon in nasal washings. Rhinitis and nasal mucosal hyperaemia were again observed in a further study in subjects given 0·5–1 mg BRL 5907 in 10, one hourly doses for five days; five out of the eight subjects had interferon present in nasal washings. In a study carried out in the author's laboratories, no interferon was obtained in six volunteers given either 2·5 or 25 μg BRL 5907 (Lees, personal communication).

Although these results were not particularly encouraging, studies in the vervet monkey had indicated that intranasally administered BRL 5907 provides some protection against rhinovirus, as measured by virus shedding, and also against parainfluenza (Boyd, personal communication). Studies were therefore initiated by Tyrrell and his group using volunteers infected with rhinovirus. BRL 5907 was given in five divided doses giving a total of 5 mg/day, on days −1, 0 and +1 in relation to rhinovirus administration on day 0. Slight activity as measured by clinical symptoms and by virus shedding was observed, but the results are not statistically significant. Overall, therefore, efficacy by the intranasal route in primates, whether monkey or man, is at best modest, and BRL 5907 is very obviously less active in these species than in rodents.

The reasons for the species variation is not yet entirely clear. It is known that man is capable of interferon production in response to a viral infection and, in some instances, best exemplified by the very high interferon titres observed in the vesicular lesions of herpes virus infections, of substantial and sustained production. However, interferon induction by polyribonucleotides is a function of both molecular weight and the double-helical conformation, and therefore dependent upon survival of the inducing molecule intact *in vivo*. Human body fluids, serum, and in particular nasal secretions contain high levels of ribonucleases capable of degrading polyribonucleotides. A reasonable, although not exclusive, explanation for the comparative ineffectiveness of these molecules in primates, is that they are rapidly degraded. The evaluation of the ribonuclease-resistant complex BRL 10739 in man could, on these grounds, be justified.

CHEMICAL AND PHYSICAL MODIFICATION

Extensive programmes have been undertaken in the Beecham laboratories to try to modigy BRL 5907 by chemical or physicochemical means in order to produce compounds with better therapeutic ratios either by increasing effectiveness or by decreasing acute toxicity. One property sought in this modification programme was increased resistance to the enzymic action of ribonucleases (Harnden *et al.*, 1973a,b,c; Heyes *et al.*, 1974). However, modification of the purine or pyrimidine bases of BRL 5907 by reaction with the amino groups at positions 7 and 8 of the purines, or at the 5,6 double bond of the pyrimidines (Figure 8.1) results in compounds with no useful improvements compared with the natural product, BRL 5907. In addition, the 2'-hydroxyl group of ribose did not prove to be amenable to modification (Harnden *et al.*, 1973b,c). The binding of BRL 5907 to polyamines, basic polypeptides, and polyquaternary compounds was promising (Harnden *et al.*, 1973*a*; Heyes *et al.*, 1974) and, in some instances, quite marked changes in biological properties were observed. A polybrene complex of BRL 5907 proved to be less toxic in several species and to give antiviral protection of longer duration. A more soluble polyquaternary ammonium complex, designated BRL 10739, gives not only better and more prolonged antiviral activity in mice but also possesses significantly increased resistance to ribonuclease. This material has been evaluated in several experimental situations (Heyes *et al.*, 1974; Planterose, 1975).

Overall, the impression gained is that where susceptibility to ribonuclease is a critical factor, as for example in primates and in cattle, BRL 10739 can be regarded as a significant improvement upon the parent molecule, BRL 5907. In antiviral studies in mice, where BRL 5907 is highly active, BRL 10739 represents a more modest improvement, although longer duration of activity has been observed. It is of interest, that, in this respect, BRL 10739 mimics the action of viral particles from *P.* stoloniferum, possibly because the particle, with its protecting protein coat, is more resistant to ribonucleases than is the naked ds-RNA (Planterose *et al.*, 1970), although the difference is less marked with viral particles derived from *P. chrysogenum* (Buck *et al.*, 1971). In accord with studies on BRL 10739, it has recently been shown that a polylysine complex of poly I:C possesses impressive activity in virus-infected monkeys (Levy *et al.*, 1974).

It is therefore becoming clearer that chemical modification of natural or semisynthetic polyribonucleotides can lead to compounds of significantly different biological activity, some of which might lend themselves to clinical exploitation in human and veterinary medicine. In this section, this possibility has been reviewed with respect to exploitation of ds-RNA as an antiviral agent. There is no doubt, however, that the polyribonucleotides initiate in avian and mammalian species a wide range of biological events in addition to the induction of interferon and protection of cells from viral invasion.

It is to be expected that some of these events, either at the initiation or induction stage, or through the activity of effector molecules, will be intrinsically detrimental to the integrity of the host and the toxicity of the molecule is the cumulative outcome of these biological events taking place at a cellular level. This is discussed further in the review of toxicity and pharmacology.

On the other hand, many of the biological pathways affected by ds-RNA are those which one wishes to modulate to achieve effects useful in the prevention or control of disease processes, and alteady already is clear that this can be achieved without overt toxicity. Thus, polyribonucleotides are proven adjuvants in many different systems allowing the development of higher and more prolonged antibody titres to, for example, viral vaccines. In experimental work it has been shown that these adjuvant properties can be exceedingly impressive in situations where the responsiveness of the host is depressed because of disease, chemotherapy, or genetic make-up. In addition, antitumour properties have been described and these are not without clinical or veterinary interest. Of relevance to the present discussion is the observation that where structure–activity relationships have been established, it is apparent that structural molecular characteristics which are essential for one type of biological responsiveness are not necessarily the same for optimal activity of another kind. Thus, antiviral activity demands the double-stranded conformation, a high molecular weight, and as a consequence, resistance to ribonucleases. Adjuvancy is much less demanding in terms of molecular integrity and a range of nucleic acid derivatives can show this activity. In this situation, it is not unrealistic to predict that it will be possible to achieve significant degrees of selectivity for polyribonucleotides by modification programmes and the result may well be a marked improvement in therapeutic ratios.

ADJUVANT PROPERTIES

The adjuvant properties of polyribonucleotides were first demonstrated by Braun and Nakano (1967) who showed that the semisynthetic polyribonucleotide, poly A : U increases the antibody responses of mice to sheep erythrocytes. Extensive studies have now been made to define the adjuvant activity of BRL 5907 in the author's laboratories, and of the synthetic materials by other workers (Cunnington and Naysmith, 1975a; Braun et al., 1971; Johnson et al., 1971; Woodhour et al., 1969). It is now possible to draw some general conclusions about the kinetics of the adjuvant effect and the physicochemical requirements of the molecule for adjuvant activity.

The adjuvant activity of polyribonucleotides is demonstrable in all mammalian species tested and in chickens, and has been shown for a wide range of thymus-dependent antigens. Table 8.3 records some of the studies with BRL 5907 which have particular bearing upon the application of this material as an adjuvant for veterinary vaccines.

BRL 5907 is most effective when given with antigen at the same site and, in some species, when given in a water-in-oil emulsion. Efficacy is dependent upon time of polyribonucleotide administration with respect to antigen. In the mouse, for example, adjuvant effects, measured by increase in antibody-forming cells in mouse spleen, are seen if the ds-RNA is given up to 24 hours after antigen, but if given before antigen a marked immunosuppressive effect is observed.

The double-stranded conformation is important to adjuvant activity but does not seem to be obligatory. It has been known for many years that oligonucleotides and nucleic acid digests have adjuvant activity although their efficiency in most studies falls short of that of the ds-RNAs. The influence of helical conformation and molecular size on biological activity is, in fact, less marked for adjuvant activity than for many other biological activities, including antiviral activity, the overall toxicity of the molecule, and its ability to act as an immunogen to stimulate the production of specific antibodies.

Thus, the strict requirement for helical conformation and a high molecular weight is less marked for adjuvant activity than for other biological properties,

Vaccine	Species	Formulation	Result	References
Newcastle disease virus inactivated	Chicken	Intramuscular in oil emulsions	increased antibody titres enhanced protection	Gough et al., 1974
Avian influenza virus inactivated	Chicken	Intramuscular in oil emulsion	increased primary and secondary antibody titres	Gough et al., 1975
Influenza virus PR8 inactivated	Cattle	Intramuscular in oil	increased antibody titres longer duration and earlier peak of antibody enhanced protection	Knight, D. personal communication
Foot and mouth disease virus inactivated	Pig	Subcutaneous in double emulsion / Subcutaneous in alhydrogel	slight increase in antibody titre	Mowat, G. N. personal communication / Mowat, G. N. personal communication
Foot and mouth disease virus inactivated	Cattle	Subcutaneous in alhydrogel	increased primary and secondary antibody titres	Mowat, G. N. personal communication
Foot and mouth disease virus inactivated	Cattle	Subcutaneous in oil emulsions or alhydrogel	no increase in antibody titres	Basarab, O. personal communication
	Pig	Intramuscular in alhydrogel or added to oil emulsions	high degree of protection in all oil-emulsion innoculated groups; added benefit of 5907 not assessable	Basarab, O. personal communication
Avian influenza virus inactivated	Turkey	Subcutaneous in oil emulsion	increased antibody titres enhanced protection	Leiper, H. personal communication
Parainfluenza 3 virus	Sheep	Intramuscular in oil emulsion	increased antibody titres enhanced protection	Wells et al., 1976
Oncornavirus cell surface antigen 10^7 inactivated cells	Cat	In oil emulsion	rapid response with low antigen dose	Jarrett, W. personal communication
Louping ill virus	Sheep	Subcutaneous in oil emulsion	increased antibody titres equivalent titres with 1/10th the antigen dose	Reid, H. and Wells, P. personal communication

notably antiviral efficacy. Acute toxicity and the ability of the molecule to stimulate specific antibodies, that is, its inherent immunogenicity are, in contrast to adjuvancy, also largely functions of the double-stranded conformation and a high molecular weight. In addition, Cunnington in the Beecham laboratories has shown that whereas a reduction in the molecular size of BRL 5907 by sonication results in a very significant reduction in immunogenicity, only a very marginal reduction in adjuvancy is obtained. Furthermore, in collaboration with Imperial College it has been shown that in most, although not all, experimental systems, toxicity and antiviral activity fall off in parallel with decreasing molecular size.

These results may give important leads to the mechanism of action of polyribonucleotides. The structural requirements for interferon-induction of high molecular weight and double-stranded molecule suggests that precise interaction is required at a receptor site. Adjuvant activity makes less precise demands upon the conformation of the molecule and, as has been suggested previously (Dewdney, 1975), might be the result of activation of the macrophage population to bring about better co-operation between different populations of lymphocytes, either through cell–cell interaction, or, perhaps more plausibly, through a macrophage-derived soluble mediator. The exploitation of polyribonucleotides as adjuvants is now a scientific, if not commercial, reality. The modern-day plagues of rabies, and foot and mouth disease for example may well be brought under control in the next decade by a combination of viral antigen purification and the improved adjuvancy afforded by a polyribonucleotide in an immunization programme.

There are few other structurally defined adjuvants. Those that are known are microbial products, *Bordetella pertussis*, Mycobacteria, Corynebacteria, or physical depots comprising oil or aluminium hydroxide. Although strenuous efforts are being made to purify and characterize these, confirmed activity has not yet been obtained from precisely defined products. Exploration therefore must continue. The means are now available to study the fundamental biology of adjuvancy and this could open up new practical concepts in the treatment of human disease.

ANTITUMOUR ACTIVITY

It has been demonstrated that statolon given shortly after infection of mice with Friend leukaemia virus can reverse the profound immunosuppression that this virus produces and can suppress the otherwise fatal erythroleukaemia of infected mice (Wheelock, 1967; Wheelock et al., 1969; Weislow et al., 1973; Wheelock et al., 1974). This remarkable effect is, however, time dependent. Pilch and Planterose (1971) using BRL 5907 showed that the suppressive effect upon erythroleukaemia was only observed if BRL 5907 was given during the phase of rapid leukaemic cell proliferation which in the experimental system used was between three to 11 days after infection. Treatment prior to infection and up to three days after infection resulted in a marked enhancement of the leukaemia as measured by splenomegaly.

Interpretation of results such as these is complex. It seems likely that the enhancement of splenomegaly seen if the ds-RNA is given prior to, or early after, infection may be a reflection of the immunosuppression observed with other antigens when the time factors between adjuvant and antigen are similar. What accounts for the dramatic antileukaemic effect? Is it a direct antiviral action mediated by interferon, which has been shown to possess some antitumour properties (Gresser and Bourali, 1969), mediated by as yet unidentified antiviral effects, or is it a direct antitumour cell action? None of these questions can be fully answered at the present time but perhaps ds-RNA will provide a tool with which to explore the complex biological interactions of host and virus which makes up the leukaemic syndrome.

More direct antitumour properties have been observed with fungal virus ds-RNAs. In the author's laboratories, Heyes and Catherall (1974) have shown that the lifespan of mice given FS6 fibrosarcoma cells intravenously is increased when BRL 5907 is administered by aerosol. In this experimental system, tumour cells systemically administered lodge in the capillary beds in the lungs. It is of interest in these studies that only topical administration of BRL 5907 is effective; the intraperitoneal route of administration fails to provide any significant benefit. The effectiveness of topical application of BRL 5907 was also demonstrated in the Lewis lung carcinoma model in which subcutaneously implanted tumour cells give rise to a primary tumour mass and subsequent metastases in the lung. BRL 5907 given by aerosol significantly reduces the number of pulmonary metastatic tumours. These workers also demonstrated the activity of the polyquaternary ammonium complex of BRL 5907, BRL 10739, given either intraperitoneally or topically against 5178Y lymphoma in mice and in the Lewis lung model (Heyes et al., 1974).

The antitumour properties of ds-RNA from *P. chrysogenum* have also been studied and reviewed by Alexander and his group (Alexander and Evans, 1971; Parr et al., 1973; Alexander, 1974). It was found that peritoneal macrophages from mice and rats treated with BRL 5907 acquire the capacity to inhibit the growth of lymphoma and sarcoma cells *in vitro*, and yet BRL 5907 has no direct antitumour cell activity (Alexander and Evans, 1971). It has been shown, in animal experiments, that ds-RNA is most effective against established tumours (Parr et al., 1973), although the overall picture is complex and appears to depend upon the route of tumour-cell administration, the nature of the tumour, and when the ds-RNA is administrated. In experiments reported by Alexander and his group, both systemic and intralesion administration of ds-RNA are effective.

The mechanisms by which antitumour effects are achieved are not clear. It is possible that macrophage activation is a critical event in the efficacy of locally administered ds-RNA against tumours having a high proportion of macrophage cells (Alexander and Evans, 1971). In other situations, for example, when the ds-RNA is given systemically, it seems that a combination of damage to vasculature and the consequent increase in accessibility of the tumour to immune effector molecules might be the explanation for the activity of ds-RNA against certain solid tumours, an activity which depends upon the antigenicity of the tumour and the immune competance of the host (Parr *et al.*, 1973; Alexander, 1974). The similarity of the antitumour activity of ds-RNAs and endotoxins is, of course, striking, as it is also with respect to general toxicity (Stinebring and Absher, 1971).

There have been several studies in cancer patients, mostly in terminal cases, with the semisynthetic polyribonucleotides poly I : C or poly A : U (Levy *et al.*, 1971; Mathe *et al.*, 1971; Tilz and Becker, 1973; Lacour *et al.*, 1974; Tilz and Sailer, 1974; Cornell *et al.*, 1975; Mathe, 1975; Wanebo *et al.*, 1975). In general, these polyribonucleotides have been given without serious toxic side effects developing but, as might be expected in these critically ill patients, efficacy has not yet been demonstrated. Clinical studies with BRL 5907 are now planned. It is hoped to be able to assess the ability of this compound to act as an anticancer agent and also to determine whether it will protect cancer patients from the life-threatening dissemination of viral diseases to which their disease, or its therapy, makes them prone. It is under just such circumstances that polyribonucleotides might be expected to be most effective, at least as immunostimulants, for the most impressive adjuvant effects of these molecules have been observed when the immunological responsiveness of the host is less than optimal, whether due to age, chemotherapy, disease, or genetic factors. The lack of understanding of the mode of action of polyribonucleotides as anticancer drugs will, however, hinder clinical studies; it is difficult to predict or determine by experimental work optimal dosage regimens.

TOXICITY AND PHARMACOLOGY

An important aspect of the preclinical evaluation of any novel compound intended for human or veterinary use is the detailed study of the biological events culminating in effects which are adverse to the functioning or even survival of the recipient; this is known as toxicity. That polyribonucleotides stimulate cellular and subcellular events which result in overt toxicity cannot be denied. On the other hand, it is important not to dismiss too readily this molecule as a potentially useful drug and to consider in depth the mechanisms by which these biological events are triggered. The complexity of such a study is clear. Polyribonucleotides stimulate the induction or release of biologically active effector molecules of which interferon, the lymphokines, and factors arising from the macrophage are the best examples. Each of these molecules has a potential toxicity. One of the most significant questions in the study of interferon inducers is whether the toxicity of the inducers as a class is an intrinsic property, or more directly a consequence of their ability to induce, or release these substances, or a consequence of the toxicity of the effector molecules themselves. This is a matter of fundamental importance to research designed to investigate the role of inducers in antiviral chemotherapy. The mechanism of toxicity must therefore be studied further. Poly I : C (reviewed by Stinebring and Absher, 1971; Phillips *et al.*, 1971), and in our experience, several naturally occurring ds-RNAs are acutely toxic in many mammalian species. Symptoms and objective findings have been compared with those following the administration of endotoxin. This is an interesting point. In species susceptibility, clinical symptoms, haemotological effects, and actions on the cardiovascular system, quite remarkable similarities have been observed, to an extent that in the author's laboratories much time has been devoted to providing indisputable data proving that the ds-RNA was not contaminated by endotoxins.

An observation of even greater importance, however, is that in very many respects the toxicity of ds-RNA resembles that of acute viral disease. In the chicken, the pathology of Newcastle disease is very similar to that induced by ds-RNA. In the baby pig, it is similar to the lesions of transmissible gastroen-teritis, while in man, when applied locally to the respiratory tract, symptoms can mimic those of the rhinoviruses and adenoviruses. The author believes that in the elucidation of the underlying biology of these events lies scientific discoveries related to virus pathogenicity.

The acute toxicity of ds-RNA at relatively high doses can be impressive. However, in the limited clinical studies performed to date, mostly admittedly in cancer patients who may not respond as healthy persons, poly I : C has not proved to be too toxic, and even by systemic routes the only common finding has been pyrexia. Clotting irregularities, nausea and vomiting, and broncho-spasm have been described occasionally (Krakoff *et al.*, 1970; de Vita *et al.*, 1970). Some local irritation has been observed after administration of polyribonucleotides to nasal mucosa, but in general this route of administration seems to avoid any systemic toxicological problems (Hill *et al.*, 1969; Niblack *et al.*, 1970; Tyrrell *et al.*, personal communication).

In the final analysis what may be more important than acute toxicity are the immunological consequences of immune stimulation. Also interference with or alteration of cell metabolism may be important, although there is to date only limited evidence of the cellular uptake of ds-RNA. Under these circumstances the ds-RNA could theoretically be considered as genetic information for mammalian cells, or to interact with host-cell DNA. The immunogenicity of these molecules must also be considered. As might be expected from their high molecular weight, polyribonucleotides are immunogenic and stimulate the production of antibodies specific for the double-stranded conformation of the molecule, although there is pronounced strain and species specificity in this response. (Cunnington and Naysmith, 1975*b*).

It is not, however, their immunogenicity *per se* which suggests that caution should be exercised in the clinical use of these molecules for there are many examples in clinical medicine of the successful use of immunogenic molecules, as for example viral and bacterial vaccines, allergens, hormones, and enzymes. It is more the specificity of the antibody raised. In certain diseases, notably systemic lupus erythematosus and to a lesser extent rheumatoid arthritis, antibody to ds-RNA is frequently found. Although anti-RNA antibody, unlike antibody to DNA, is not an indication of disease severity and its significance, if any, to pathology is unknown, while its role is not defined, any material which enhances or stimulates *de novo* such antibody must be treated with care in clinical use. On the other hand, the opportunity now exists to utilize polyribonucleotides in order to shed light on just this type of problem, and their value as biological tools is now being recognized.

SUMMARY AND CONCLUSIONS

The polyribonucleotides derived from fungal viruses are macromolecules which exhibit a wide spectrum of biological activity which includes interferon induction, the ability to protect animals from viral disease, amplification of immune responsiveness, and antitumour activity. The exploitation of these properties in human and veterinary medicine is still at the exploratory stage. It seems likely that in the future the outstanding potency of these molecules will be safely harnessed for clinical use in the control of disease. Important though this objective is, in the longer term the value of polyribonucleotides may be seen differently. These are powerful biological tools with which it may be possible to explore a number of disease processes and biological phenomena. It cannot be pure chance that their activity mimics so closely that of systemic viral disease. From a study of the toxicology, pathology, and pharmacology of ds-RNAs, much of importance may be learned in relation to viral induced pathology, its initiation, and mediation. Moreover, the nature of the interactions between presumptive virus and immunological dysfunction which underlies many chronic diseases, which have defeated so far all attempts at therapy, may be elucidated by means of polyribonucleotides. In this respect, the development of iridocyclitis in primates treated with high intravenous doses of ds-RNA has been studied (Kelvin, personal communication). This condition in man is frequently associated with diseases in which immunological dysfunction, including immune responsiveness to nucleic acids, is a feature. Perhaps ds-RNA will be the means whereby this relationship can be explained.

The target cells for polyribonucleotides include the lymphocytes and cells of reticuloendothelial systems. These cells are concerned with defence and the maintenance of homeostasis, critical functions in relation to health, and survival of the individual and the species. There can be no more important objective than to learn more about the control of these functions in health and disease, and polyribonucleotides may be the means whereby this knowledge can be obtained.

Finally, any discussion of penicillin, the metabolic product of *Penicillium* culture, notes the selectivity of action of this drug. It acts specifically upon enzymes in the bacterial cell wall to kill the micro-organism with no concomitant effect on mammalian cells. Any discussion of ds-RNA derived also from *Penicillium* culture stresses, not selectivity, but the breadth of biological effects stimulated in mammalian species by them. The problems, therefore, are different from those of penicillin research but not less demanding and the rewards may be as great. The future challenge to Sir Ernst and all others involved in this work, which is one of the most exciting biological endeavours of recent times, is to bring to bear upon the problem imagination, scientific observation, and determination to achieve sufficient selectivity of action to allow full exploitation of the biology of polyribonucleotides.

ACKNOWLEDGEMENTS

The author is grateful to her colleagues at the Chemotherapeutic Research Centre of Beecham Pharmaceuticals Research Division for permission to publish in this form previously unpublished data and for their helpful suggestions.

REFERENCES

Alexander, P. (1974) *Johns Hopkin Med. J.*, **3** (Suppl.), 321.
Alexander, P., and Evans, R. (1971) *Nature, New Biol.*, **232**, 76.
Banks, G. T., Buck, K. W., Chain, E. B., Darbyshire, J. E., and Himmelweit, F. (1969*a*) *Nature (London)*, **222**, 89.
Banks, G. T., Buck, K. W., Chain, E. B., Darbyshire, J. E., and Himmelweit, F. (1969*b*) *Nature (London)*, **223**, 155.
Banks, G. T., Buck, K. W., Chain, E. B., Darbyshire, J. E., Himmelweit, F., Ratti, G., Sharpe, T. J., and Planterose, D. N. (1970) *Nature (London)*, **227**, 505.
Banks, G. T., Buck, K. W., Chain, E. B., Himmelweit, F., Marks, J. E., Tyler, J. M., Hollings, M., Last, F. T., and Stone, O. M. (1968) *Nature (London)*, **218**, 542.
Border, D. J., Buck, K. W., Chain, E. B., Kempson-Jones, G. F., Lhoas, P., and Ratti, G. (1972) *Biochem. J.*, **127**, 4P.
Bozarth, R. F., Wood, H. A., and Manselbrot, A. (1971) *Virology*, **45**, 516.
Braun, W., Ishizuka, M., Yajima, Y., Webb, D., and Winchurch, R. (1971) in *Biological Effects of Polynucleotides. Proceedings of the Symposium on Molecular Biology.* (Beers, R. F., and Braun, W., eds.), Springer-Verlag, New York, pp. 139–156.
Braun, W., and Nakano, M. (1967) *Science, N.Y.*, **157**, 819.
Brown, A. G. (1971) *Rep. Prog. Appl. Chem.*, **56**, 686.
Buck, K. W., Chain, E. B., and Himmelweit, F. (1971) *J. Gen. Virol.*, **12**, 131.
Buck, K. W. and Kempson-Jones, G. F. (1970) *Nature (London)*, **225**, 945.
Chain, E. B. (1972) *Proc. R. Inst. G.B.*, **45**, 241.
Cole, M., and Planterose, D. N. (1968) Brit. Pat. 1 230 011.
Cornell, G. J., Smith, K. A., Cornwell, G. G., Grace, W. R., and McIntyre, O. R. (1975) *Proc. Am. Ass. Cancer Res.*, **16**, 265.
Cox, R. A., Kanagalingen, K., and Sutherland, E. S. (1970) *Biochem. J.*, **120**, 549.
Cunnington, P. G., and Naysmith, J. D. (1975*a*) *Immunology*, **28**, 451.
Cunnington, P. G., and Naysmith, J. D. (1975*b*) *Immunology*, **29**, 1001.
de Clerq, E., and Merigan T. (1970) *Ann. Rev. Med.* **21**, 17.
de Vita, V., Canellos, G., Carbone, P., Baron, S., Levy, H., and Graenick, H. (1970). *Proc. Am. Ass. Cancer Res.*, **66**, Abs. 79.
Dewdney, J. M. (1975) Presentation to the British Society for Immunology.
Ellis, L. F., and Kleinschmidt, W. J. (1967) *Nature (London)*, **215**, 649.
Gough, R. E., Allan, W. H., Knight, D. J., and Leiper, J. W. G. (1974) *Res. Vet. Sci.*, **17**, 280.

168

Gough, R. E., Allan, W. H., Knight, D. J., and Leiper, J. W. G. (1975) *Res. Vet. Sci.*, 19, 185.

Gresser, I., and Bourali, C. (1969) *Nature (London)*, 223, 844.

Harnden, M. R., Brown, A. G., Sharpe, T. J., and Vere Hodge, R. A. (1973a) *Am. Chem. Soc.*, Abs. No. 48.

Harnden, M. R., Brown, A. R., and Vere Hodge, R. A. (1973b) *Experientia*, 29, 1344.

Harnden, M. R., Brown, A. R. and Vere Hodge, R. A. (1973c) *J. Chem. Soc. Perkin I*, 333.

Heyes, J., and Catherall, E. J. (1974) *Nature (London)*, 247, 485.

Heyes, J., Catherall, E. J., and Harnden, M. J. (1974) *Eur. J. Cancer*, 10, 431.

Hill, D. A., Perkins, J. C., Worthington, M., Kapikian, A. Z., Chanock, R. M., and Baron, S. (1969) in *Proc. 3rd Int. Symp. on Medical and Applied Virology*. p. 405.

Ho, M., Postic, B., and Ke, Y. H. (1968) in *Ciba Foundation Symp. on Interferon*. J. and A. Churchill, London, p. 19.

Hollings, M. (1962) *Nature (London)*, 196, 962.

Hollings, M., and Stone, O. M. (1969) *Sci. Prog. (Oxford)*, 57, 371.

Hollings, M., and Stone, O. M. (1971) *Ann. Rev. Phytopathol.*, 9, 93.

Isaacs, A., and Lindenmann, J. (1957) *Proc. Roy. Soc., Ser. B*, 147, 258.

Johnson, A. G., Cone, R. E., Friedman, H. M., Han, I. H., Johnson, H. G., Schmidtke, J. R., and Stout, R. D. (1971) in *Biological Effects of Polynucleotides. Proceedings of the Symposium on Molecular Biology*. (Beers, R. F., and Braun, W., eds.), Springer-Verlag, New York, pp. 157–177.

Kleinschmidt, W. J. (1972) *Ann. Rev. Biochem.*, 41, 517.

Kleinschmidt, W. J., Cline, J. C., and Murphy, E. B. (1964) *Proc. Nat. Acad. Sci., U.S.A.*, 52, 741.

Kleinschmidt, W. J., Ellis, L. F., van Frank, R. M., and Murphy, E. B. (1968) *Nature (London)*, 220, 167.

Kleinschmidt, W. J., and Probst, G. W. (1962) *Antibiot. Chemother.* 12, 298.

Krakoff, I. H., Young, C. W., and Hilleman, M. R. (1970) *Proc. Am. Ass. Cancer Res.*, 11, 45.

Lacour, J., Lacour, F., Spira, A., Delage, G., and Michelson, A. M. (1974) *Bull. Cancer*, 61, 275.

Lampson, G. P., Tytell, A. A., Field, A. K., Nemes, M. M., and Hilleman, M. R. (1967) *Proc. Nat. Acad. Sci., U.S.A.*, 58, 782.

Lemke, P. A., and Ness, T. M. (1970) *J. Virol.*, 6, 813.

Levy, H. B., Adamson, R., Carbone, P., De Vita, V., Gazdar, A., Rhim, J., Weinstein, A., and Riley, F. (1971) in *Biological Effects of Polynucleotides. Proceedings of the Symposium on Molecular Biology*. (Beers, R. F., and Braun, W., eds.), Springer-Verlag, New York, pp. 55–65.

Levy, H. B., Baer, G., Baron, S., Gibbs, C. F., Iadakola, M., London, W., and Rice, J. M. (1974) *J. Int. Res. Commun.*, 2, 1643.

Lewis, U. J., Rickes, E. L., McClelland, L., and Brink, N. G. (1959) *J. Am. Chem. Soc.*, 81, 4115.

Mathe, G. (1975) *Nouv. Presse Med.*, 4, 1335.

Mathe, G., Amiel, J. L., Schwartzenberg, L., Schneider, M., Hayat, M., de Vassal, F., Jasmin, C., Rosenfeld, C., Sakouhi, M., and Choay, J. (1971) in *Biological Effects of Polynucleotides. Proceedings of the Symposium on Molecular Biology*. (Beers, R. F., and Braun, W., eds.), Springer-Verlag, New York, pp. 225–230.

Naficy, K., and Carver, D. H. (1963) *Proc. Soc. Exp. Biol. Med.*, 114, 175.

Niblack, J. F., Knirsch, A. K., and Vora, L. R. M. (1970) personal communication quoted by Hilleman, M. R. *et al.*, (1971). In *Biological Effects of Polynucleotides. Proceedings of the Symposium on Molecular Biology*. (Beers, R. F., and Braun, W., eds.), Springer-Verlag, New York, pp. 27–44.

169

Pallett, I. H. (1975) in *Proceedings of the 4th Int. Symp. on Yeasts and Other Protoplasts,* (Peberdy, J. F., Rose, A. H., Rogers, H. J., and Cocking, E. C., eds.), Academic Press, New York and London, p. 107.

Panusarn, C., Stanley, E. D., Dirda, V., Rubens, M., and Jackson, G. G. (1974) *New Eng. J. Med.,* **291,** 57.

Parr, I., Wheeler, W., and Alexander, P. (1973) *Brit. J. Cancer,* **27,** 370.

Phillips, F. S., Fleisher, M., Hamilton, L. D., Schwartz, M. K., and Sternberg, S. S. (1971) in *Biological Effects of Polynucleotides. Proceedings of the Symposium on Molecular Biology.* (Beers, R. F., and Braun, W., eds.), Springer-Verlag, New York, pp. 259–273.

Pilch, D. J. F., and Planterose, D. N. (1971) *J. Gen. Virol.,* **10,** 155.

Planterose, D. N. (1975) in *Effects of Interferon on Cells, Viruses, and the Immune System.* (Geraldes, A., ed.), Academic Press, New York and London, pp. 629–637.

Planterose, D. N., Birch, P. J., Pilch, D. J. F., and Sharpe, T. J. (1970) *Nature (London),* **227,** 504.

Powell, H. M., Culbertson, C. G., McGuire, J. M., Hoehn, M. M., and Baker, L. A. (1952) *Antibiot. Chemother.,* **2,** 432.

Rytel, M. W., Shope, R. E., and Kilbourne, E. D. (1966) *J. Exp. Med.,* **123,** 577.

Sellers, R. F., Herniman, K. A. J., Leiper, J. W. G., and Planterose, D. N. (1973) *Vet. Rec.,* **93,** 90.

Sellers, R. F., and Herniman, K. A. J. (1974) *Brit. Vet. J.,* **130,** 440.

Sharpe, T. J., Birch, P. J., and Planterose, D. N. (1971) *J. Gen. Virol.,* **12,** 331.

Shope, R. E. (1953*a*) *J. Exp. Med.,* **97,** 639.

Shope, R. E. (1953*b*) *J. Exp. Med.,* **97,** 627.

Stinebring, W. R., and Absher, M. (1971) in *Biological Effects of Polynucleotides. Proceedings of the Symposium on Molecular Biology.* Beers, R. F., and Braun, W., eds.), Springer-Verlag, New York, pp. 249–257.

Sutherland, E. S., and Bessell, C. J. (1969) Brit. Pat. 1 170 929.

Theil, K. W., Mohanty, S. B., and Hetnick, F. M. (1971) *Proc. Soc. Exp. Biol. Med.,* **137,** 1176.

Tilz, G. P., and Becker, H. (1973) *Med. Welt.,* **24,** 1487.

Tilz, G. P., and Sailer, S. (1974) *Wien. Med. Wochenschr.,* **124,** 617.

Tsunoda, A., and Ishida, N. (1970) *Ann. N.Y. Acad. Sci.,* **173,** 717.

Wanebo, H. J., Oettgen, H. F., Lundy, J., Stock, C. C., and Old, L. J. (1975) *Proc. Am. Ass. Cancer Res.,* **16,** 179.

Weislow, O. S., Friedman, H., and Wheelock, E. F. (1973) *Proc. Soc. Exp. Biol. Med.,* **142,** 401.

Wells, P. W., Sharp, J. M., Burrells, C., Rushton, B., and Smith, W. D. (1976) *J. Hygiene,* in press.

Wheelock, E. F. (1967) *Proc. Soc. Exp. Biol. Med.,* **124,** 855.

Wheelock, E. F., Caroline, N. L., and Moore, R. D. (1969) *J. Virol.,* **4,** 1.

Wheelock, E. F., Toy, S. T., Weislow, O. S., and Levy, M. H. (1974) *Prog. Exp. Tumour Res.,* **19,** 369.

Wood, H. A., Bozarth, R. F., and Mislivec, P. B. (1971) *Virology,* **44,** 592.

Woodhour, A. F., Friedman, A., Tytell, A. A., and Hilleman, M. R. (1969) *Proc. Soc. Exp. Biol. Med.,* **131,** 809.

9
Pathways of Glucose Absorption and Metabolism

F. Pocchiari and G. D'Agnolo

Istituto Superiore di Sanità, Rome, Italy

I started working with Sir Ernst when he first came to our Institute in Rome more than 25 years ago. When the late Professor Marotta summoned me to the corner room at the top floor, where Sir Ernst and Lady Anne had just made their headquarters, I certainly had no idea of how momentous that meeting would be for my career and for my whole life. In spite of my inexperience in biochemical research, the guidance of Sir Ernst during our first set of experiments was so patient and thorough that an enthusiastic team was soon established, leading to the collection of a large amount of valuable data. We were often in discussion until late in the night (and I mean late even by Italian standards), and next morning meeting me in the lift, Sir Ernst would ask me: 'Well, Francesco, have you got new results?'

GLUCOSE ABSORPTION

The mechanism of glucose uptake is rather complex. Glucose enters the cell at a rate far higher than its ability to diffuse through the cell membrane would suggest. The specialized transport system required is mediated by constituents of the membrane. A plausible model is that sugars cross the membrane through hydrophilic channels. The sugars are then further transported by random absorption or desorption between neighbouring binding sites within these channels. The flux of a sugar into the cell is a function of its affinity for the binding sites.

The so-called 'carrier hypothesis' has gained wider acceptance as a molecular model for facilitated diffusion of substrates into the cell. Glucose, for example, is thought to combine with a carrier molecule which permits the sugar to move across the plasma membrane. Kinetic analysis of glucose transport has revealed that there is a limited number of carriers within the membrane, and when the concentration of substrate molecules on one side of the membrane increases, the limited number of sites on the carrier molecule is progressively filled. With further increases of substrate concentration, the carrier is saturated and transport becomes independent of concentration. The kinetics of facilitated transport are therefore identical to those of enzyme catalysed reactions.

Although the specificity of the system which facilitates diffusion of sugars may vary in different tissues, in some early experiments with rabbits (Beloff-Chain *et al.*, 1951, 1953), it was observed that intravenously injected glucose rapidly disappears from the blood, reaching an equilibrium value in about one hour. In the same experiment, it was observed that both glucose 1-phosphate and glucose 6-phosphate penetrate the tissues. Generally, sugar phosphates are found only within the cells and do not escape, nor do they serve as readily available carbohydrates. For this reason, little attention was paid to their transport properties across mammalian cell membranes. However, a special transport mechanism has been suggested in *Escherichia coli* mutants which can utilize glucose 6-phosphate supplemented in the medium (Hagihira *et al.*, 1963).

Figure 9.1 shows the amounts of glucose, glucose 1-phosphate, and glucose 6-phosphate in the blood as a function of time, replotted on a semi-log scale from data of Beloff-Chain *et al.* (1953). The linearity of the plot indicates that hexose monophosphate transport displays first-order kinetics, which suggests that glucose 1-phosphate and glucose 6-phosphate are metabolized at a rate faster than the rate of transport across the cell membrane, even at the high hexose phosphate concentrations employed in these experiments. The rate of glucose uptake is not a linear function of time, but becomes saturated within one hour because, while intracellular glucose concentration rises, its rate of removal by metabolism, that is by phosphorylation, becomes rate limiting. These results are not due to a breakdown of the hexose phosphate esters in the blood, since *in vitro* incubation of glucose 1-phosphate and of glucose 6-phosphate with rabbit blood for two hours at 37°C shows no significant hydrolysis.

The stereospecificity of hexose transport has been extensively studied in mammalian cells. Affinity for carriers is higher for sugars whose pyranose ring tends to assume the 'chain' conformation in which the number of –OH or –CH$_2$OH groups oriented in the equatorial position is greater (Reeves, 1951). Even if glucose 1-phosphate and glucose 6-phosphate meet these requirements it cannot be assumed that they are using the same carrier system as glucose. A consequence of the Michaelis–Menten kinetics observed with carrier systems is the phenomenon of countertransport during which a substance A moves out of the cell, against its concentration gradient, using the free energy liberated by coupled transport of a related substance B which moves into the cell. Another consequence is that the rate of entry of B is changed by the presence of A if they share the same carrier. When glucose is present simultaneously with one of the hexose phosphates they do not compete for the same carrier, since no appreciable variation in the rate of uptake was observed as compared to when present alone. A similar study was carried out in alloxan-diabetic rabbits (Figure 9.2). The glucose level in the blood remains high for a considerable time after injection, while glucose 6-phosphate and glucose 1-phosphate are taken up at

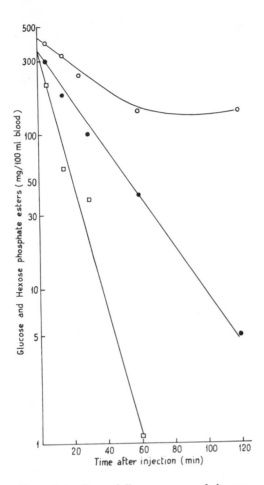

Figure 9.1 Rate of disappearance of glucose, glucose 1-phosphate and glucose 6-phosphate (1 g/kg, i.v.) in rabbits. Glucose, (○); glucose 1-phosphate, (●); glucose 6-phosphate, (□). Redrawn, with permission, from data of Beloff-Chain *et al.* (1953)

the normal rate. The complex physiological phenomena involved in an *in vivo* experiment do not warrant any conclusion as to the nature of the hexose phosphate carriers involved. Attention should be focused on the role of the ester phosphate groups which are completely ionized at neutral pH. However, the absence of countertransport and of inhibition by alloxan gives grounds for suspecting different transport systems exist for glucose and hexose phosphate.

It is not possible to estimate, from these data, the role of tissue phosphatases in the uptake of the injected phosphate esters. About 30–50 per cent of the phosphate injected as hexose ester is excreted as inorganic phosphate in the urine within 24 hours. It does not seem reasonable to assume that glucose

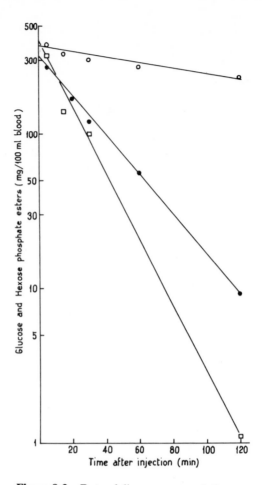

Figure 9.2 Rate of disappearance of glucose, glucose 1-phosphate and glucose 6-phosphate (1 mg/kg, i.v.) from the blood of alloxan-diabetic rabbits. The alloxan-diabetic rabbits were maintained on a carbohydrate-free diet prior to the experiments to reduce the blood glucose to normal. Glucose, (○); glucose 1-phosphate, (●); glucose 6-phosphate, (□). Redrawn, with permission, from data of Beloff-Chain *et al.* (1953)

6-phosphatase may be involved in the absorption of the phosphate esters, since glucose 6-phosphate supplemented in the medium (Table 9.1) accumulates in a tissue lacking the enzyme (von Fellenberg *et al.*, 1962). The data for similar experiments with glucose 1-phosphate are not reported because it was found that it is converted rapidly and quantitatively to glucose 6-phosphate. These results are consistent with the fact that phosphoglucomutase activity has been

Table 9.1 Accumulation of glucose and glucose 6-phosphate by rat diaphragm muscle

Substrate	Substrate concentration in the medium (per cent)	Intracellular concentration after 90 minutes (μmol/100 mg wet weight)
Glucose	0·1	0·32
	0·5	1·18
	1·0	2·53
Glucose 6-phosphate	0·1	0·03
	0·5	0·13
	1·0	0·41

Tissue extracts in 0·6 ml phosphate buffer (pH 6·8) were prepared according to Beloff-Chain *et al.* (1955).

found in rat tissues in excess of the activities of the enzymes of the glycogen cycle (Villar-Palasi and Larner, 1960*a*), providing a rapid step in the utilization of the glucose 1-phosphate derived from glycogen.

Another important result of these experiments is the fundamental difference observed between glucose 1-phosphate which, in the presence of isolated rat diaphragm, gives rise to a net synthesis of glycogen, and glucose 6-phosphate which in turn reaches a rapid equilibrium with fructose 6-phosphate and is a relatively poor substrate for glycogen formation. These observations, in striking contrast with the reported phosphoglucomutase activity, gave rise to Sir Ernst's intuition that glycogen synthesis in muscle could not be explained 'with the generally accepted theories of glucose metabolism' (Beloff-Chain *et al.*, 1953) and to most of our subsequent work on the early stages of glucose metabolism.

GLUCOSE METABOLISM

No attempt will be made here to outline in detail the stepwise degradation of glucose to pyruvate, its conversion to glycogen, or the regulation of the two processes since excellent reviews are available covering the subject as a whole (Axelrod, 1967; Florkin and Stotz, 1969). Many enzymes of glucose utilization are covered individually in a recent treatment (Boyer, 1973).

In mammalian tissues, the amount and routes of glucose utilization are geared to the different metabolic characteristics of the different tissues. Using quantitative two-dimensional paper radiochromatography (Chain *et al.*, 1956), developed at the Institute from an idea of Sir Ernst, it was possible to follow the fate of labelled glucose in different tissues. It was found that while in muscle (Beloff-Chain *et al.*, 1964), as well as in liver (Beloff-Chain *et al.*, 1956*a,b,c*), radioactivity is incorporated into glycogen and oligosaccharides, in brain (Chain *et al.*, 1960) it is all converted into amino acids (glutamate, aspartate, alanine, γ-aminobutyrate, and glutamine); in all tissues some lactate is formed from glucose. An extensive study of the influence of non-radioactive glucose on the metabolism of labelled glutamate in rat cortical slices was also undertaken (Sellinger et al., 1962). The presence of glucose stimulated glutamate accumulation into the cell and its oxidation simultaneously. The three-fold enhanced conversion into glutamine is accompanied by an analogous decrease in the conversion into aspartate. Moreover, the observed increase in glutamine-specific activity was the first observation, among the large body of now available data, indicating that various pools concerned with the glutamate–glutamine system exist in brain.

In rat diaphragm muscle at concentrations of glucose in the medium going from the physiological value of 0·1 per cent (w/v) to 1·0 per cent (w/v), there is an eight-fold increase in glucose concentration in the tissue (Table 9.1). Under the same conditions, the amount of glucose utilized increases only two-fold. Although rates of glycolysis cannot be calculated from the concentrations of glycolytic intermediates, relative rates can be inferred from changes in such intermediates. An indicator of the rates of glucose utilization can be obtained both from the rate of carbon dioxide production and that of glycogen synthesis (Table 9.2). Then in a tissue, such as rat diaphragm muscle devoid of a functional glucose 6-phosphatase (von Fellenberg et al., 1962), the rate of glucose utilization will be equal to the rate of its conversion to glucose 6-phosphate. The latter metabolite may undergo one of the several different

Table 9.2 Influence of substrate concentration on the metabolism of glucose

Results are expressed as μmoles of converted substrate/100 mg of tissue wet weight, after incubation for 90 minutes in 0·6 ml of phosphate-buffered medium, pH 6·8 at 37°C in O_2. The concentration of [U-^{14}C]glucose was as indicated (w/v). Tissue extracts were prepared according to Beloff-Chain et al. (1955). Metabolites were determined according to Beloff-Chain et al. (1964). Mean values of four experiments ± S.E.M.

	Metabolite concentration after 90 min. (μmole converted substrate/100 g wet weight)	
	0·1 per cent [U-^{14}C]glucose	1·0 [U-^{14}C]glucose
Glycogen	123 ± 29	775 ± 93
Lactate	75 ± 15	187 ± 9
CO_2	612 ± 27	983 ± 53

Tissue extracts in 0·6 ml phosphate buffer (pH 6.8) were prepared according to Beloff-Chain et al. (1955). Metabolite concentrations were determined by the method of Beloff-Chain et al. (1964).

fates. It can enter into the energy-yielding glycolytic pathway or into the 6-phosphogluconate pathway, or it can be converted into glycogen. Beloff-Chain et al. (1964) have shown that in rat diaphragm lactate formation from glucose is reduced markedly in the presence of glucose 6-phosphate. A comparable decrease in glycolysis was also observed with glucose 1-phosphate, due to its almost quantitative conversion to glucose 6-phosphate.

The possible explanation for the reported effect that the rate of glucose 6-phosphate removal in the 6-phosphogluconate pathway is of importance in determining the rate of glucose utilization is not possible in rat diaphragm muscle, where glucose metabolism proceeds only by way of glycolysis and the oxidative shunt pathway is activated only under anaerobic conditions. (Beloff-Chain et al., 1962). Another possible explanation may be that glucose 6-phosphate inhibition of hexokinase exercises control over glucose utilization (Crane and Sols, 1953). The level of glucose 6-phosphate (28 μmole/100 g wet tissue) found in rat diaphragm incubated with 0·1 per cent (w/v) glucose is well above the K_i value (approximately 10^{-5} M) reported for most mammalian hexokinases (Florkin and Stotz, 1969). The high sensitivity of the hexokinase to glucose 6-phosphate inhibition will make the glycolytic rate sensitive to any effect which alters the glucose 6-phosphate concentration. The interconversion of glucose 6-phosphate and fructose 6-phosphate could be a metabolic block imposed on glucose utilization (Table 9.3). The ratios of intracellular glucose 6-phosphate to fructose 6-phosphate are consistently higher than the ratio of 2·3 obtained at equilibrium for phosphoglucoisomerase (Axelrod, 1967).

Table 9.3 Influence of glucose 6-phosphate concentration on glycolytic intermediates of isolated rat diaphragm muscle

Substrate concentration (per cent)	Glycolytic intermediates (μmole/100 g wet weight)					
	G 1-P	G 6-P	F 6-P	F 1,6-P	3-PGA	Lactate
0·1	—	0·03	—	0·023	0·22	0·44
0·5	0·01	0·13	0·026	0·046	0·27	0·54
1·0	0·034	0·41	0·064	0·23	0·39	0·73

Experimental conditions as in Table 9.1. G 1-P, glucose 1-phosphate; G 6-P, glucose 6-phosphate; F 6-P, fructose 6-phosphate; F 1,6-P, fructose 1,6-disphosphate; 3-PGA, 3-phosphoglycerate.

Because the ratio, which averages five, does not attain the equilibrium value at the highest glucose 6-phosphate concentration employed, phosphogluco-isomerase is apparently a rate-limiting step for glycolysis under the experimental conditions employed by the author. However, the fructose 1,6-diphosphate concentration increases faster than that of fructose 6-phosphate suggesting that the rate of phosphorylation of fructose 6-phosphate rather than its formation from glucose 6-phosphate, is an important rate-limiting step in glucose utilization.

It seems reasonable to assume that the concentration of glucose 1-phosphate varies with that of glucose 6-phosphate, since the equilibrium of phosphoglucomutase observed in vivo is maintained in vitro (Tables 9.3 and 9.4), and

Table 9.4   Influence of glucose 1-phosphate concentration on glycolytic intermediates of isolated rat diaphragm muscle

Substrate Concentration	Glycolytic intermediates (μmole/100 g wet weight)					
	G 1-P	G 6-P	F 6-P	F 1,6-P	3-PGA	Lactate
0·1	—	0·034	—	0·065	0·12	0·51
0·5	—	0·073	0·02	0·075	0·20	0·81
1·0	0·01	0·157	0·035	0·12	0·31	1·05

Experimental conditions as in Table 9.1.

thus glucose 1-phosphate would have the same effect as glucose 6-phosphate on glucose utilization.

As can be seen in Tables 9.3 and 9.4, the fructose 6-phosphate concentration in the muscle is approximately 50 per cent lower, relative to the concentration of glucose 6-phosphate, than would be expected from the equilibrium values obtained *in vitro*. Since there is no proportional increase in the concentrations of the intermediates beyond the phosphofructokinase step, with respect to hexose monophosphate concentration in the medium or in the tissue, one should assume that there is no prominent rate-limiting step after the sequence glucose 6-phosphate → fructose 6-phosphate → fructose 1,6-diphosphate.

HEXOSE MONOPHOSPHATE–PENTOSE PATHWAYS

An understanding of the place of the pentose phosphate pathway in glucose economy requires a knowledge of the flux through the pathway and the mechanism by which that flux is controlled. The most logical regulatory step is the first one since glucose 6-phosphate is the substrate of four competing enzymes: glucose 6-phosphatase, phosphoglucomutase, phosphoglucoisomerase, and glucose 6-phosphate dehydrogenase. The favoured pathway would appear to be hexose monophosphate oxidation since the reaction catalysed by glucose 6-phosphate dehydrogenase is greatly displaced from equilibrium and, among the four enzymes, the dehydrogenase possesses the lowest K_m for glucose 6-phosphate. There is clear evidence, however, that there are relatively small changes in 6-phosphogluconate levels when glucose 6-phosphate levels are varied by different agents (Gumaa and McLean, 1969; Kauffman *et al.*, 1969). Other factors deserving consideration suggest that glucose 6-phosphate dehydrogenase is tightly regulated. Among others, Salas *et al.* (1965) have indicated the anomeric specificity of the four enzymes mentioned above. While hexokinase produces both α- and β-glucopyranose 6-phosphate, glucose 6-phosphate dehydrogenase acts only on β-glucopyranose-6-phosphate, and phosphoglucoisomerase acts on α-glucopyranose 6-phosphate (Figure 9.3).

In β-glucopyranose all the hydroxyl groups, as well as the phosphate ester group, are equatorial. This minimizes steric interactions, so that the β-anomer

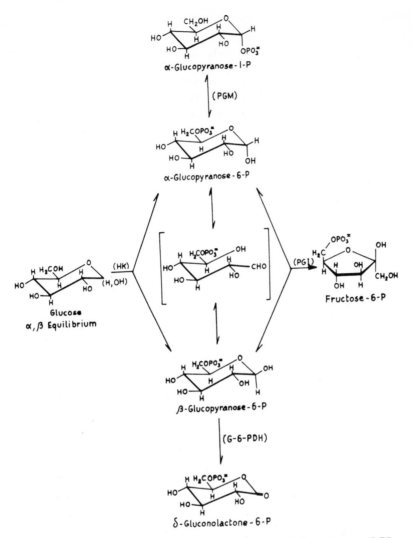

Figure 9.3 Glucose 6-phosphate metabolism. HK, hexokinase; PGI, phosphoglucoisomerase; PGM, phosphoglucomutase; G 6-PDH, glucose-6-phosphate dehydrogenase

is the predominant form in solution. It is known that in spontaneous, that is general acid–base, catalysis the open-chain aldehyde is the most likely inter-mediate formed during the interconversion of the chair form of the glucose derivative anomers (Bentley and Bhate, 1960), and that there appears to be a relationship between the proportion of open-form and anomerization rate.

α-Glucose 6-phosphate is formed in the hexokinase and phosphoglucomut-ase reactions, while β-glucose 6-phosphate is formed only in the hexokinase reaction, and since neither phosphoglucoisomerase nor phosphoglucomutase can act on the latter, the rate of anomerization may be significant in control of glucose utilization. Thus, in a tissue in which the rate of spontaneous anomerization of glucose 6-phosphate is limiting with respect to the rate of glucose 6-phosphate dehydrogenase, any factor accelerating this process will accelerate the oxidative pathway. As can be seen from Figure 9.3 phosphoglucoisomerase accelerates the process by forming open glucose 6-phosphate. Phosphoglucoisomerase has a greater affinity for the open form of the hexose phosphate esters than for the cyclic-related compounds and can catalyse the anomerization of α-glucose 6-phosphate but not of β-glucose 6-phosphate. For these reasons, the enzyme has been extensively studied as a possible switch of the glycolytic flux towards the pentose phosphate pathway.

A possible regulatory role has been attributed to erythrose 4-phosphate since the anomerization activity, together with the conversion of glucose 6-phosphate into fructose 6-phosphate, is inhibited by this compound (Grazi et al., 1960). According to in vitro experiments this substance should depress, in a co-ordinate fashion, both glycolysis and hexose monosphosphate oxidation. In tissues in which the pentose phosphate pathway has been estimated to contribute less than 2 per cent to glucose metabolism, erythrose 4-phosphate concentrations were found to be five times higher than the observed K_i for phosphoglucoisomerase using glucose 6-phosphate as substrate (Gumaa and McLean, 1969). However, interpretation of the changes in the pentose phosphate intermediate levels is complicated by the fact that the experimental data yield equilibrium values which are in every case lower than the apparent equilibrium constants of the enzymic reactions involved (Kauffman et al., 1969). In order to explain these discrepancies and the one reported previously on the equilibrium value of phosphoglucoisomerase the possibility should be considered of a compartmentation of glucose metabolism within the cell.

CELL COMPARTMENTATION OF GLUCOSE METABOLITES

The existence of two separate and distinct glycolytic pathways which differ in cellular localization and metabolic function was postulated by Shaw and Stadie (1959). The first was thought to be intracellular, responsive to insulin, and involved in glycogen formation, while the second was thought to be located on the cell surface and involved in lactic acid production. Evidence that glucose 6-phosphate formation is not a necessary intermediate step in glycogen synthesis from glucose had been obtained by Sir Ernst's group (Beloff-Chain et al., 1955) from studies on the effect of insulin on the metabolism of glucose in rat diaphragm muscle. Other investigators have later questioned the position of glucose 6-phosphate as a required intermediate of glycogen synthesis (Nigam, 1967; Threlfall, 1966; London, 1966; Landau and Sims, 1967; Threlfall and Heath, 1968). Further evidence for glucose 6-phosphate compartmentation stems from the fact that the hexokinases of most mammalian cells are found both in the soluble and in the particulate fractions of homogenates (Katzen et al., 1970; Gots and Bessman, 1974).

Table 9.5 Influence of the composition of the incubation medium on the metabolism of glucose incubated in the presence of glucose 6-phosphate

	Metabolite concentration (μmole/100 g wet weight)			
	Phosphate medium		Bicarbonate medium	
	$-$G 6-P	$+$G 6-P	$-$G 6-P	$+$G 6-P
Glycogen and oligosaccharides	96 ± 2	124 ± 12	250 ± 6	172 ± 20
Zone G	228 ± 20	344 ± 4	174 ± 10	216 ± 7
Lactate	856 ± 50	584 ± 40	1018 ± 100	880 ± 60

Tissue extracts were prepared in buffer (0·6 ml) according to the method of Beloff-Chain *et al.* (1955). After incubation for 90 minutes in 0·6 ml Krebs-Ringer bicarbonate buffer or phosphate buffer containing [U-^{14}C]glucose (0·1 per cent) with or without G 6-P (1 per cent), metabolite concentrations were determined according to Beloff-Chain *et al.* (1964).

The compartmentation was also deduced by studying *in vitro* parallel reactions in which glucose and glucose 6-phosphate were alternately labelled. In this manner, the fate of glucose 6-phosphate coming from the external medium and the fate of glucose 6-phosphate coming from glucose can be compared. The results have been interpreted both in terms of two pools of glucose 6-phosphate and of a pathway for the conversion of glucose into glycogen not involving glucose 6-phosphate as an intermediate. The assumption that glucose 6-phosphate is an obligatory intermediate in the metabolism of glucose is an essential feature of the former hypothesis. D'Agnolo *et al.* (1969), however, showed that in rat diaphragm muscle reactions of glucose 6-phosphate metabolism did occur in a homogeneous phase without compartments when the amount of glucose 6-phosphate added to the medium was greater than its threshold concentration. Glucose 6-phosphate requires a threshold concentration before it can be utilized (Beloff-Chain *et al.*, 1964). Moreover, glucose 6-phosphate behaves as a real intermediate of glycogen synthesis, even when glucose is the labelled precursor, in bicarbonate but not in phosphate buffer (Table 9.5). A point of interest arising out of these data is that while glucose 6-phosphate decreases both glycogen synthesis and glucose utilization in bicarbonate medium, it has a stimulatory effect on glycogen synthesis in phosphate buffer. The results obtained cannot be explained on the basis of regulatory effects only, since orthophosphate is an inhibitor of UDP–glucosepyrophosphorylase (Oliver, 1961), and an activator of glycogen synthetase (Rosell-Perez and Larner, 1964). On the other hand, one should expect a similar stimulatory effect of glucose 6-phosphate on glycogen synthetase in both media. The reported concentration of glucose 6-phosphate required for half maximal activation of the enzyme of several mammalian tissues is about 5×10^{-4} M (Florkin and Stotz, 1969). The concentration found in rat diaphragm muscle is in both cases about three times higher than that required for the modification of the enzyme activity.

Additional evidence for the existence of two pools of glucose 6-phosphate is associated with leakage of the enzymes of the glycolytic system into the medium, after incubation with rat diaphragm. It was suggested that some glucose utilization may occur at the surface of the cell, without penetration by glucose. Extensive leakage of different enzymes, under different conditions of incubation, has been reported by several workers (Beloff-Chain et al., 1953; Shaw and Stadie, 1957; Zierlier et al., 1953). Nevertheless, it is conceivable that some of the substrate which disappeared from the medium during incubation of rat diaphragm can be utilized by enzymes which leak into the medium. However, when the diaphragm was removed from the medium, Randle and Smith (1958) did not observe any further glucose metabolism; analogous observations were made by Landau and Sims (1967) using labelled glucose 6-phosphate and fructose 1,6-diphosphate. Failure to demonstrate any effect led these authors to postulate that glycolytic enzymes may be located on the cell surface or in the intracellular space of the diaphragm. Advantage was taken of a sensitive chromatographic technique developed by Bedetti et al. (1970) to determine which glycolytic intermediates are present in the medium. As can be seen from Table 9.6, when the diaphragm was incubated with labelled glucose most radioactivity was found in the medium as unchanged glucose and as lactate. Only small amounts of the hexose phosphates were present at non-equilibrium ratios indicating a tissue capable of rapid glycolysis.

Table 9.6 Distribution of [U-^{14}C]glucose in rat diaphragm muscle
Results are expressed as μmoles of substrate present/g of tissue wet weight after incubation for 90 minutes in 3 ml of phosphate-buffered medium, pH 6·8 at 37° in O$_2$. The glucose concentration was 0·5 per cent (w/v). Extracts were prepared as described in Table 1.

Intermediate	Concentration (μmole/g tissue wet weight)	
	Extract	Medium
Glucose	4·440	17·250
Glucose 1-phosphate	—	0·078
Glucose 6-phosphate	0·250	0·058
Fructose 6-phosphate	0·058	0·064
Fructose 1,6-diphosphate	0·060	0·026
Dihydroxyacetone-phosphate	0·160	—
Glyceraldehyde 3-phosphate	0·063	—
3-Phosphoglycerate	0·070	—
2,3-Disphosphoglycerate	0·056	—
Phosphoenolpyruvate	0·083	—
Lactate	2·030	5·020

Failure to show clear-cut evidence for the existence of two glucose 6-phosphate pools suggests that the results obtained in vitro should be interpreted with caution. Even if the experiments cannot rule out completely the existence of two pools of glucose 6-phosphate, they seem to indicate the existence of a pathway for the conversion of glucose into glycogen not involving glucose 6-phosphate.

GLYCOGEN SYNTHESIS

Pharmacological, hormonal, and neural stimuli affect the synthesis and degradation of glycogen. The response to such stimuli appears to be mediated through the formation of cylic AMP. Synthesis and degradation cannot occur simultaneously, and periodic changes of enzymic activities and of glycogen concentration can be observed in response to the levels of such controlling factors.

Studies, now in progress in several laboratories, are being directed towards an understanding of the molecular mechanisms involved in the control of glycogen synthesis and degradation. It is significant that two types of control mechanisms (covalent modification and non-covalent allosteric control) are used to regulate glycogen metabolism. Both have been extensively reviewed (Leloir, 1971; Fischer et al., 1971; Boyer, 1973). The role of the non-covalent effectors, which are substrates of other reactions in the pathways of glucose utilization, will be briefly discussed.

In muscle, two forms of glycogen synthetase have been recognized on the basis of different degrees of stimulation by glucose 6-phosphate (Villar-Palasi and Larner, 1960b). The form active in absence of modifier has been named the independent or I form. The other which is dependent for activity on glucose 6-phosphate is the dependent or D form. There is considerable evidence that glycogen synthetase D is an allosteric enzyme with a V_{max} which is markedly increased by glucose 6-phosphate, while the I form is not truly independent of the activator. Glucose 6-phosphate increases the affinity by up to eight-fold of the I enzyme for the substrate. It has been suggested that the non-covalent regulation of the synthetase by glucose 6-phosphate may operate during muscle contraction when the glucose 6-phosphate levels increase up to 10-fold. The interconversion between the D and I forms, achieved by phosphorylation and dephosphorylation reactions, will have full significance at lower glucose 6-phosphate levels encountered in resting muscle.

In the light of recent discoveries that the conversion from the I to the D form of glycogen synthetase occurs via the phosphorylation of two different sites with different kinetic properties (Soderling, 1975), it is quite possible that the role of glucose 6-phosphate is more complex than that of a simple effector. Hizukuri and Larner (1964) have shown the participation of glucose 6-phosphate in the conversion of the D to the I form in liver. Alternative possibilities have been put forward by Nimmo and Cohen (1974) who found a kinase which could phosphorylate the glycogen synthetase without any corresponding change in glucose 6-phosphate dependence. Thus, if the I-to-D conversion occurs as a two step process in vivo, this would provide an additional

184

regulatory mechanism in which the degree of enzyme-subunit phosphorylation will influence glucose 6-phosphate dependence (Huang et al., 1975).

It has been known for a long time that glucose administered to fed or fasted animals induces, after a short lag, a deposition of glycogen in the liver (Cori, 1926). The mechanism of this rapid rise in the rate of glycogen synthesis has been investigated by deWulf and Hers (1967). The increase in glycogen synthesis is paralleled by an increase in the amount of glycogen synthetase, and a decrease in the concentrations of both UDP–glucose and glucose 6-phosphate. Thus, the glycogenic effect cannot be attributed to a rise in the hepatic concentrations of the metabolites involved in the conversion of glucose to glycogen, brought about by the glucose load in the blood. Interestingly, Neely et al. (1967) observed a decrease in glycogenolysis in isolated rat heart perfused with glucose, while Holmes and Mansour (1968a, b) reported a lower level of phosphorylase a, the active form, in isolated rat diaphragm incubated with glucose. Incubation of phosphorylase a with glucose promotes the formation of an inactive dimer which can be converted back to the active tetrameric state by glycogen and glucose 1-phosphate (Fischer et al., 1968). A similar effect on phosphorylase b, the less active form, has been described for glucose 6-phosphate. The sugars stabilize the inactive conformations.

More work is needed on degradation mechanisms since glucose and glucose 6-phosphate could act not only on the a and b forms of phosphorylase but also on the partially phosphorylated forms that have been described by Fischer et al. (1970). Finally, it is doubtful whether such high concentrations (10^{-3} M) as are required for the in vitro effect of glucose and glucose 6-phosphate would be found in vivo.

At present, no enzymic studies have been carried out which support the notion of an alternative pathway for glycogen synthesis. However, in vivo and in vitro evidence has pushed several authors to postulate the existence of two separate pools of glucose 6-phosphate, one involved in glycogen formation and the other in lactic acid production. Although much information has been accumulated on the chemical and physical properties of the enzymes involved in the co-ordinate control of glycogen synthesis and of glycolysis, it is obvious, in agreement with Sir Ernst's original ideas, that information concerning the initial stages of glucose utilization is still lacking today.

REFERENCES

Axelrod, B. (1967) in *Metabolic Pathways*, Vol. 1 (Greenberg, D. M., ed.), Academic Press, London and New York, pp. 112–145.
Bedetti, G., D'Agnolo, G., and Pocchiari, F. (1970) *J. Chromatog.*, **49**, 53.
Beloff-Chain, A., Betto, P., Catanzaro, R., Chain, E. B., Longinotti, L., Masi, I., and Pocchiari, F. (1964) *Biochem. J.*, **91**, 620.
Beloff-Chain, A., Bovet, D., Chain, E. B., and Pocchiari, F. (1951) *R. C. Accad. Lincei*, **8**, 280.
Beloff-Chain, A., Bovet, D., Catanzaro, R., Chain, E. B., Kohn, R., Masi, I., and Pocchiari, F. (1956a) *Select. Sci. Papers Ist. Super. Sanità*, **1**, 304.

Beloff-Chain, A., Catanzaro, R., Chain, E. B., Kohn, R., and Pocchiari, F. (1956b) *Select. Sci. Papers Ist. Super. Sanità*, **1**, 328.

Beloff-Chain, A., Catanzaro, R., Chain, E. B., Longinotti, L., Masi, I., and Pocchiari, F. (1962) *Biochim. Biophys. Acta*, **56**, 153.

Beloff-Chain, A., Catanzaro, R., Chain, E. B., Masi, I., Pocchiari, F., and Rossi, C. (1955) *Proc. Roy. Soc., Series B*, **143**, 481.

Beloff-Chain, A., Catanzaro, R., Chain, E. B., Masi, I., and Pocchiari, F. (1956c) *Select. Sci. Papers Ist. Super. Sanità*, **1**, 293.

Beloff-Chain, A., Chain, E. B., Bovet, D., Pocchiari, F., Catanzaro, R., and Longinotti, L. (1953) *Biochem. J.*, **54**, 529.

Bentley, R., and Bhate, D. S. (1960) *J. Biol. Chem.*, **235**, 1225.

Boyer, P. D. (1973) *The Enzymes*, Vol. IV–IX, 3rd edn., Academic Press, London and New York.

Chain, E. B., Frank, M., Pocchiari, F., Rossi, C., Ugolini, F., and Ugolini, G. (1956) *Select. Sci. Papers Ist. Super. Sanità*, **1**, 241.

Chain, E. B., Larsson, S., and Pocchiari, F. (1960) *Proc. Roy. Soc., Series B*, **152**, 283.

Cori, C. F. (1926) *J. Biol. Chem.*, **70**, 577.

Crane, R. K., and Sols, A. (1953) *J. Biol. Chem.*, **203**, 273.

D'Agnolo, G., Baroncelli, V., Betto, P., Catanzaro, R., Longinotti, L., and Pocchiari, F. (1969) *Experientia*, **25**, 697.

DeWulf, H., and Hers, H. G. (1967) *Eur. J. Biochem.*, **2**, 50.

Fischer, E. H., Heilmeyer, L. M. G., Jr., and Haschke, R. (1971) *Curr. Top. Cell. Reg.*, **4**, 211.

Fischer, E. H., Hurd, S. S., Koh, P., Seery, V. L., and Teller, D. C. (1968) in *Control of Glycogen Metabolism; Proc. 4th Meeting of the Federation of European Biochemical Societies* (Whelan, W. J., ed.), Academic Press, London, Universitetsforlaget, Oslo, pp. 19–33.

Fischer, E. H., Pocker, A., and Saari, J. C. (1970) in *Essays in Biochemistry*, Vol. 6 (Campbell, P. N., and Dickens, F., eds.), Academic Press, London and New York, pp. 23–68.

Florkin, M., and Stotz, E. H. eds. (1969) *Comprehensive Biochemistry*, Vol. 17, Elsevier Publishing Co., Amsterdam.

Gots, R. E., and Bessman, S. P. (1974) *Arch. Biochem. Biophys.*, **163**, 7.

Grazi, E., DeFlora, A., and Pontremoli, S. (1960) *Biochem. Biophys. Res. Commun.*, **2**, 121.

Gumaa, K. A., and McLean, P. (1969) *Biochem. J.*, **115**, 1009.

Hagohira, H., Wilson, T. H., and Lin, E. C. C. (1963) *Biochim. Biophys. Acta*, **78**, 505.

Holmes, P. A., and Mansour, T. E. (1968a) *Biochim. Biophys. Acta*, **156**, 266.

Holmes, P. A., and Mansour, T. E. (1968b) *Biochim. Biophys. Acta*, **156**, 275.

Hizukuri, S., amd Larner, J. (1964) *Biochemistry*, **3**, 1783.

Huang, K.-P., Huang, F. L., Glinsmann, W. H., and Robinson, J. C. (1975) *Biochem. Biophys. Res. Commun.*, **65**, 1163.

Katzen, H. M., Soderman, D. D., and Wiley, C. E. (1970) *J. Biol. Chem.*, **245**, 4081.

Kauffman, F. C., Brown, J. G., Passonneau, J. V., and Lowry, O. (1969) *J. Biol. Chem.*, **244**, 3647.

Landau, B. R., and Sims, E. A. H. (1967) *J. Biol. Chem.*, **242**, 163.

Leloir, L. F. (1971) *Science, N.Y.*, **172**, 1299.

London, W. P. (1966) *J. Biol. Chem.*, **241**, 3008.

Neely, J. R., Liebermeister, H., and Morgan, H. E. (1967) *Am. J. Physiol.*, **212**, 815.

Nimmo, H. G., and Cohen, P. (1974) *FEBS Letters*, **47**, 162.

Nigam, V. N. (1967) *Biochem. J.*, **105**, 515.

Oliver, I. T. (1961) *Biochim. Biophys. Acta*, **52**, 75.

Randle, P. J., and Smith, G. H. (1958) *Biochem. J.*, **70**, 490.

Reeves, R. E. (1951) *Adv. Carb. Chem.*, **6**, 107.

186

Rosell-Perez, M., and Larner, J. (1964) *Biochemistry*, **3**, 773.
Salas, M., Vinuela, E., and Sols, A. (1965) *J. Biol. Chem.*, **240**, 561.
Sellinger, O. Z., Catanzaro, R., Chain, E. B., and Pocchiari, F. (1962) *Proc. Roy. Soc.*, *Series B*, **156**, 148.
Shaw, W. N., and Stadie, W. C. (1957) *J. Biol. Chem.*, **227**, 115.
Shaw, W. N., and Stadie, W. C. (1959) *J. Biol. Chem.*, **234**, 2491.
Soderling, T. R. (1975) *J. Biol. Chem.*, **250**, 5407.
Threlfall, C. J. (1966) *Nature (London)*, **211**, 1192.
Threlfall, C. J., and Heath, D. F. (1968) *Biochem. J.*, **110**, 303.
Villar-Palasi, C., and Larner, J. (1960a) *Arch. Biochem. Biophys.*, **86**, 270.
Villar-Palasi, C., and Larner, J. (1960b) *Biochim. Biophys. Acta*, **39**, 171.
Von Fellenberg, R., Eppenberger, H., Richterich, R., and Aebi, H. (1962) *Biochem. Z.*, **336**, 334.
Zierler, K. L., Levy, R. I., and Andres, R. (1953) *Johns Hopkin Hosp. Bull.*, **92**, 7.

DISCUSSION:

Sir Ernst Chain

Dr. Das, have you any comment, in view of your interesting experiments in this field?

Dr. I. Das

Glucose 6-phosphate as a necessary step in the transformation of glucose to glycogen has been questioned. Several reports using homogenates and slices of rat liver, incubated rat diaphragm, pigeon liver homogenate (Das, I., and Sie, H. G. (1972) *FEBS Letters*, **20**, 203, and references therein) lead others— Smith, E. E., Taylor, P. M., and Whelan, W. J. (1967) *Nature (London)*, **213**, 733—to suggest that glucose 6-phosphate might not be the only immediate product of glucose phosphorylation.

An investigation was undertaken to evaluate the relative roles of glucose 6-phosphate and glucose 1-phosphate in the synthesis of glycogen in perfused rat heart and the effect of diabetes and insulin on the precursors of glycogen. The full results are presented in *Biochem. J.*, (1976) **154**, 765.

The specific radioactivities of glucose 6-phosphate, glucose 1-phosphate, fructose 6-phosphate, uridine diphosphate glucose (UDP–glucose), and glycogen, derived from [^{14}C]glucose, were determined in the normal and insulin-deficient (streptozotocin-diabetic) perfused non-working and working rat heart.

The specific radioactivities of all glucose metabolites reached a plateau after about 10 minutes, except that for glycogen which increased slightly but steadily over the whole observation period of 30 minutes.

Mechanical work in the normal rat heart increased the specific radioactivities of glucose 1-phosphate, UDP-glucose, and glycogen, but had little effect on glucose 6-phosphate and fructose 6-phosphate. In the normal and streptozotocin-diabetic rat heart, insulin strongly increased the specific radioactivities of all glucose metabolites under all conditions tested. The most noteworthy result of the investigation is that in all cases the specific radioactivity of glucose 1-phosphate was invariably found to be higher than that of glucose 6-phosphate. This phenomenon had been previously observed in rat liver after intravenous injection of [U-^{14}C]glucose—Das, I., Sie, H. G., and Fishman, W. H. (1971) *Arch. Biochem. Biophys.*, **144**, 715—and in pigeon liver homogenate after incubation with [U-^{14}C] glucose—Das, I., and Sie, H. G. (1972) *FEBS Letters*, **20**, 203.

There are two possible explanations. If, according to the conventional concepts of glucose metabolism, the first reaction product of glucose is glucose 6-phosphate, it could be assumed that a small compartment exists, which is transformed into glucose 1-phosphate, UDP-glucose, and glycogen. Alternatively, a pathway of glucose metabolism different from the conventional one could be envisaged in which glucose 1-phosphate is the first reaction product—Das, I., and Chain, E. B. (1976) *Biochem. J.*, **154**, 765.

10
Mechanism of Insulin Action

A. Beloff-Chain

Dept. of Biochemistry, Imperial College of Science and Technology, London, U.K.

and

A. J. M. Kits van Heijningen

Jan Swammerdam Institute, Amsterdam, Holland

INTRODUCTION

a. History

Long before the discovery of insulin, the pancreas had been linked to the regulation of blood glucose by Bouchardat (1845). Matteucci wrote in 1847: 'Je prends le pancreas d'un pigeon, je le pile et j'ajoute la substance du pancréas ainsi trituré à la fécule et je chauffe jusqu'à 40°. La fécule se dissout et se convertit en dextrine et sucre .... Il resterait à s'assurer maintenant si les fécules ainsi converties par la salive et le suc pancréatique en dextrine et sucre, passent en cet état dans le sang, ou plutot converties en acide laxtique. Ce n'est que dans le sang de quelques diabétiques que le sucre a été retrouvée .... Bouchardat le premier a émis l'opinion qui a été generalement adoptée que dans cette maladie la fécule était convertie dans les intestins en sucre, et que dans cet état il passait dans le sang et les urines.' It was also Bouchardat who pointed out that diabetics often showed lesions like fibrosis in the pancreas.

The conception of hormones and internal secretions, together with the notion of a link between the pancreas and blood glucose, prepared the way for the interpretation of the findings of von Mering and Minkowsky (1889, 1890), and of de Dominicis (1889, 1894) in pancreatectomized dogs. Yet it took 30 years before Banting and Best (1922) elegantly demonstrated that the pancreatic islets, and not the exocrine part of the pancreas, are responsible for the effect of pancreatectomy on blood sugar. By ligaturing the pancreatic duct, they caused all the exocrine tissue to degenerate, leaving the islets intact and functioning.

When larger quantities of purified insulin became available (Banting et al., 1922), clinical trials were undertaken and after the dramatic cure of a severely diabetic boy with an extract of pancreatic islets, research into diabetes concentrated mainly on experiments with more or less intact animals. In those days, the discussion as to the cause of diabetes was centred around the non-utilization and the over-production theories; both of which contain part of the truth.

Concepts were simple at that time—diabetes is caused by a lack of internal insulin production, the administration of insulin will cure the disease in very much the same way as the administration of a vitamin will cure the symptoms of its deficiency. The question of how this occurs has proved far more difficult to answer.

b. Scope of present review

As in the age of reason, the development of modern science started with the bringing together of existing knowledge by the French encyclopaedists, so, in this case, the acquisition of data on the action of insulin on various tissues in all kinds of animals, and even in plants, was the first step towards an attempt to understand its mode of action. This vast accumulation of experimental data still has not led to the unravelling of the mechanism of the action of the hormone on metabolic processes. In fact this approach has produced such an abundance of findings that there is now the danger of missing the wood for the trees!

In the present discussion, therefore, only the short-term effects—occurring up to 90 minutes—of insulin will be considered on major insulin-sensitive tissues of mammals, including diaphragm muscle, cardiac muscle, and adipose tissue, in so far as they have been related to different theories on the mechanism of action of insulin. Furthermore, as the most striking and rapid effect of insulin administered to an animal is the dramatic fall in blood glucose levels, much of this paper will be devoted to considering studies which relate to glucose metabolism and insulin action.

INSULIN AND SINGLE ENZYME REACTIONS

Gemmill (1940, 1941) first demonstrated an *in vitro* effect of insulin on glucose uptake and glycogen synthesis in diaphragm muscle. This observation stimulated a tremendous amount of research into the action of the hormone in this tissue preparation. Incidentally, one would hate to think of all the rats which sacrificed their diaphragms to this end joining us in this celebration!

This work led to a new line of research, the object of which was to find a single enzymic reaction in the known course of glucose metabolism in muscle, which might explain this *in vitro* effect of insulin. Thus, Price *et al.* (1945) proposed the hexokinase theory, in which insulin acts by accelerating the phosphorylation of glucose to glucose 6-phosphate by hexokinase and ATP, all other effects being secondary. Relevant to this concept was the theory proposed by Bessman (1966) (Figure 10.1), in which he suggests that all the effects of insulin in muscle could be explained if the hormone acts as a structural connection between hexokinase and the mitochondrion so that the former is brought in closer proximity to the site of ATP generation, thus increasing the

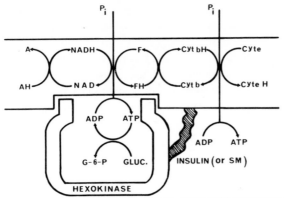

THE PROPOSED ROLE OF INSULIN IN ATTACHING HEXOKINASE
TO THE APPROPRIATE SITE IN THE ELECTRON TRANSPORT
CHAIN

Figure 10.1 The proposed role of insulin in attaching
hexokinase to the appropriate site in the electron transport chain. G 6-P, glucose 6-phosphate; gluc, glucose.
From Bessman (1966). Reproduced by permission of
the *Amer. J. Med.*

efficiency of the system. This model provided for the first time an explanation
for the necessity for an intact cellular structure to obtain the hormonal effect.
Further interest in the relationship of hexokinase and insulin action has come
from studies on the multiple forms of mammalian hexokinases, by Katzen and
his colleagues (1967). It has been anticipated that the hexokinases are a
complex group of isoenzymes, consisting of at least four in the liver and three in
other tissues. These workers have shown that hexokinase type II is predominant in insulin-sensitive tissues, is reduced in insulin deficiency, and can be
rapidly restored by insulin treatment. In this connection, it is of interest that
Walters and McLean (1967) demonstrated that in the mammary gland, which is
insensitive to insulin before lactation and which becomes increasingly insulin-
sensitive as lactation develops, there is a concomitant increase in glucose–ATP
phosphotransferase activity and the ratio of type II/type I increases three-fold
during lactation.

Another enzyme which has been implicated in the stimulation by insulin of
glycogen synthesis in muscle has been glycogen synthetase. Villar-Palasi and
Larner (1961) showed that incubation of diaphragm muscle with insulin does
not affect the total activity of UDPG–glycogen transglucosylase, but increased
the percentage of the enzyme active in the absence of glucose 6-phosphate, that
is in the I form.

PERMEABILITY THEORY OF INSULIN ACTION

In defiance of the fashion, Levine and his colleagues (1950) returned to the
earlier approach of studying hormonal action, by working with depancreatized,

eviscerated, nephrectomized dogs in preference to *in vitro* systems. They reported that in these animals insulin increases the rate of disappearance of galactose from the blood, suggesting an increased uptake of this non-metabolizable sugar by the tissues. They developed from this finding the theory that insulin acts by stimulation of the passage of glucose through the cell membrane, all other phenomena being secondary to this crucial point. These findings were later supported by Fisher and Zachariah (1961) (Figure 10.2)

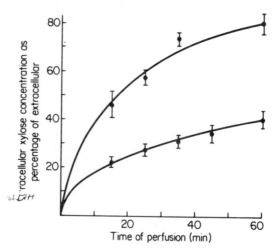

Figure 10.2 Time course of penetration of D-xylose (30 mM) into the cells of the perfused heart. From Fisher and Zachariah (1961). Reproduced by Permission of the *Journal of Physiology*

studying the influence of insulin on non-metabolizable pentoses in the per-fused heart. The permeability theory became one of the most widely accepted theories of insulin action, supported by many groups of investigators, including Wick and Drury (1953), Park *et al.* (1955), Park and Johnson (1955), and Nakada and Wick (1956).

BOOK-KEEPING OF INTERMEDIATES

Villee and Hastings (1949) studied the fate of radioactive glucose in rat diaphragm *in vitro* on a semiquantitative basis. They found that, as far as their balance sheet went, the larger part of the glucose metabolized by the normal or the insulin-treated diaphragm was unaccounted for (Table 10.1). However, they showed a marked effect of insulin on glucose uptake and incorporation into glycogen, thus confirming for the first time using isotopically labelled glucose the findings of Gemmill (1940, 1941). Beloff-Chain *et al.* (1955) were the first to study the effects of insulin on carbohydrate metabolism in its complexity, using two-dimensional quantitative radiochromatography (Table

Table 10.1 *In vitro* utilization of [^{14}C]glucose by rat diaphragm muscle

	Without insulin (mg/g tissue hr^{-1})	With insulin (mg/g tissue hr^{-1})
Total glucose disappearing from medium	1·53	2·87
Glucose metabolized to CO_2	0·11	0·22
Glycogen synthesized	0·17	0·62
Glucose unaccounted for	1·25	2·03

Mean of 14 experiments. Adapted from Villee and Hastings (1949). Reproduced by permission of the American Society of Biological Chemists, Inc.

10.2). They provided a proper book-keeping of all the counts from radioactive glucose which went into the diaphragms with the aid of a whole row of then very fancy electric typewriters, disfigured into automatic chromatogram scanners. To a straightforward administrator it must have seemed a sorry waste, so many luxury machines with only 10 of their 40-odd keys put to use!

Table 10.2 Influence of insulin on glucose metabolism in rat diaphragm muscle

	Glucose conversion in 90 min (μg/50 mg tissue)	
	−insulin	+insulin
Glycogen and oligosaccharides	10·4	23·7
Maltose	3·0	5·6
Glucose	18·0	21·6
Lactate	24·8	28·4
Glycogen of insoluble residue	14·9	25·4
CO_2	13·8	13·6

* Glucose 0·1 per cent Mean value of 8 experiments.
Adapted from Beloff-Chain *et al.* (1955), with permission.

It was at about this time that one of the authors (A. J. M. K. v. H.) isolated an insulin-sensitive, mysterious pink spot by paper chromatography after incubation of diaphragms with glucose. As this spot, although a simple glucose metabolite, defied all attempts at identification, the author turned in despair to colleagues at Oxford, as a result of which Professor Chain then invited her to come to work with his magic machines in Rome, to turn the 'spot gazing' into more scientific spot counting, and to make an attempt at its isolation and identification. Some three years later (Kits van Heijningen, 1965, 1966), the spot was thought to be 1,2-biphosphenolpyruvate. Recently, however, some doubt has arisen as to the validity of this structure, especially as far as its molecular weight, and hence the number of carbon atoms involved is concerned. Work on this metabolite is at present in progress. Meanwhile, further work on the biological activity of this compound has been carried out and the results will be discussed below.

With the aid of the automatic chromatogram scanners, Beloff-Chain *et al.* (1955) could account for all the glucose which Villee and Hastings (1949) had been missing. They also demonstrated (Beloff-Chain *et al.*, 1956*a*) that a simple increase in intracellular glucose concentration cannot reproduce the effect of insulin on the pattern of glucose metabolites. The effect of insulin is specifically on glycogen and oligosaccharides, whereas the increase in intracellular glucose also increases the production of carbon dioxide and lactic acid up to the highest glucose concentrations tested. However, increases in glucose incorporation into glycogen and oligosaccharides stop at a glucose concentration of 27·7 mM. Insulin, however, even at the highest glucose concentrations, can still specifically increase glycogen and oligosaccharide formation (Figure 10.3). This effect of insulin is very rapid; it can be demonstrated after three

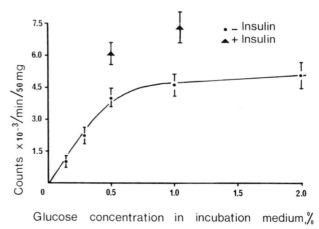

Figure 10.3 Influence of glucose concentration and insulin on labelling of glycogen in isolated rat diaphragm muscle. Adapted from Beloff-Chain *et al.* (1956*a*)

minutes. These findings cannot be reconciled with either the hexokinase or the glucose permeability theory. However, it was also demonstrated (Beloff-Chain *et al.*, 1964) that the influence of insulin preceded glucose phosphorylation, as neither the incorporation of [^{14}C]glucose 1-phosphate nor [^{14}C]glucose 6-phosphate into glycogen is stimulated by insulin; both hexose phosphates are oxidized by the muscle to about the same extent, although the incorporation of glucose 1-phosphate into glycogen is much higher than that of glucose 6-phosphate (Table 10.3). Villee *et al.* (1952) demonstrated that the intact glucose molecule was required to obtain an effect of insulin on glycogen synthesis. Thus, although pyruvate was incorporated into glycogen in diaphragm muscle, the incorporation was not stimulated by insulin. Results obtained later by Chain and his colleagues in perfused intact diaphragm (Beloff-Chain *et al.*, 1971), and perfused Langendorff and working hearts of

Table 10.3 Influence of insulin on the metabolism of glucose, glucose 1-phosphate and glucose 6-phosphate in rat diaphragm muscle

	Glucose*		Glucose 1-Phosphate*		Glucose 6-Phosphate*	
	−insulin	+insulin	−insulin	+insulin	−insulin	+insulin
Glycogen and						
oligosaccharides	236·1	460·9	410·8	412·7	61·3	53·8
CO_2	124·9	132·4	217·0	219·7	291·2	324·1

* Results expressed as nmol substrate converted/50 mg tissue in 90 minutes. Substrate concentration 10 mg/ml. Mean values given. Adapted from Beloff-Chain *et al.* (1964). Reproduced by permission of the Biochemical Society.

insulin-deficient and normal animals (Chain *et al.*, 1969) corroborate the findings on isolated diaphragm. Furthermore, using the perfused working heart from rats made insulin-deficient with streptozotocin, they showed that glucose uptake, oxidation, and lactate production are normal, and only glucose incorporation into glycogen is decreased in insulin-deficient hearts. This is completely restored to normal by the addition of insulin to the perfusion fluid, being the first metabolic defect in diabetes which was shown to be corrected immediately by the addition of insulin *in vitro*. (Table 10.4).

These experiments provide a striking demonstration of the specifity of the action of insulin being confined to glucose metabolism concerned with glycogen synthesis. As in diaphragm muscle, increased availability of glucose substrate does not simulate the effect of insulin. The significance of these findings as to the exact mechanism of insulin action at the molecular level, and their possible relevance to the findings on the hexokinase isoenzyme system are not clear. It leads one to speculate on the possible importance of compartmentation within the cell in influencing the metabolic pathway of the substrate; thus for example, hexokinase II might be specifically involved in directing glucose metabolism towards glycogen synthesis.

Table 10.4 Effect of insulin on glucose metabolism in perfused working hearts from normal and streptozotocin-treated diabetic rats

	Glucose uptake*	Lactate production*	$^{14}CO_2$*	Glycogen*
Diabetic (8)	246	22	199	2·4
Control (18)	270	28	196	7·4
Diabetic + insulin (11)	405	135	187	19·0
Control + insulin (12)	538	80	334	26·0

* Results expressed as μmoles of glucose equivalent/g dry tissue weight in 30 minutes perfusion. Mean values given. Number of hearts in parentheses. Adapted from Chain *et al.* (1969). Reproduced by permission of the Biochemical Society.

INFLUENCE OF INSULIN ON AMINO ACID TRANSPORT
AND PROTEIN SYNTHESIS

Forker et al. (1951) were the first to demonstrate the increased incorporation of [^{35}S]methionine into protein of diabetic dogs treated with insulin, (thereby confirming earlier results using unlabelled amino acids). These findings were corroborated by Sinex et al. (1952) who studied the incorporation of [^{14}C]alanine into the protein of rat diaphragm. Manchester and Young (1958) extended this work using other labelled amino acids and concluded that stimulation by insulin of the incorporation of these amino acids into the diaphragm muscle protein occurs in the absence of glucose (Figure 10.4). Similar findings were reported by Wool and Krahl (1959). However, as was

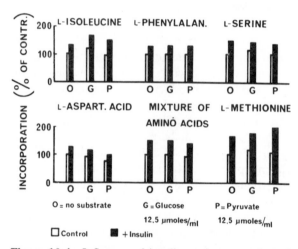

Figure 10.4 Influence of insulin on incorporation of labelled amino acids into protein in isolated rat diaphragm muscle. Adapted from Manchester and Young (1958). Reproduced by permission of the Biochemical Society

pointed out by Chain and Sender (1973), no effort had been made to exclude the role of an insulin effect on the endogenous glycogen, which is always present in considerable amounts in these tissues. They therefore performed a series of experiments on perfused rat hearts depleted of endogenous glucose, glycogen, and glucose 6-phosphate by a 35-minute perfusion with glucose-free medium. The results showed that this treatment does not affect the stimulation of the incorporation of amino acids into protein by insulin. They thus concluded that insulin can exert an effect on a metabolic reaction in cardiac muscle which is not dependent on glucose metabolism, a fact which has obvious implications for any theory on the mechanism of insulin action.

Chain and Sender (1973) were unable to demonstrate any abnormality in the [^{14}C]amino acid incorporation into proteins in perfused hearts from streptozotocin-diabetic rats, in contrast to the findings of Manchester and Young (1960), who reported a decreased protein synthesis in diaphragm muscle from alloxan-diabetic rats. Furthermore, Wool et al. (1968) reported a decreased capacity of ribosomes from alloxan-diabetic rat skeletal muscle to synthesize proteins and also an abnormal profile of these ribosomes on sucrose gradients. However, neither of these observations were confirmed by Chain and Sender (1973) using ribosomes prepared from cardiac muscle of streptozotocin-diabetic rats. This divergence of results could be due to differences between skeletal and cardiac muscle, or to a specific toxicity of alloxan. This latter explanation is supported by the findings of Wool et al. (1968) who were unable to reverse the abnormality by the addition of insulin to the ribosomes.

INFLUENCE OF INSULIN ON ADIPOSE TISSUE

The conclusion that insulin plays a role in fat synthesis could be drawn from the studies of Drury (1940), and Stetten and Boxer (1944). The latter using ^2H as a tracer showed that lipogenesis from carbohydrate is greatly reduced in diabetes. Two important in vitro systems for the study of the rapid effect of insulin on carbohydrate and lipid metabolism in adipose tissue have been the isolated mammary gland and the epididymal fat pad. Balmain et al. (1952) made the interesting observation that the incorporation of $[^{14}C]$acetate into lipids in rat mammary gland is stimulated by insulin only in the presence of glucose (Table 10.5). Similar observations have been reported by Winegrad and Renold (1958a) in the epididymal fat pad. The effect of insulin on lipid synthesis from glucose has been shown in white adipose tissue by these authors, and in brown fat by Beloff-Chain et al. (1956b). Winegrad and Renold (1958b) using glucose specifically labelled at C1 and C6 showed that insulin stimulates

Table 10.5 Effect of insulin on the incorporation of ^{14}C from $[^{14}C]$acetate into fatty acids of rat mammary gland slices

	Exp. No.					
Addition	1	2	3	4	5	6
Substrate [carboxy-^{14}C] acetate						
Insulin	86	40	97	43	58	58
None	50	43	40	50	58	40
Substrate [carboxy-^{14}C] acetate + glucose						
Insulin	9061	7567	10847	6383	7132	1991
None	5951	3805	5886	3532	3215	1069

Results expressed as counts/min/mg fatty acid C. From Balmain et al. (1952), with permission.

oxidation of glucose metabolized by the phosphogluconate oxidative pathway, and not *via* the glycolytic pathway or the tricarboxylic acid cycle (Table 10.6). Similar findings were reported by Abraham *et al.* (1957) using the mammary gland. A number of investigators have suggested that the increased supply of NADPH produced by stimulation of the dehydrogenase enzymes involved in the the phosphogluconate pathway of glucose metabolism is itself a factor in promoting lipid synthesis.

Table 10.6 Effect of insulin added *in vitro* on the metabolism of [1-^{14}C]glucose and [6-^{14}C]glucose by rat adipose tissue

	Oxidation to CO_2		Incorporation into lipid		Incorporation into fatty acid	
	[1-^{14}C]	[6-^{14}C]	[1-^{14}C]	[6-^{14}C]	[1-^{14}C]	[6-^{14}C]
−insulin	0·92	0·24	0·26	0·55	0·19	0·38
+insulin	6·36	0·33	3·14	6·39	3·06	6·31

Results expressed as μmole glucose/mg tissue nitrogen after 3 hour incubation. Adapted from Winegrad and Renold (1958*b*). Reproduced by permission of the American Society of Biological Chemists, Inc.

However, according to Flatt and Ball (1964), and Wise and Ball (1964) the amount of reduced coenzymes produced in phosphogluconate pathway will, in the presence of insulin, furnish only about 60 per cent of the reducing equivalents in the form of NADPH required for fatty-acid synthesis. They calculated that during the oxidation of triose phosphates to acetyl-CoA more reduced coenzyme (NADH) is generated than is needed to provide the other 40 per cent. They suggested that the malic enzyme described by Ochoa *et al.* (1948) would then perform what is essentially a transhydrogenase reaction between NADH and NADP. As pointed out by Wise and Ball, the malic enzyme activity would thus serve the dual function of providing the necessary NADPH for fatty acid synthesis and would regenerate NAD to permit formation of more acetyl-CoA.

It was later demonstrated, using the ^3H_2O technique (Jungas, 1968) to measure the rate of lipogenesis in the absence of ^{14}C-labelled precursors, that insulin activates one or more steps in the lipogenic pathway independent of glucose metabolism (Halperin, 1970; Halperin and Robinson, 1971). A number of investigators have shown that pyruvate dehydrogenase is at least one of the enzymic steps involved in insulin stimulation of lipogenesis in adipose tissue. (Jungas, 1970, 1971; Coore *et al.*, 1971)). Taylor *et al.* (1973) proposed that the activation of this enzyme by insulin is associated with a decreased degree of phosphorylation of the enzyme. It has been established by Linn *et al* (1969*a,b*) that the mammalian pyruvate dehydrogenase complex is active in the dephosphorylated form. A possible mechanism for the insulin control of this enzyme activity proposed by some investigators will be discussed below.

Another glucose independent effect of insulin has been demonstrated by Hepp *et al.* (1968) who showed that insulin stimulates the incorporation of inorganic phosphate into ATP in isolated adipocytes.

INTERACTION WITH OTHER HORMONES

When Houssay (1936), Long and Lukens (1936), and Young (1937) demonstrated that the pituitary and the adrenal cortex exert anti-insulin effects, it became clear that there is an interplay of hormonal actions on the target cells. The anti-insulin effects of growth hormone in man have been demonstrated by Zierler and Rabinowitz (1963), using the elegant technique of human forearm perfusion, and later by Luft and Cerasi (1968) from glucose tolerance curves in hypophysectomized patients treated with insulin with or without growth hormone.

With the introduction of *in vitro* techniques this concept has been expanded. The antagonistic effects of insulin and adrenaline on glycogen metabolism have been studied in the diaphragm by Kits van Heijningen (1963). The simultaneous action of insulin and adrenaline results in a net decrease in free glycogen and a net increase in the fixed glycogen fraction; alterations in specific activities of both fractions indicate an increased turnover.

One of the very widely studied effects of insulin has been its antilipolytic action in the presence of lipolytic hormones and some of this work has been reviewed by Ball (1970). He described experimental work showing that this antilipolytic effect can be distinguished from the influence of insulin on the re-esterification of free fatty acids due to the increased formation of glycerol phosphate from glucose. The concept that the antipolytic effect is associated with levels of cyclic AMP will be discussed below.

Goldfine (1975) has demonstrated that thymocytes of hypophysectomized rats show an increased sensitivity to insulin, which is due to an increased number of insulin receptors.

IS THERE A SINGLE MECHANISM FOR INSULIN ACTION?

In summarizing the metabolic effects of insulin discussed above, it is evident that the overall effect of this hormone is to specifically promote anabolic reactions, including glycogen, lipid, and protein synthesis.

In addition to these metabolic effects, insulin has been shown to influence ionic distribution in the cell, thus affecting the membrane resting potential. In fact, insulin increases the entry of K^+ into the cells to such an extent that it is one of the best drugs in the treatment of human hyperkalaemia. Insulin also brings about an increase in K^+ efflux, the change in the ratio of $K^+_{inside}/K^+_{outside}$ is however insufficient to account for the hyperpolarization produced by insulin (Zierler, 1957, 1959).

While this catalogue of insulin actions is growing like the expanding universe and is equally awe-inspiring to anyone seeking to grasp the essence of it, some investigators have turned away from it all to ask a few fundamental questions.

(*i*) Is a unitary concept of insulin action possible?
(*ii*) If so, in what direction is the solution to be sought?
(*iii*) Any one action which could be regarded as the key to all subsequent effects of insulin on intracellular metabolism should precede all other reactions in time. The first conceivable reaction of insulin with its target cell is the contact of insulin with the cell membrane. Is this a fleeting contact or a more permanent one? Could this in itself trigger the intracellular effects, or would it alter the membrane structure so as to stimulate or inhibit a secondary reaction which might produce a translator or second messenger to act inside the cell?

Stadie *et al.* (1949) has already drawn attention to the fact that after diaphragm muscle has been exposed to insulin *in vitro*, even for a relatively short space of time, the effect of the hormone on glucose metabolism in the muscle is retained even after prolonged washing of the tissue. These findings were subsequently extended using [^{125}I]insulin (Stadie *et al.*, 1952). Although their results have been criticized subsequently, workers have become aware of a possibility that insulin becomes attached to the cell membrane. The proposition that insulin acts directly on the cell membrane has been supported by demonstrating the biological activity of insulin–agarose derivatives on isolated adipocytes (Cuatrecasas, 1969), and of an insulin–dextran complex both *in vivo* and *in vitro* (Suzuki *et al.*, 1972).

The subsequent development of this line of insulin research has been fraught with technical troubles. Further progress in the understanding of the binding of insulin to specific receptors has depended on the preparation of a homogeneously labelled mono-iodinated insulin. This has been achieved by Freychet and his colleagues (1971), and by Cuatrecasas (1971), who demonstrated that the insulin-binding capacity of liver plasma membranes and of fat cells can be quantitatively measured by the amount of [^{125}I]insulin which is displaced by non-labelled insulin.

Recently the significance of the specific insulin receptors on the cell membrane has received a lot of attention, and has been correlated both with the biological action of insulin as well as with insulin resistance. (Freychet *et al.*, 1971; Desbuquois and Cuatrecasas, 1973). It is of interest that Zierler (1957; 1959) had already suggested that hyperpolarization is the primary effect of insulin which serves as a signal which activates or inactivates membrane-bound carrier and enzyme systems.

In an article by Levine (1974) on mechanisms of insulin action, it was proposed that the hormone–receptor interaction may result in the perturbation of the cell membrane causing changes in permeability, which as discussed above, have been demonstrated in the case of non-metabolizable sugar as well as of ions. Levine suggested that the other intracellular anabolic effects of insulin and its anticatabolic effects may be secondary to the hormone–receptor interaction, possibly with the formation of an unknown 'second messenger'. A number of investigators have proposed that insulin action can be explained by an effect of the hormone on the lowering of cyclic AMP levels, either due to inhibition of adenyl cyclase or to an activation of phosphodiesterase. However, there appears to be little correlation so far between cyclic nucleotide levels and the very marked cellular responses of synthetic reactions to insulin, as has been discussed recently by Fraser and his colleagues (Kissebah et al., 1975). They demonstrated that insulin can inhibit adrenaline-induced lipolysis at concentrations which do not affect the cyclic AMP levels, whereas with larger doses of insulin which can produce a small decrease in cyclic AMP levels, the time sequence for a cause–effect relationship is wrong, the inhibition of lipolysis preceding the decrease in cyclic AMP levels. Moreover, insulin is only able to lower levels of the cyclic nucleotide in cells if levels have been previously increased by the administration of adrenaline or glucagon. Mangiello et al. (1971) have demonstrated that insulin can stimulate lipogenesis and protein synthesis in fat cells, in the absence of glucose, without altering cyclic AMP levels.

Walaas et al. (1972) have suggested that insulin may interfere with the activation of protein kinase by cyclic AMP. Therefore the phosphorylation of some of the enzymes which are inactive in the phosphorylated forms will be reduced, thus increasing the enzyme activity. Examples of such enzymes which may be involved are glycogen synthetase and pyruvate dehydrogenase.

Several authors have postulated a second messenger for insulin, as this would solve many problems. It would mean that insulin acts on a single enzymic reaction without having to enter the cell, its antagonists might inhibit the same reaction, and the second messenger produced could, for instance, act as a coenzyme in the stimulation of key reactions in the chain leading to all the widespread effects of insulin on intermediary metabolism.

Such a second messenger should fulfill several conditions.

(i) It should be the first intermediate to be increased upon contact of insulin with the cell.

(ii) It should be able to simulate the known effects of insulin on intermediary metabolism.

(iii) Inhibition of production of the second messenger should inhibit the effect of insulin on tissue.

With regard to the concept of a second messenger, it is of interest that Kits van Heijningen et al. (1973) have been able to demonstrate that insulin increases 1,2-biphospenol pyruvate (bis-PEP) release from diaphragm muscle in vitro by about 70 per cent within 30 seconds (Figure 10.5); this seems to be the fastest known effect of insulin on the intermediates of tissue metabolism. Only Volfin (1970) claims an equally rapid effect of insulin on pyruvate in the rat diaphragm.

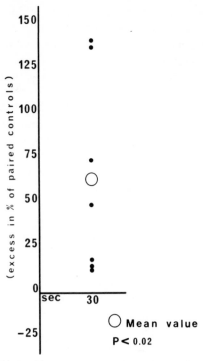

Figure 10.5 Short-time effect of insulin on labelled 1,2–biphosphenol pyruvate formation from [^{14}C] glucose in isolated rat diaphragm muscle. Adapted from Kits van Heijningen *et al.* (1973), Reproduced by permission of Springer-Verlag

The investigation of the second condition requires the preparation of pure natural or synthetic bis-PEP in order to study its effects on tissue metabolism *in vitro*. Treitjel and Visser (Kits van Heijningen *et al.*, 1976) have been able to isolate bis-PEP in sufficient quantities from erythrocytes to be able to study its effects *in vitro*. Work on the preparation, determination of chemical structure, and biological activity of this compound is now in progress. Thus far, a statistically significant stimulation of the incorporation of glucose into free glycogen of the diaphragm, of glucose oxidation *via* the hexose monophosphate pathway by epididymal fat, and a significant increase of fat synthesis, as measured with ^{3}H$_2$O and labelled glucose in mesenteric and parametrial adipose tissue, have been demonstrated by Kits van Heijningen *et al.* (1976) (Figures 10.6–10.9).

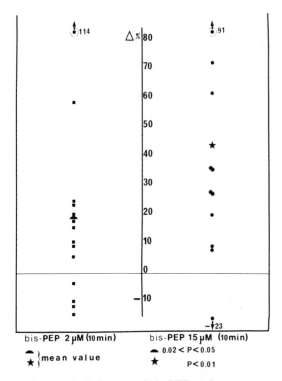

Figure 10.6 Influence of bis-PEP on incorporation of [^{14}C] glucose into free glycogen of isolated rat diaphragm. From Kits van Heijningen *et al.* (1976)

An interesting recent hypothesis on the mechanism of insulin action has been proposed by Fraser and his colleagues (Kissebah *et al.*, 1975), which offers a unitary theory explaining both the membrane and intracellular effects of insulin. These workers suggest that Ca^{2+} may provide the intracellular second messenger for insulin action, while the displacement of Ca^{2+} from the plasma membrane enhances transport of substrate as well as of ions. According to this hypothesis the binding of insulin to its specific receptors produces a change in the conformation of the plasma membrane which results in the displacement of Ca^{2+} from high-affinity binding sites on the endoplasmic reticulum and the inhibition of Ca^{2+} release from intracellular pools, thus the free cytoplasmic Ca^{2+} is increased. This inhibits the cyclic AMP-dependent protein kinase and activates the adipose tissue protein phosphatase, thus inhibiting lipase and phosphorylase, and stimulating glycogen synthetase. They also suggest that an increase in mitochondrial Ca^{2+} would activate pyruvate dehydrogenase and consequently lipogenesis. In this model, however, it is hard to see how insulin, while remaining outside the cell, can have such a specific effect on the

204

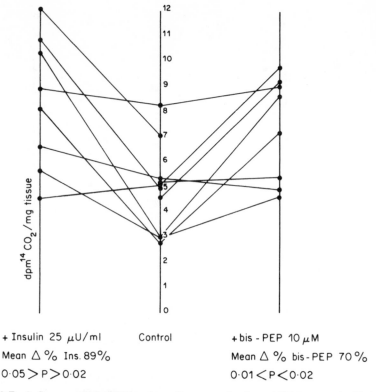

+ Insulin 25 μU/ml   Control   + bis - PEP 10 μM

Mean Δ % Ins. 89%   Mean Δ % bis - PEP 70 %

$0.05 > P > 0.02$ $0.01 < P < 0.02$

Figure 10.7   Influence of bis-PEP and insulin on production of $^{14}CO_2$ from [1-^{14}C] glucose in epididymal fat pads. From Kits van Heijningen *et al.* (1976)

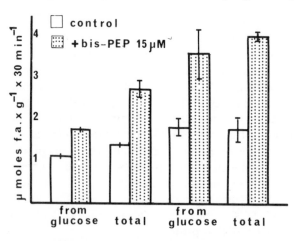

Figure 10.8   Influence of bis-PEP on synthesis of fatty acids in mouse adipose tissue *in vitro*. From Kits van Heijningen *et al.* (1976)

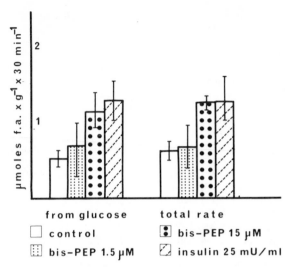

from glucose   total rate

☐ control   ⦙⦙ bis–PEP 15 µM

⦙⦙ bis–PEP 1.5 µM   ⧄ insulin 25 mU/ml

Figure 10.9 Influence of bis-PEP and insulin on synthesis of fatty acids in mouse adipose tissue *in vitro* (14 mM CaCl$_2$). From Kits van Heijningen *et al.* (1976)

intracellular Ca^{2+} distribution, unless this could depend on the stimulation by insulin of a specific Ca^{2+} carrier.

CONCLUSION

At present, the second messenger theory seems to offer the best prospects for clarifying the mechanism of action of insulin. As it will have been realized, the work of Sir Ernst has contributed to this insight in two different methods.

Firstly, by pointing out, again and again, that elucidation of the mechanism of action of insulin will come from studying the first steps in the effects of insulin on tissue metabolism. He was the first to emphasize the specific anabolic effects of insulin, particularly in muscle, which could not be explained by a simple increase in the permeability of the cell membrane to glucose.

Secondly Sir Ernst has contributed in a way which perhaps does not make the solution easier. He has added a great deal to our knowledge of the many effects of insulin on tissue metabolism, thus increasing the long list of requirements to be met by any theory on the mechanism of insulin action, and thus reminding us strongly of Pascal's vision on knowledge—'Knowledge is like a sphere in space: the greater its volume, the larger its contact with the unknown.'

REFERENCES

Abraham, S., Cady, P., and Chaikoff, I. L. (1957) *J. Biol. Chem.*, **224**, 955.
Ball, E. G. (1970) *Adipose Tissue, Regulation, and Metabolic Function* (Jeanrenaud, B., and Hepp, D., eds.), Academic Press, New York and London, p. 102.

206

Balmain, J. H., Folley, S. J., and Glascock, R. F. (1952) *Biochem. J.*, **52**, 301.
Banting, F. G., and Best, C. H. (1922) *J. Lab. Clin. Med.*, **7**, 251.
Banting, F. G., Best, C. H., Collip, J. B., Campbell, W. R., and Fletcher, A. A. (1922) *Can. Med. Ass. J.*, **12**, 141.
Beloff-Chain, A., Betto, P., Catanzaro, R., Chain, E. B., Longinotti, L., Masi, I., and Pocchiari, F. (1964) *Biochem. J.*, **91**, 620.
Beloff-Chain, A., Catanzaro, R., Chain, E. B., Masi, I., Pocchiari, F., and Rossi, C. (1955) *Proc. Roy. Soc., Series B*, **143**, 481.
Beloff-Chain, A., Catanzaro, R., Chain, E. B., Masi, I., and Pocchiari, F. (1956*a*) *Sel. Sci. Pap. Ist. Super. Sanità*, **1**, 356.
Beloff-Chain, A., Catanzaro, R., Chain, E. B., Masi, I., and Pocchiari, F. (1956*b*) *Sel. Sci. Pap. Ist. Super. Sanità*, **1**, 345.
Beloff-Chain, A., Chain, E. B., and Rookledge, K. A. (1971) *Biochem. J.*, **125**, 97.
Bessman, S. P. (1966) *Am. J. Med.*, **40**, 740.
Bouchardat and Sandras (1845) *Gaz. Med.*, **13**, 252.
Chain, E. B., Manford, K. R. L., and Opie, L. H. (1969) *Biochem. J.*, **115**, 537.
Chain, E. B., and Sender, P. M. (1973) *Biochem. J.*, **132**, 593.
Coore, H. G., Denton, R. M., Martin, B. R., and Randle, P. J. (1971) *Biochem. J.*, **125**, 115.
Cuatrecasas, P. (1969) *Proc. Nat. Acad. Sci., U.S.A.*, **63**, 450.
Cuatrecasas, P. (1971) *Proc. Nat. Acad. Sci., U.S.A.*, **68**, 1264.
Desbuquois, B., and Cuatracasas, P. (1973) *Ann. Rev. Med.*, **24**, 233.
de Dominicis, G. (1889) *Giorn. Intern. Sci. Med.*, **1889**, 801.
de Dominicis, G. (1894) *Atti congr. intern. Roma*, **3**, 391.
Drury, D. R. (1940) *Am. J. Physiol.*, **131**, 536.
Fisher, R. B., and Zachariah, B. (1961) *J. Physiol.*, **158**, 73.
Flatt, J. P., and Ball, E. G. (1964) *J. Biol. Chem.*, **239**, 675.
Forker, L. L., Chaikoff, I. L., Entenman, C., and Tarver, H. (1951) *J. Biol. Chem.*, **188**, 37.
Freychet, P., Roth, J., and Neville, D. M. (1971) *Proc. Nat. Acad. Sci., U.S.A.*, **68**, 1833.
Gemmill, C. L. (1940) *Johns Hopkin Hosp. Bull.*, **66**, 232.
Gemmill, C. L. (1941) *Johns Hopkin Hosp. Bull.*, **68**, 329.
Goldfine, T. D. (1975) *Endocrinology*, **97**, 948.
Halperin, M. L. (1970) *Can. J. Biochem.*, **48**, 1228.
Halperin, M. L., and Robinson, B. H. (1971) *Metabolism*, **20**, 78.
Hepp, D., Challoner, D. R., and Williams, R. H. (1968) *J. Biol. Chem.*, **243**, 4020.
Houssay, B. A. (1936) *N. Eng. J. Med.*, **214**, 961.
Jungas, R. L. (1968) *Biochemistry*, **7**, 3708.
Jungas, R. L. (1970) *Endocrinology*, **86**, 1368.
Jungas, R. L. (1971) *Metabolism*, **20**, 43.
Katzen, H. H. (1967) *Adv. Enz. Reg.*, **5**, 335.
Kissebah, A. H., Hope-Gill, H., Vydelingun, N., Tulloch, B. R., Clark, P. V., and Fraser, T. R. (1975) *Lancet*, *i*, 144.
Kits van Heijningen, A. J. M. (1963) *Arch. Biochem. Biophys.*, **102**, 456.
Kits van Heijningen, A. J. M. (1965) *Biochim. Biophys. Acta*, **97**, 165.
Kits van Heijningen, A. J. M. (1966). M.D. Thesis, University of Amsterdam.
Kits van Heijningen, A. J. M., Lankhorst-Santaguida, I., and Wientjes, C. (1973) *Pflugers Arch.*, **345**, 353.
Kits van Heijningen, A. J. M., Rath, E., Treitjel, B., Visser, N., Wientjes, C., and Beloff-Chain, A. (1976) *F.E.B.S. Letters*, **72**, 58.
Levine, R. (1974) *Adv. Metab. Disord.*, **7**, 183.
Levine, R., Goldstein, M. S., Huddlestun, B., and Klein, S. P. (1950) *Am. J. Physiol.*, **163**, 70.

Linn, J. C., Pettit, F. H., Hucho, F., and Reed, L. J. (1969a) *Proc. Nat. Acad. Sci.*, *U.S.A.*, **64**, 227.
Linn, T. C., Pettit, F. H., and Reed, J. L. (1969b) *Proc. Nat. Acad. Sci.*, *U.S.A.*, **62**, 234.
Long, C. N. H., and Lukens, F. D. W. (1936) *J. Exp. Med.*, **63**, 465.
Luft, R., and Cerasi, E. (1968) *Diabetologia*, **4**, 1.
Manchester, K. L., and Young, F. G. (1958) *Biochem. J.*, **70**, 353.
Manchester, K. L., and Young, F. G. (1960) *Biochem. J.*, **77**, 386.
Manganiello, V. C., Murad, F., and Vaughan, M. (1971) *J. Biol. Chem.*, **246**, 2195.
Matteucci, C. (1847). Leçons sur les Phenomenes Physiques des corps vivants. Paris, (Masson, V., Pub. and ed.).
von Mering, J., and Minkowski, O. (1889) *Zent. bl. Klin. Med.*, **10**, 393.
von Mering, J., and Minkowski, O. (1890) *Arch. exp. Path. Pharmak.*, **26**, 371.
Nakada, H. I., and Wick, A. N. (1956) *Am. J. Physiol.*, **185**, 23.
Ochoa, S., Mehler, A. H., and Kornberg, A. (1948) *J. Biol. Chem.*, **174**, 979.
Park, C. R., Bornstein, J., and Post, R. L. (1955) *Am. J. Physiol.*, **182**, 12.
Park, C. R., and Johnson, L. H. (1955) *Am. J. Physiol.*, **182**, 17.
Price, W. H., Cori, C. F., and Colowick, S. P. (1945) *J. Biol. Chem.*, **160**, 633.
Sinex, F. M., MacMullen, J., and Hastings, A. B. (1952) *J. Biol. Chem.*, **198**, 615.
Stadie, W. C., Haugaard, N., Hills, A. G., and Marsh, J. B. (1949) *Am. J. Med. Sci.*, **218**, 265.
Stadie, W. C., Haugaard, N., and Vaughan, M. (1952) *J. Biol. Chem.*, **199**, 729.
Stetten, D., and Boxer, G. E. (1944) *J. Biol. Chem.*, **156**, 271.
Suzuki, F., Daikuhara, Y., Ono, M., and Takeda, Y. (1972) *Endocrinology*, **90**, 1220.
Taylor, S. I., Mukherjee, C., and Jungas, R. L. (1973) *J. Biol. Chem.*, **248**, 73.
Villar-Palasi, C., and Larner, J. (1961) *Archiv. Biochem. Biophys.*, **94**, 436.
Villee, C. A., and Hastings, A. B. (1949) *J. Biol. Chem.*, **179**, 673.
Villee, C. A., White, V. K., and Hastings, A. B. (1952) *J. Biol. Chem.*, **195**, 287.
Volfin, P. (1970) *FEBS Letters*, **9**, 317.
Walaas, O., Walaas, E., and Gronnerod, O. (1972) *Is. J. Med. Sci.*, **8**, 353.
Walters, A., and McLean, P. (1967) *Biochem. J.*, **109**, 737.
Wick, A. N., and Drury, D. R. (1953) *Am. J. Physiol.*, **173**, 229.
Winegrad, A. I., and Renold, A. E. (1958a) *J. Biol. Chem.*, **233**, 267.
Winegrad, A. I., and Renold, A. E. (1958b) *J. Biol. Chem.*, **233**, 273.
Wise, E. M., and Ball, E. G. (1964) *Proc. Nat. Acad. Sci.*, *U.S.A.*, **52**, 1255.
Wool, I. G., and Krahl, M. E. (1959) *Am. J. Physiol.*, **196**, 961.
Wool, I. G., Stirewalt, W. S., Kurihara, K., Low, R. B., Bailey, P., and Oyer, D. (1968) *Rec. prog. Horm. Res.*, **24**, 139.
Young, F. G. (1937) *Lancet*, **ii**, 372.
Zierler, K. L. (1957) *Science*, *N.Y.*, **126**, 1067.
Zierler, K. L. (1959) *Am. J. Physiol.*, **197**, 515.
Zierler, K. L., and Rabinowitz, D. (1963) *Medicine*, **42**, 385.

DISCUSSION

Dr. A. B. Hastings

Anne, would you like to comment? No? Sir Ernst will comment for you!

Sir Ernst Chain

People get very sensitive when you talk about the mechanism of insulin action. The most pronounced effects of insulin in muscle are on two areas of metabolic reactions. These are glucose and glycogen metabolism, and protein metabolism. We must find out what motivates these reactions. If a factor influences them, it will then influence all sorts of other reactions. I believe one superimposed reaction can influence both glucose and protein metabolism. This reaction features ATP. This is difficult to study in muscle because so much ATP is used for the contraction, but in adipose tissue a definite effect of insulin on ATP metabolism has been demonstrated. From this you can explain various other effects.

11
Liver Metabolism in Diabetes

D. A. Hems

Department of Biochemistry,
St. George's Hospital Medical School, London, U.K.

INTRODUCTION

Diabetes is one of the most widespread disorders of man, and was one of the first to be described systematically. Egyptian papyri contain descriptions of a fatal polyuria, and a vivid and accurate description was given by Aretaeus the Cappedocian. About 2000 years later, chemical pathology was founded by Thomas Willis, who tasted the urine of diabetics and found it sweet 'as if imbued with sugar or honey'. Thus, diabetes mellitus was differentiated from other kinds of polyuria. Further major landmarks were the discovery that pancreatectomy causes diabetes (von Mering and Minkowski, 1889; de Dominicis, 1889) and of course the elucidation by Banting of insulin as the active principle concerned.

Diabetes is a metabolic disorder, so it seems likely that the liver as the major metabolic organ plays a key role in the disease. This notion is more recent than it might seem. The Babylonians stared balefully at the liver, among the surrounding entrails, to foretell the future. The Greeks credited the liver with the manufacture of humour (black, in particular). In medieval times, a humorous man was sometimes liverish, and Titian thought man was a rodent, because he painted the liver in the left hypogastrium. Now it is realized that the liver is essential for life, and can generate bile, heat, red cells, and many types of molecule. In different kinds of liver disease, there may be diabetes ('hepatogenous') or hypoglycaemia. In insulin-deficient states, it is probable that almost all aspects of liver function are at least marginally altered. These alterations have not been well characterized, although a few metabolic changes have been elucidated, as will be seen.

The purpose of this article is to discuss those metabolic aspects of diabetes in which the liver plays a role. The hidden theme of any such attempt concerns the question of action of insulin on the liver; these can be long, medium, or short term, directly hepatic or indirect. This paper presents arguments on these aspects of insulin action.

GENERAL CHARACTERISTICS OF DIABETES

Commonly diabetes reflects a deficiency of circulating insulin, due to inadequate function of the B-cells of the pancreatic islets of Langerhans. Many of the characteristics of diabetes are reversed by insulin administration. Indeed, the discovery and the therapeutic application of insulin constitutes the greatest achievement of biochemical endocrinology; approximately 140 million lives have been saved using insulin during the past 50 years. Whether this number exceeds those saved by penicillin is a moot point.

Diabetes can be a serious disorder in which acidotic coma supervenes if blood insulin levels become low. In this state, there are excessive levels of glucose, free fatty acids, ketone bodies, triglyceride, and some amino acids in the blood. Diabetes could in fact be described as 'hypersubstrataemia'. Acidosis is mainly due to ketone bodies, and there are associated complex electrolytic disturbances. Administration of insulin rapidly reverses all these features; thus insulin is the hormone concerned with blood substrate clearance. No other hormone serves a similar role and no other hormone, except perhaps aldosterone, is so critical to life.

There is a second major type of diabetes in which the main pathogenic factor is the failure of insulin action, rather than insulin secretion. If insulin fails to act on muscle and adipose tissue, in particular, the metabolic pattern of hypersubstrataemia again develops, but is now less responsive to the action of insulin, which may already be present at high concentrations in blood. Typically, these diabetic patients are older and more obese than patients in which the more straightforward insulin deficiency is apparent.

The therapeutic success achieved using insulin has tended to mask the fact that several outstanding problems of diabetes still remain unsolved. For example, the malign sequelae of diabetes still ensue in many patients, who develop renal, neurological, or vascular syndromes which are intractable to insulin therapy. Also, the aetiology of the pancreatic dysfunction is still not understood, although a viral origin appears possible. Diabetes is a generalized disorder, affecting all tissues, and many of the features, apart from the major metabolic ones, have not been properly characterized. Finally, synthetic insulin is still not available, although there is an enormous potential market in view of the world shortage of pancreatic tissue.

Above all, the mechanism of insulin action remains unknown. It is not surprising that this problem came to fascinate Sir Ernst, (before most other scientists, as so often in his career) since insulin occupies a prime place among hormones, much as penicillin does among antibiotics. Other analogies exist between insulin and penicillin, which explains why Sir Ernst Chain became interested in insulin (Chain et al., 1956). As far as is known he has not attempted to treat infections with insulin or diabetes with penicillin, but if this was appropriate, he would have the imagination to attempt it! During the period spent in Italy Sir Ernst and collaborators tackled the problem of insulin action, in liver (Beloff-Chain et al., 1956a–c) and (Chain et al., 1956). In this phase of his research, and in later work featuring the perfused heart preparation, as well as in studies involving diaphragms, Sir Ernst came up with several concepts which will one day seem to be almost clairvoyant, such as the multiple cellular sites for the pathway of glycolysis, the relevance of oxidative processes in insulin action, and the notion of an indirect insulin effect on the liver, perhaps *via* release of a muscle factor. The problem of the mechanism of insulin action is even yet proving difficult to solve in liver (Fain, 1974; Pilkis and Park, 1974) as in other tissues. In general, it appears possible that insulin may act as an ionophore (Maina *et al.*, 1975) rather than *via* a 'second' messenger.

ANIMAL MODELS OF DIABETES

Just as the discovery of insulin and the early work with penicillin depended on experiments with animals, so does current knowledge of the metabolic characteristics of diabetes. Diabetes may be produced in animals in a variety of ways: (*i*) use of B-cell toxins, such as alloxan and streptozotocin; it is always uncertain whether such agents act solely on the B-cell, but the test for this aspect is whether a particular feature is reversible on insulin treatment; (*ii*) injection of antibodies to insulin; (*iii*) administration of compounds, such as mannoheptulose, which impede glucose-dependent activation of insulin secretion; (*iv*) surgical removal of part or all of the pancreas; (*v*) genetic obesity in mice and rats; (*vi*) administration of an excess of glucocorticoid hormones, or their trophic peptide (ACTH), or growth hormone.

In general, diabetes produced by the first four manoeuvres is of an insulin-deficiency type and exhibits a common set of metabolic features (Table 11.1). Administration of insulin reverses these alterations. Genetic or hormone-induced diabetes, on the other hand, presents a syndrome of insulin-resistant type. Although there are intergeneric differences in the details of diabetic

Table 11.1 Alterations of hepatic carbohydrate and lipid metabolism in insulin-deficient diabetes

Change in blood substrate	Intrinsic alteration in liver capacity	Relevant changes in blood hormones
Increase in glucose	Increased gluconeogenesis Decreased glycolysis Decreased glycogen storage	Insulin fall Glucagon rise (Adrenaline and angiotensin II rise, may be relevant)
Increase in ketone bodies	Increased ketogenesis Decreased lipogenesis	
Increase in triglyceride	Decreased triglyceride export and synthesis	Insulin fall
Increase in free fatty acids	No change in uptake Fatty liver develops	

syndromes, the use of animal models undoubtedly will continue to illumine rather than undermine our insights into diabetes.

NATURE OF INSULIN IN BLOOD

Before turning more specifically to the role of the liver in diabetes, the nature of insulin in blood will be briefly considered. As organs in mammals are functionally inter-linked by blood, this matter is of enormous significance, yet there are gaps in knowledge. The greater part of blood-borne insulin-like activity is not 'suppressible' by antibodies, and little is known at present about this component (Oelz et al., 1972). Immunoreactive insulin is present in blood for several days after pancreatectomy (Penhos et al., 1975). The full details of the roles of the C-peptide and pro-insulin are not yet available. For the purpose of this article, 'insulin' denotes the conventional peptide (employed in diabetes therapy, and therefore of unquestionable significance).

HYPERGLYCAEMIA, GLUCOSE TOLERANCE, AND THE LIVER

The simplest definition of diabetes is that it is a state in which handling of a glucose load is impaired—although it is imperative to remember that this is a vastly over-simplified definition of a complex disease. The question arises as to the role of the liver in glucose tolerance; this has been estimated to be 8–70 per cent of the disposal of a net load. Usually, these estimates are based on experiments with [^{14}C]glucose or after hepatectomy, both of which can give misleading results. The only real measure of net hepatic glucose changes is by monitoring differences in glucose in the three major hepatic blood vessels. Few studies of this type are available except in animals under nonphysiological conditions, for example because of a portacaval shunt or because of the antecedent diet. Data in man suggest that there may be significant hepatic glucose uptake in the fed state (Felig, 1975; Felig and Wahren, 1975).

In animals which have been starved for moderate periods, it appears that a glucose load is not assimilated through net uptake by the liver, although glucose output by the liver may be suppressed. The majority of such uptake is by muscle or adipose tissue. This conclusion arises from several lines of evidence including experiments with perfused liver from starved rats, which show that glucose can suppress glucose release, but that even at high concentrations of glucose (30 nM) net glycogen synthesis is entirely supported by glucogenic precursors such as lactate, glycerol, and amino acids if they are available (Hems et al., 1972). In the starved animal which receives glucose, synthesis of glycogen from continuing gluconeogenesis obviates any requirement for extensive glucokinase activity, since net glucose uptake is negligible. In this situation, glucose does serve a regulatory purpose, however, in redirecting gluconeogenic hexose phosphate products to glycogen (Hems et al., 1972; Hers et al., 1974; Hue et al., 1975).

As far as fed animals are concerned, the significance of net glucose uptake by the liver is still a problem. Most likely, there is a net uptake during starch ingestion (Felig, 1975; Felig and Wahren, 1975). A major fate of this glucose in the liver of fed animals is its conversion to glycogen (Whitton and Hems, 1975a). Thus blood-borne glucose may not be an important source of acetyl units for lipogenesis in the liver even during feeding (Hems et al., 1975b; Figure 11.1). Indeed, consumption of circulating glucose by glycolysis may not be important in the liver in the aerobic state.

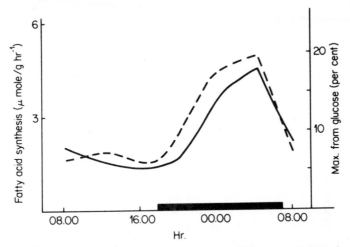

Figure 11.1 Hepatic fatty acid synthesis. Mice were injected with ^3H_2O and [^{14}C]glucose at times throughout the 24 hr cycle. The rate of fatty acid synthesis (hr^{-1}) (——) was calculated from ^3H values after one hour and the maximal contribution of glucose (– – –) to lipogenesis in liver from the ratio ($^{14}C/^3H$ in adipose tissue)/($^{14}C/^3H$ in liver). The shaded area indicates the dark periods during which most feeding occurred. Modified from Hems et al. (1975b). Reproduced by permission of the Biochemical Society

SEQUENCE OF METABOLIC ALTERATIONS IN THE LIVER IN DIABETES

The questions arise of the origin of the alterations in blood substrates in insulin-deficient diabetes, which organs are implicated, and which alterations of metabolism in a given organ are the result of a failure of insulin action. Essentially, these problems may only be tackled by studies of preparations from single organs *in vitro*. Such studies have become more informative recently, particularly in the case of the liver with the advent of perfusion techniques, improved preparation of cell suspensions, and the availability of pure substrates and hormones.

From such studies, modifications in liver metabolism have been identified (Table 11.1), which contribute to the changes in profile of blood substrates. The possibility exists that some of the alterations listed in Table 11.1 are secondary consequences of other events in diabetes. One approach to this problem is to elucidate the time course of changes in the liver, either following the onset of insulin-deficiency or after the administration of insulin. Such studies suggest that the impairment in glycogen synthesis and the increase in ketogenesis are the first events to occur in the liver in insulin deficiency, as both of these responses are apparent within one to two hours of insulin lack or administration (Whitton and Hems, 1975b; McGarry et al., 1974). Such rapid enhancement of ketogenesis, however, may still be secondary to the decline in glycogen-storage function (McGarry et al., 1974; Woodside and Heimberg, 1976).

INSULIN DEFICIENCY AND LIVER GLYCOGEN METABOLISM

The high blood glucose concentration occurring in diabetes is commonly associated with a diminished hepatic glycogen content, implying that there is a defect in the accumulation or retention of glycogen by the liver. Under these conditions, hexose phosphate products of gluconeogenesis tend to form free glucose rather than glucogen. After insulin injection, the glycogen content of the liver is replenished (Steiner, 1966). These aspects of hepatic glycogen metabolism in diabetes have been studied using the perfused liver of streptozotocin-diabetic rats, (Whitton and Hems, 1975b), in which there is a marked decrease in rates of net glycogen accumulation compared with rates in normal rats starved for 48 hours (Table 11.2). The defect in net glycogen

Table 11.2 Net hepatic glycogen synthesis in diabetes

	In vivo pretreatment	Net glycogen synthesis (μmole glucose/g min^{-1})	Glucose release into perfusate (mM increase)
Normal	None	0·75	0·6
Diabetic	None	0·19	1·6
Diabetic	Glucose, fructose	0·81	2·6
Diabetic	Insulin	0·51	1·5
Diabetic (insulin in perfusate)	None	0·10	—

Data from Hems et al. (1972), and Whitton and Hems (1975b).
Reproduced by permission of the Biochemical Society.

synthesis observed in perfusions containing glucose (30 mM) plus either fructose or a mixture of C_3 substrates (lactate, glycerol, and pyruvate) is reversed by administration of a mixture of glucose plus fructose in vivo, 50 minutes before perfusion (Table 11.2). Glucose alone is not effective in correcting impaired synthesis from glucose plus fructose or other substrates.

Under all conditions studied, there is net output of glucose during perfusion of livers of diabetic rats, yet if glucose is not added to perfusions of diabetic rat livers no glycogen accumulates.

These results suggest that there is an intrinsic impairment of the capacity for net glycogen accumulation in the liver of diabetic rats (see also Hastings *et al.*, 1955) which is rapidly reversible within one to two hours by insulin, and perhaps fructose, *in vivo* but *in vitro*. Thus, insulin in intact animals appears to exert a medium-term effect to regulate the capacity for hepatic glycogen synthesis by a complex and novel mechanism. This action probably involves the initiatory role of glucose in synthesis, exerted despite its lack of role as a carbon source, through mechanisms such as a glucose receptor, which are defective if there is a lack of insulin.

The lack of capacity for glycogen deposition in diabetes requires explanation at the enzymic level. The metabolism of glycogen is controlled by a complex group of enzymes whose function can be conditioned by glucose to promote synthesis (Hers *et al.*, 1974; Hue *et al.*, 1975; Whitton and Hems, 1975*b*, 1976*a*). Synthetase activity can also increase in response to gluconeogenic precursors (Whitton and Hems, 1975*b*). These changes in glycogen synthetase during perfusion may be assessed from the activities in sequential liver samples. In livers from diabetic rats, the response of synthetase to substrates is impaired (Table 11.3), and in rats in which pretreatment has restored net glycogen accumulation, there is an increase in the proportion of glycogen synthetase *a* which presumably reflects the return of the effect of substrates on synthetase, as observed in livers of normal (starved) rats. This response is less pronounced in perfusions of diabetic rat livers where glycogen synthesis is low. Thus, the impairment of the capacity for net glycogen synthesis in the liver of diabetic rats may reside at least partly in an inadequate responsiveness of the hepatic glycogen synthetase system to substrates. In perfusions with fructose, there is no such relationship; in the absence of pretreatment, glycogen synthesis is not

Table 11.3   Glycogen synthetase activity in perfused liver of diabetic rats

	In vivo pretreatment	Addition to perfusate glucose (30 mM)	Increase in synthetase *a* (per cent)	Net glycogen synthesis (μmole glucose/g min^{-1})
Normal	None	C_3 substrates	17	0·61
Diabetic	None	C_3 substrates	12	0·17
Diabetic	None	Fructose	34	0·35
Diabetic	Glucose, fructose	C_3 substrates	29	0·81
Diabetic	Insulin	C_3 substrates	18	0·59
Diabetic	None	C_3 substrates (insulin in perfusate)	1	0·26

Data from Whitton and Hems (1975*b*, 1976*a*).
Reproduced by permission of the Biochemical Society.

rapid, despite the extensive conversion of the synthetase into the *a* form during perfusion. The attainment of a high proportion of synthetase *a* during perfusion with fructose suggests that the enzymic apparatus for glycogen synthesis is not fundamentally lacking in the diabetic rat liver. Yet such activation by fructose is not a sufficient condition for maximal net glycogen accumulation. Thus the defect, which cannot be corrected in the perfused liver of diabetic rats, may involve the initiatory or cofactor role of glucose, which is implicated in net glycogen deposition in the normal liver and apparently in maintaining the full sensitivity of synthetase. This would be in accord with the established impairment in hepatic glucose uptake in diabetes (Renold *et al.*, 1956); and would also explain why the capacity for hepatic glycogen deposition in diabetes can be corrected more rapidly than is accounted for by the restoration of glucokinase activity (Steiner, 1966).

A general implication of these observations is that, in diabetes the hexose phosphate products of gluconeogenesis which are produced at an increased rate, are directed towards free glucose formation rather than to glycogen synthesis. Results obtained in the perfused liver confirm this suggestion, in that during maximal glycogen synthesis the net carbon sources of glycogen are gluconeogenic precursors, in either normal rat livers (Hems *et al.*, 1972) or in diabetic rat livers (Whitton and Hems, 1975*b*), or in adrenalectomized rat livers (Whitton and Hems, 1976*a*).

The lack of direct action of insulin on glycogen synthesis when added alone to the perfused liver is reminiscent of its lack of action—as the sole added hormone—on glycogen breakdown during perfusion with a full complement of red cells (Mondon and Burton, 1971, Mondon *et al.*, 1975). Perhaps in the presence of glucagon insulin would de-inhibit glycogen synthesis.

These experiments also demonstrate that hepatic glycogen synthesis is not sensitive to long-term insulin deprivation, since the lesion in diabetic animals is reversible within one to two hours *in vivo*.

HEPATIC GLUCONEOGENESIS IN DIABETES

A fundamental feature of diabetes is hyperglycaemia, and the major source of this glucose is hepatic gluconeogenesis. During insulin lack, there is an inherent increase in the capacity of gluconeogenesis as has been amply documented in the perfused liver (Exton *et al.*, 1972*a*, 1973), or in suspensions of isolated hepatocytes (Wagle *et al.*, 1974). The extra gluconeogenic capacity is most clearly seen with substrates which enter the metabolic routes to glucose *via* the tricarboxylic acid cycle, or phosphopyruvate. In general, there is a moderate increase in the activities of the key enzymes of glucose synthesis, and also a decline in the maximal assayable activities of the glycolytic enzymes. These alterations in the concentrations of the enzymes of carbohydrate metabolism in the liver during diabetes appear to involve slight changes in the rates of both synthesis and destruction of the specific catalytic proteins. These processes and their control are not fully understood, but it is reasonable to suggest that cyclic AMP is involved. Adrenal glucocorticoids have also been implicated in the increases in concentrations of the enzymes of gluconeogenesis in the diabetic liver (Exton *et al.*, 1973).

PRODUCTION OF KETONE BODIES BY THE LIVER

The most deleterious of the components of the hypersubstrataemia of diabetes, at least in the short-term, as in diabetic coma, is hyperketonaemia. This leads to severe metabolic acidosis, which contributes to the onset of the coma, but whose effects are mitigated as a result of neutralization of the acid by ammonia produced in the kidney (Hems, 1975*b*). The excess of ketone bodies in diabetes is largely due to the breakdown of triglycerides in adipose tissue resulting in the release of free fatty acids into the plasma. These fatty acids in turn, are converted rapidly to ketone bodies by the liver as a result mainly of their increased concentrations.

In addition, in diabetic animals there is an inherent increase in the capacity of the liver to generate ketone bodies from free fatty acids. This may be shown in experiments with the perfused liver, in which ketogenesis at any given concentration of free fatty acid may be seen to be increased if the donor animal is diabetic (Woodside and Heimberg, 1976; Heimberg *et al.*, 1974; McGarry and Foster, 1972; McGarry *et al.*, 1974, 1975). This increased capacity for ketogenesis probably has very complex origins. These include adjustments in the disposal of long-chain fatty acyl-coesters within cells, so that conversion to glycerides becomes less favoured at the expense of increased degradation by β-oxidation, a major product of which is ketone bodies. This conclusion has emerged from the imaginative and comprehensive work in Foster's laboratory using the perfused liver in particular (McGarry and Foster, 1972; McGarry *et al.*, 1974, 1975). However, many pieces of this jigsaw remain to be identified, let alone put in their right place.

LIPID METABOLISM IN DIABETES

a. Hepatic triglyceride metabolism in diabetes

The alterations to lipid metabolism in diabetes are of the utmost importance in view of their direct manifestation as vascular disease, and their more subtle effects on membranes which may well underlie most of the consequences of this disorder. Quite possibly, the hyperglycaemia associated with diabetes is of less pathogenic significance than the alterations in lipid metabolism, except perhaps in regard to ophthalmic complications.

The liver fulfills a crucial role in glyceride metabolism (Hems, 1975*a*). The major alterations of glyceride metabolism in diabetes listed in Table 11.1 include hypertriglyceridaemia. This change may be partly understood in the light of the increased influx of free fatty acids from extrahepatic tissues, to the liver, which are converted to glycerides and accumulate in the liver—particularly in the form of triglyceride—thus resulting in a 'fatty' liver. This trend is exacerbated by the impaired export of hepatic glycerides which ensues in diabetes, at least in its later stages (Basso and Havel, 1970; Heimberg et al., 1974; Reaven and Reaven, 1974).

b. Fatty acid synthesis in the liver

The most extensive alteration in hepatic lipid metabolism in diabetes is the decline in the rate of hepatic synthesis of fatty acids *de novo* (lipogenesis). This decrease, which may easily be demonstrated in the intact animal, is largely due to an intrinsic alteration in the hepatic capacity for lipogenesis and fatty acid desaturation (Bloch and Kramer, 1948; Gellhorn and Benjamin, 1966).

Measurements of hepatic lipogenesis, carried out with ^{14}C-labelled precursors cannot provide valid quantitative estimates of this process, as no single precursor contributes predominantly to the acetyl pool in cytoplasm. The simplest technique for measuring the total rate of hepatic lipogenesis is by determining the incorporation of ^3H from ^3H_2O into fatty acids (Windmueller and Spaeth, 1967). This method can be used to quantify carbon flow from all acetyl pools to fatty acids, as the entry of hydrogen from water into fatty acids is very rapid, virtually complete (in the sense that all hydrogen atoms in the product are derived from water, partly by exchange at some step during synthesis), and non-exchangeable once located in the fatty acid methylene groups. The main routes of entry of this hydrogen into fatty acids appear to be either *via* exchange of malonyl ester methylene hydrogen, or by reductive steps which feature NADPH and H^+ as reducing equivalent source. The main problem in the use of ^3H_2O to measure conversion of acetyl residues into fatty acid arises from the significant isotope effect, that is the discrimination in the relevant steps of synthesis, against ^3H compared with ^1H; the discrimination is estimated to be about 2·4. From this factor, lipogenesis may be calculated from ^3H-incorporation values. These aspects of the technique of measuring lipogenesis with ^3H_2O have been discussed (for refs. see Salmon et al., 1974; Hems et al., 1975b, Ma and Hems, 1975).

Experiments with ^3H_2O have shown that hepatic lipogenesis is faster than has hitherto been thought; maximal rates approach 1 μmol acetyl unit/g liver min.$^{-1}$ converted to fatty acid, which is of the same general order as the citrate cycle (Table 11.4). These experiments have also shown that the favoured precursors for fatty-acid synthesis are glycogen and lactate, and presumably related C_3 precursors, in livers perfused during glycogenolytic conditions (that is at glucose concentrations of less than 20 mM) as shown for rat (Clark et al., 1974; Kirk et al., 1976), and mouse (Salmon et al., 1974; Ma and Hems, 1975; Hems and Ma, 1976). Glucose is not a preferred precursor for hepatic fatty acid synthesis even during feeding, as has also been demonstrated *in vivo* (Hems et al., 1975b; Figure 11.1). During feeding and simultaneous net glycogen synthesis from both glucose and simpler precursors (Whitton and Hems,

Table 11.4 Fatty acid synthesis in the liver in fed animals, measured with either ^3H_2O (total rate of synthesis) or with ^{14}C-labelled precursors

Species	Condition	State of animal	Fatty acid synthesis Total rate, C_2 units (μmole/g min^{-1})	Precursor, max. contribution per cent
Rat	*In vivo*	Normal	0·15	Glucose 15
Rat	Perfusion	Normal	0·3–0·5	Glucose 20
Rat	Perfusion	Diabetic	0·05	Lactate 30
Rat	Perfusion	Adrenalectomized	0·2–0·4	Lactate 30
Mouse	*In vivo*	Normal	0·6 (night) 0·3 (day)	Lactate 30
Mouse	Perfusion	Normal	1·0 (maximum)	Glucose 20 Lactate 30–50

Values calculated from data of Salmon *et al.* (1974), Hems *et al.* (1975*b,c*), and Kirk *et al.* (1976). Reproduced by permission of the Biochemical Society.

1976*b*), lipogenesis in the liver appears to involve only simple precursors, such as lactate (Hems *et al.*, 1975*b*).

Despite these findings, which force a complete reappraisal of the significance of hepatic lipogenesis, there is no doubt about the extent of the massive decline in lipogenesis in diabetes, for example as shown with ^3H_2O in streptozotocin-diabetic rats. In longer-term diabetes, the decline in hepatic lipogenesis is in general a result of decreases in maximal assayable activities of regulatory enzymes in the liver. The details of these events remain to be elucidated in regard to the roles of synthesis and degradation of enzymes, time courses of acute changes, and significance of inactive forms of enzymes, for example, acetyl-CoA carboxylase and fatty acid synthetase. In contrast, cholesterol synthesis in the liver is not much altered in diabetes (Kirk *et al.*, 1976: Table 5).

DIRECT HEPATIC EFFECTS OF INSULIN

There has long been controversy over whether there are any important direct hepatic actions of insulin. This has mainly been due to the fact that the liver slice is a rather dysfunctional preparation—more so than in the case of slices from other tissues. The importance of the small insulin effects which have been observed cannot be reliably assessed.

Recently, the availability of more viable preparations, namely perfused livers and suspensions of hepatocytes, has permitted a group of short-term potent actions of insulin on the liver to be identified. The major effect of insulin at low concentrations is to prevent the action of glucagon in stimulating glycogen breakdown. This was first reported from Mortimore's laboratory (Glinsmann and Mortimore 1968; Figure 11.2) and has been confirmed (Exton *et al.*, 1972*b*; Exton and Park, 1972; Mackrell and Sokal, 1969). In a similar

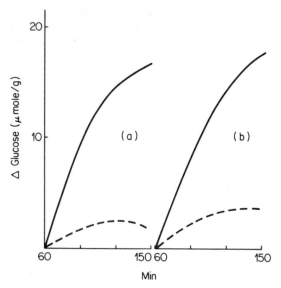

Figure 11.2 Action of glucagon on glucose release in the perfused liver. Livers from fed rats were perfused for one hour, during which glucose concentration stabilized at about 10 mM in perfusate. Then glucagon (a) or cyclic AMP (b) was added, in the absence (——) or presence (– – –) of insulin. Modified, with permission, from Glinsmann and Mortimore (1968)

way, insulin can prevent adrenaline-stimulated glycogen breakdown and glucose output in the perfused rat liver (Exton and Park, 1972).

Systematic study of the actions of insulin in the perfused liver has shown that additional actions which are exerted by concentrations of the hormone in the physiological range (10–500 μU/ml portal vein plasma) are stimulation of K^+ uptake and prevention of proteolysis and urea output (Mondon et al., 1975). Also, insulin can inhibit hepatic gluconeogenesis (Claus and Pilkis, 1976). The sensitivity of this action is not well-documented, and it may be an unimportant effect, compared to suppression of glycogen breakdown (Chiasson et al., 1976), which itself may not be highly sensitive to insulin action, as shown in perfusion experiments with sufficient erythrocytes (Mondon et al., 1975; Mondon and Burton, 1971; Haft, 1967, 1968).

Turning to lipid metabolism, here there is also controversy about the significance of direct hepatic insulin effects. In fact no really sensitive action—occurring at less than 1mU/ml—has been established. Effects which occur at relatively low insulin concentrations may include: (*i*) stimulation of fatty acid synthesis (Bloch and Kramer, 1948) although not always in optimal substrate conditions (Salmon and Hems, 1975); (*ii*) promotion of synthesis and export of triglycerides in lipoproteins (Topping and Mayes, 1972); (*iii*) increased accumulation of newly synthesized monoenoic fatty acids in hepatic triacyl glycerols (Salmon and Hems, 1975); (*iv*) inhibition of ketone body production (Topping and Mayes, 1972; Woodside and Heimberg, 1976); and (*v*) prevention of net triglyceride degradation (Salmon and Hems, 1976; Table 11.5). For a variety of reasons, these effects of insulin, mooted to be direct on the liver, remain problematical. Nevertheless, there seems no reason to doubt that some of these actions will turn out to be of physiological significance.

Table 11.5 Effect of insulin on content of triglyceride in mouse liver perfused with glucose and lactate

| | Triglyceride fatty acids (μmole/g) | | |
Fatty acid	Initial content	Final content − insulin	Final content + insulin (5 mU/ml)
16·0	8·6	7·2	9·0
18·0	0·9	0·8	1·2
16·1	0·9	0·6	1·4
18·1	11·5	6·8	9·7
18·2	5·0	2·7	3·5
Total:	26·9	18·1	24·8

Data are mean values from Salmon and Hems (1976).
Reproduced by permission of the Biochemical Society.

There is also a group of putative long-term actions of insulin on the liver, all to promote biosynthetic processes. Few of these have been shown to involve direct action, which will require the use of viable systems, such as tissue culture or long-term perfusion. Such studies are beginning to reveal the expected effects on, for example, lipogenesis (Alberts *et al.*, 1974) or glycogen metabolism (Plas and Nunez, 1976), although the sensitivity of these responses is not yet clear. Insulin can also promote protein synthesis in the perfused liver, at least at high concentrations (John and Miller, 1969).

SIGNIFICANCE OF THE ACTION OF GLUCAGON ON THE LIVER

The most clearcut example of a rapid hormonal effect on any tissue which is mediated by cyclic AMP is the ability of glucagon to stimulate glycogen breakdown in the liver (Exton *et al.*, 1971*a*, and *b*, 1972*b*, 1973; Glinsmann and Mortimore, 1968; Figure 11.2). This effect can be largely prevented by insulin, partly due to the inhibition of cyclic AMP formation (Exton and Park, 1972). This dual hormonal system assumes particular elegance in view of the fact that both insulin and glucagon are secreted into the hepatic portal vein, so that the first organ they reach is the liver. Therefore, the concerted actions of the two hormones on the liver (Parrilla *et al.*, 1974, 1975) may have a major role in glucose homeostasis in normal animals in particular (Unger, 1971). Also in insulin-deficient diabetes, circulating glucagon concentrations are increased; the ratio of glucagon/insulin in plasma thus increases significantly, apparently contributing to hyperglycaemia, through increases in the tissue cyclic AMP levels (Pilkis *et al.*, 1974).

Nevertheless, there are reasons to doubt the importance of pancreatic glucagon in short-term glucose homeostasis. Firstly, glucagon injections do not produce hyperglycaemia, in rats at least, unless the injected dose is large (Hems *et al.*, 1975c). Also, administration of antiglucagon antibodies do not produce hypoglycaemia in fed rats (Barling and Beloff-Chain, 1973). Thirdly, diabetes due to pancreatectomy closely resembles that due to specific B-cell toxins, certainly in regard to the occurrence of hyperglycaemia and hyperlipaemia, as has been shown in animals (Chernick and Scow, 1959; Scow, 1960; Basso and Havel, 1970; Migliorini, 1972) and in man (Barnes and Bloom, 1976). Finally, it is significant that there is no clinical disorder due to pancreatic A-cell loss or glucagon deficiency. Therefore, the significance of the short-term glucagon action on liver glucose metabolism is still questionable. Glucagon can exert many other short-term effects on liver metabolism (Exton *et al.*, 1972b) but so far most appear too insensitive to be of great importance. One of the most acceptable of its actions is the longer-term stimulation of gluconeogenesis during starvation or in diabetes exerted through the effects of cyclic AMP on the concentrations of the key enzymes of gluconeogenesis.

PROMOTION OF HEPATIC CATABOLISM BY HORMONES

In addition to glucagon, other hormones can exert a short-term catabolic effect on hepatic metabolism. Such hormones could be implicated in the events of diabetes, such as in causing hyperglycaemia. One such major action which has been known for many years is that of adrenaline (Exton *et al.*, 1971b; Hems *et al.*, 1976). This effect can occur at adrenaline levels of 10^{-8} M (Figure 11.3) which are observed in stressed animals; thus the old idea of insulin–adrenaline antagonism in glucose homeostasis is perfectly valid. Another hormone which can stimulate glycogen breakdown or inhibit its synthesis is vasopressin (Hems and Whitton, 1973; Kirk and Hems, 1974; Ma and Hems, 1975; Hems *et al.*, 1975c, Whitton and Hems, 1976b; Hems *et al.*, 1976); stimulation of glycogenolysis occurs at physiological concentrations (0·1–1 mU/ml) (Figure 11.3; Hems and Whitton, 1973, Hems *et al.*, 1976). Similar effects are exerted by parathyroid hormone (Figure 11.4; Hems *et al.*, 1975a), oxytocin (Figure 11.4; Whitton and Hems, 1976b), various intestinal peptides, including the vasoactive intestinal peptide and enteroglucagon, and angiotensin II (Figure 11.3; Hems *et al.*, 1976).

The potent glycogenolytic action of vasopressin, adrenaline, and angiotensin II is reflected particularly in the activation of glycogen phosphorylase in the perfused liver by low concentrations of hormone—about 5×10^{-11} M for the peptides and 10^{-8} M for adrenaline (Hems *et al.*, 1976). Such concentrations can be observed in a wide variety of stress states, especially circulatory shock

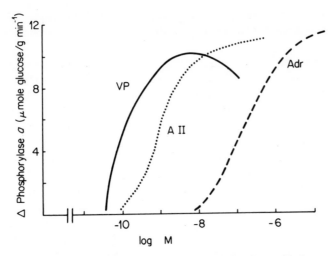

Figure 11.3 Increase in amount of hepatic glycogen phosphorylase *a* in response to hormones. Livers from fed rats were perfused for about 40 minutes. Perfusate glucose concentration was stable at about 10 mM. Liver samples were rapidly frozen and phosphorylase *a* was assayed. The change in activity during five minutes is shown for ——, vasopressin (VP); ······, angiotensin II (AII); – – –, adrenaline (Adr). Redrawn from Hems *et al.* (1976). Reproduced by permission of the Biochemical Society

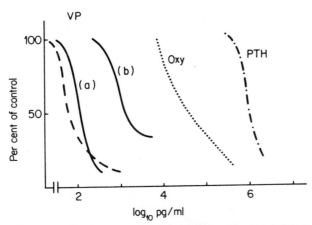

Figure 11.4 Actions of hormones on liver to inhibit biosynthesis of glycogen or fatty acid. Inhibition of glycogen synthesis with 8-arginine-vasopressin (——, (a)); 8-lysine vasopressin (– – –); oxytocin (······); and parathyroid hormone (– · – ·). Inhibition of fatty acid synthesis with 8-arginine-vasopressin (——, (b)). Data modified, with permission, from Hems and Whitton (1973), Hems *et al.* (1975a), Whitton and Hems (1976b), and Ma and Hems (1975). Reproduced by permission of Pergamon Press Ltd., and the Biochemical Society

(see Hems et al., 1976 for references). Activation of glycogen phosphorylase in livers of fed animals may be the most potent effect of these hormones (Hems et al., 1976).

Vasopressin, adrenaline, and angiotensin II can all produce hyperglycaemia in vivo (see Hems et al., 1976 for refs.). All are vasoconstrictors, although only adrenaline and angiotensin II can exert such an action directly on the liver (Hems et al., 1976). Their role in pathological states, and shock in particular, clearly involves a concerted pressor effect in addition to a glycogenolytic action on the liver. A simple concept would be that glucose is produced from liver glycogen both for consumption within the liver by glycolysis and for release as free glucose for consumption by other tissues (Hems et al., 1976).

This picture of the role of these catabolic hormones—all with actions and turnover among the most rapid of any in the animal—is not compatible with the notion that they stimulate hepatic gluconeogenesis in fed animals (Hems et al., 1976). In starved animals however, just as glucagon and adrenaline can stimulate gluconeogenesis (Exton, 1971; Exton et al., 1972; Lardy et al., 1974; Pilkis et al., 1975; Fain et al., 1975), so can vasopressin (Hems and Whitton, 1973).

a. Role of catabolic hormones in diabetes

Except perhaps in acute circulatory stress states the overall function of vasopressin, adrenaline, and angiotensin II appears to be to increase hepatic glucose production from glycogen and by gluconeogenesis. Therefore, they could all contribute to the hyperglycaemia of diabetes. So far, glucagon has been suggested to be relevant (Unger 1971, 1976) during insulin-deficiency hyperglycaemia, (but see the discussion in the previous section). The possible significance of increased circulating adrenaline observed in diabetes (Christensen, 1974) has not been adequately studied. Plasma levels of renin may also be increased in diabetic patients (Christlieb et al., 1975). Plasma vasopressin levels in diabetes have not been reported.

b. Mechanisms of hormone action

Another interesting question in regard to these hormones which act like glucagon is whether they act via cyclic AMP (Sutherland and Robison, 1969). Already it is clear that a major route of adrenaline action—the α-receptor route—does not involve cyclic AMP (Fain et al., 1975), and that the action of vasopressin in rat liver also does not involve cyclic AMP (Kirk and Hems, 1974). Parathyroid hormone can stimulate cyclic AMP formation in the liver, but not markedly so (for refs, see Hems et al., 1975a). Adrenaline, angiotensin II, and vasopressin also do not act via cyclic GMP (Siddle, Davies, and Hems, unpublished results). Extracellular Ca^{2+} is implicated in the action of vasopressin on glycogen metabolism (Stubbs et al., 1976).

In general, it can be concluded that the roles of the above hormones in aspects of liver metabolism (including diabetes), and their mechanism of action, remain to be settled.

ADRENAL GLUCOCORTICOIDS, INSULIN, AND LIVER METABOLISM

There are complex relationships between the functions of insulin and glucocorticoids in the intact animal. In regard to the liver, one of the simplest concerns the long-established effect of these hormones in promoting glycogen and fat accumulation in the liver. These actions are among the most immediate and extensive which glucocorticoids produce. Although that on glycogen was well-documented many years ago (Long et al., 1940), its mechanism is still not clear.

One way to tackle this problem is to study the liver of adrenalectomized animals. In such livers, there is a total loss of capacity for net glycogen deposition, revealed by experiments with the perfused liver (Whitton and Hems, 1976a; Table 11.6). There is also no glycogen synthesis in perfusions containing cortisol and insulin. Restoration of synthesis in the perfused liver of

Table 11.6 Hepatic glycogen metabolism in adrenalectomized rats

Rat	In vivo pretreatment	Perfusate + glucose 30 mM	Glycogen metabolism	
			Net synthesis (μmole glucose/ g min^{-1})	Increase in synthetase a after 30 min (per cent)
Normal (sham operated)	None	C$_3$ substrates	0·65	23
Adrenalectomized	None	C$_3$ substrates	0	0
Adrenalectomized	None	Fructose	0	7
Adrenalectomized	None	C$_3$ substrates, insulin, cortisol	0	−4
Adrenalectomized	Cortisol, (5 hr)	C$_3$ substrates	0·75	—
Adrenalectomized	Insulin (3 hr)	C$_3$ substrates	0·48	—

Data are taken from Whitton and Hems (1976a).
Reproduced by permission of the Biochemical Society.

adrenalectomized rats is achieved after about two hours treatment in vivo with hexoses plus either insulin or cortisol, or after four to five hours following treatment with cortisol alone. In these perfusions, there is consistent glucose output (Whitton and Hems, 1976a); thus the net carbon sources of glycogen

226

were the C_3 substrates, as in similar perfusions of starved, normal (Hems *et al.*, 1972), or diabetic rats (Whitton and Hems, 1975*b*; Table 11.2).

As in previously described studies of glycogen synthesis in diabetes, insight into the lesion after adrenalectomy has been obtained by assaying glycogen synthetase and phosphorylase. The response of these enzymes to substrates during perfusion is defective (Table 11.6), and is restored to normal in parallel with the capacity for net glycogen synthesis (Whitton and Hems, 1976*a*; Table 11.6; Figure 11.5). This total loss of the liver's ability to synthesize glycogen

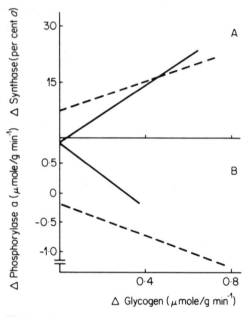

Figure 11.5 Changes in activity of glycogen synthetase and phosphorylase during liver perfusion, and their relationship to rates of net glycogen synthesis. Livers of starved rats were perfused with glucose plus glucogenic substrates. A, increase in synthetase (per cent of *a*) and B, decrease in phosphorylase in livers of rats which were either adrenalectomized (——) or diabetic (----). Redrawn from data of Whitton and Hems (1974, 1975*b*, 1976*a*). Reproduced by permission of the Biochemical Society

after adrenalectomy and starvation constitutes a more severe intrinsic alteration in hepatic metabolism than is shown by any other process. The most likely explanation for this impairment following adrenalectomy is that it reflects insulin lack; a fall in blood insulin after adrenalectomy has been observed by

Van Lan *et al.* (1974). Full details of the reasons for this conclusion are given by Whitton and Hems (1976*a*).

From these studies of diabetic and adrenalectomized rats, the overall conclusion emerges that adrenal corticosteroids promote hepatic glycogen accumulation (Long *et al.*, 1940), not by direct hepatic action, but *via* insulin acting indirectly on the liver. Furthermore, this is a novel mechanism involving the initiatory role of glucose in synthesis, discussed above, and also involving the complex properties of the phosphatase reactions which bring about activation of synthetase (Tan and Nuttall, 1976).

Fatty acid synthesis has been reported to be both increased and decreased by adrenalectomy. This type of problem may be studied using ^3H_2O to measure fatty acid synthesis. If the perfused liver is used for such experiments, then an intrinsic impairment in fatty acid synthesis and triglyceride export is observed after adrenalectomy which resembles that due to insulin deficiency (Kirk *et al.*, 1976). So again, as in the studies of glycogen synthesis, it appears that adrenal glucocorticoids serve to stimulate fatty acid synthesis and triglyceride export by increasing insulin levels. Insulin may act directly on the liver to stimulate these processes (Topping and Mayes, 1972).

Finally, both adrenal glucocorticoids and insulin acting synergistically have been shown to promote hepatic protein biosynthesis and export (John and Miller, 1969). Conversely, in diabetic animals protein synthesis is impaired, (Alford *et al.*, 1975*a,b*) at least in regard to the lipoprotein–apoproteins (Wilcox *et al.*, 1968) if not in respect to some general hepatic proteins (Pain and Garlick, 1974). In adrenalectomized animals, these aspects have not been studied systematically.

In the case of all these biosynthetic processes therefore, adrenal corticoids and insulin act to promote synthesis. There appears to be no 'insulin resistance' due to steroids, in respect of the hepatic biosynthesis of glycogen or fat. The functional significance of these promotions of biosynthesis by glucocorticoids, which are supposedly hormones of stress and catabolism, remains obscure.

A different picture may be obtained in the case of gluconeogenesis. In intact animals, the capacity of this pathway is increased by adrenal glucocorticoids and diminished by insulin (Weber *et al.*, 1974). These changes reflect alterations in the amount of enzymes in liver, probably due to direct hepatic action of the hormones, although such concerted responses—enzyme induction—have not been systematically reproduced *in vitro*. Enzymes affected include those of pyruvate metabolism (Exton *et al.*, 1976).

Interrelationships of this type shed light on the well-established observation that adrenalectomy or hypophysectomy can ameliorate the hyperglycaemia of diabetes. On the above arguments, adrenal glucocorticoids would be expected to be implicated in the increase in gluconeogenic capacity which ensues in diabetes, and indeed this has been demonstrated (Exton *et al.*, 1973). However, most of the effects of steroids in the intact animal to offset insulin actions are likely to be exerted on muscle or adipose tissue, which are the major insulin-sensitive tissues.

CIRCULATING SUBSTRATES AND CONTROL OF LIVER METABOLISM

It is not well enough recognized that cirulating substrates can control metabolic processes in the same manner as do hormones. The paradigm for this type of phenomenon is the so-called glucose–fatty acid cycle (Randle *et al.*, 1963). Its central features are that cirulating free fatty acids inhibit glucose uptake and glycolysis in heart, and that glucose suppresses triglyceride breakdown to free fatty acids in adipose tissue. An oscillatory situation is thus created whereby an increase in blood glucose at first causes a decrease in free fatty acids, but glucose is then consumed faster and the process is reversed. This kind of regulatory device is of significance since substrates in blood can alter several-fold between the different states of the animal. Some hormone concentration changes, such as those of glucagon, are no greater than this.

As far as the liver is concerned, one such control process is the stimulation of gluconeogenesis which can be observed in response to free fatty acids. Although the significance of this effect is the subject of controversy, it clearly could be relevant to the enhancement of hepatic gluconeogenesis which occurs in diabetes. In addition, carbohydrate substrates can exert regulatory influences on hepatic metabolism. Circulating glucose, in particular, although of minor importance as a carbon source for glycogen synthesis in starved animals (Hems *et al.*, 1972) and for the biosynthesis of fatty acids (Salmon *et al.*, 1974; Kirk *et al.*, 1976; Hems *et al.*, 1975*b*), can initiate the synthesis of both glycogen (Hems *et al.*, 1972, Hers *et al.*, 1974) and fatty acids (Salmon *et al.*, 1974), even during net glucose release. In each instance, lactate and related C_3–C_5 precursors provides carbon for conversion to the biosynthetic product. Glucose may also be implicated in longer-term events of enzyme induction, including liver fatty acid synthetase (Volpe and Vagelos, 1974); enzymes of glycogen metabolism do not appear to alter significantly in this respect.

Glycogen not only contributes carbon for fatty acid synthesis in the perfused mouse liver (Salmon *et al.*, 1974), and perhaps *in vivo* (Hems *et al.*, 1975*b*), but the rate of synthesis, even from glucose or acetate, is proportional to the initial glycogen content (Salmon *et al.*, 1974), suggesting that glycogen can stimulate lipogenesis independently of its role as a carbon source. The same may also apply to protein synthesis (Wagle and Sampson, 1975).

In addition, lactate can not only contribute significant carbon for hepatic lipogenesis—and perhaps the only carbon in conditions where there is simultaneous glycogen deposition, for example during ingestion of glucose—but also can stimulate this process (Salmon *et al.*, 1974). This may be through events of extra-mitochondrial reducing equivalent transfer.

All of these substrate effects are of the same general type as those of hormones (so perhaps a neologism is required here—metabolone, hormite?). It is interesting to speculate whether these effects are exerted partly *via* cyclic nucleotides, which would be analogous to catabolite repression occurring in microorganisms. Some of these actions also occur in a direction such as to be relevant to metabolic alterations in the liver in diabetes, for example promotion of lipogenesis by glycogen, and of gluconeogenesis by free fatty acids.

A GLUCOSE RECEPTOR IN THE LIVER?

The effects of glucose in stimulating hepatic biosynthesis of glycogen or fat are particularly interesting. In regard to glycogen synthesis, this effect may partly derive from the ability of glucose to activate glycogen phosphorylase phosphatase, thus lowering the phosphorylase a activity in liver, and secondarily de-inhibiting glycogen synthetase phosphatase, since phosphorylase a is an inhibitor of synthetase phosphatase (Hers et al., 1974).

However, this may not be the whole story, as suggested by the characteristics of livers from diabetic animals. In this situation, there is a major impairment in the hepatic capacity for net glycogen deposition (Whitton and Hems, 1975a) which is due to a reduced response of the glycogen synthetase system to substrates, as has been described previously. It seems unlikely that glucose itself can be exerting an inadequate effect on enzymes in diabetes, as this is a disease in which glucose is abundantly available. The clue here arises from the observation that although fructose can maximally stimulate synthetase activation in the perfused liver, there still is not full restoration of net glycogen synthetic capacity (Whitton and Hems, 1975b). Therefore, there must be an additional lesion in the liver in diabetes. This impairment in glycogen synthetic capacity is corrected within one to two hours by insulin in vivo (Whitton & Hems, 1975b). It is unlikely that this impairment resides in the glucokinase enzyme since this enzyme, which is greatly diminished in diabetes, does not return to normal levels within this time period following treatment (Steiner, 1966). If the process of glucose phosphorylation is not implicated in the stimulatory role of glucose in glycogen deposition in the normal liver, which depends on insulin in vivo for its maintenance, this implies that there may be a glucose receptor in the liver, other than that operated through the phosphorylase and synthetase phosphatases, by which glucose promotes the glycogen synthetic capacity. Thus similar receptors in the pancreatic B-cells may be defective in diabetes (Robertson and Porte, 1973). Studies of the influence of hexose analogues on glycogen synthesis support the notion of a glucose-receptor which can lead to stimulation of hepatic glycogen synthesis (Whitton and Hems, 1977).

DIABETES AND OBESITY

Obesity (measured as overweight or adiposity) appears to bring about a predisposition to diabetes. This may be understood in terms of pancreatic endocrine function and tissue insulin needs as follows. Obesity is a consequence of over-eating, as a result of which there is stimulation of insulin secretion by the pancreas. As long as the gland can respond to this stimulus, there is no impairment in the assimilation of dietary constituents by tissues.

However, if the endocrine pancreas begins to fail to respond to this extra demand and/or if more and more insulin is required to act upon muscle and adipose tissue then the handling of substrates in blood becomes sluggish. Obesity, which may be defined as an absolute *or relative* excess of body fat, may be due to overeating, and can be reversed if food intake is diminished. This fact may have obscured the true nature of obesity, which should be regarded as an entity rather than as a mere description of body weight. Obese individuals are prone to serious conditions such as diabetes and heart disease; *this may be true regardless of their weight.* Obesity is a complex disorder in which many endocrine glands and metabolic processes are implicated. Its study is inseparable from that of diabetes.

Certain lines of circumstantial evidence strongly suggest that there are inherent metabolic or endocrine factors implicated in the development of obesity. This particularly follows from the existence of a variety of types of obesity in animals, in which pair-feeding studies show that, even at 'normal' weight, the fat content of the body is increased. This is a sign of true obesity. Such types of obesity are (*i*) neurogenic following hypothalamic damage; (*ii*) hormonal, for example in Cushingoid states; (*iii*) physiological, for example pregnancy, pre-hibernation, or pre-migratory; (*iv*) in-bred, as in pigs or old dogs; (*v*) dietary; and (*vi*) mutant.

a. Studies in genetically obese hyperglycaemic mice

There are obvious limitations to the investigation of fundamental aspects of obesity in human subjects, hence increasing attention is being directed towards obesity in animals. Genetically obese mice or rats provide some of the most clearcut models of obesity. The most widely studied obese rodent is the homozygote for the abnormal recessive gene obese or *ob*. Such mice are diabetic, as shown by glucose tolerance studies (Beloff-Chain *et al.*, 1975), partly due to the relative inadequacy of the insulin action (Abraham and Beloff-Chain, 1971). The characteristics of genetically obese, hyperglycaemic rodents are described in several excellent review articles (Bray and York, 1971; Loten *et al.*, 1974).

Liver metabolism is altered in genetically obese, hyperglycaemic mice. For example the organ is hypertrophied, by a factor of about two. As obesity is a matter of fat, the role of the liver in fat synthesis must be considered. Obese mice may gain as much as 0.5 g/day of adipose tissue triglyceride. The rate of synthesis *de novo* of fatty acid from dietary non-fat precursors such as glucose, may exceed 1 g/day, since some fatty acid is burned by the mouse. Measurements of fatty acid synthesis with ^3H_2O have shown that most of this extra lipogenesis occurs in adipose tissue (Hems *et al.*, 1975*b*), although fatty acid synthesis is also enhanced in liver (Table 11.7; Salmon and Hems, 1973; Hems *et al.*, 1975*b*). Despite the fact that this fatty acid is synthesized ultimately from dietary glucose, the major precursors used by the liver in obese, hyperglycaemic mice are blood-borne lactate and glycogen, at least

Table 11.7 Metabolic characteristics of genetically obese, hyperglycaemic (*ob/ob*) mice

	Lean	Obese
Rates of fatty acid synthesis *in vivo* (μmole/g hr^{-1})		
liver, daytime	2	5
adipose tissue, daytime	1	2
liver, nighttime feeding	4	12
adipose tissue, nighttime feeding	3	3
liver, starved	1	2
Rates of metabolism in perfused liver (μmole/g min^{-1})		
gluconeogenesis from lactate (starved mice)	0·89	0·95
glucose released from glycogen	0·97	4·19
ketogenesis from oleate (starved mice)	0·67	0·52
Composition of liver		
total weight (g)	1·0–1·5	1·5–3·0
per cent fat	5–7	10
Turnover of substrates in blood (μmole/mouse min^{-1})		
triglyceride fatty acid	0·25	1·0
glycerol	0·31	1·13
free fatty acid	0·9	1·8
Half life of triglyceride removal from blood (min)		
fed mice	5–7	2·5–3·5
diet-restricted starved mice	7–8	2·7–3·3

Mean values are taken from Elliott *et al.* (1971, 1974), Salmon and Hems (1973), and Hems *et al.* (1975*b*).
Reproduced by permission of the Biochemical Society.

during times of net glycogen breakdown, but not blood-borne glucose (Salmon *et al.*, 1974; Hems *et al.*, 1975*b*). As would be expected from this inference, their hepatic glycogen synthesis and breakdown are both enhanced compared to matched lean controls (Abraham *et al.*, 1971; Elliott *et al.*, 1971; Das and Hems, 1974; Elliott *et al.*, 1974) whereas gluconeogenesis in liver is not significantly altered (Elliott *et al.*, 1971), except that there may be an enhancement from glycerol (Elliott *et al.*, 1974). In general, the alterations in carbohydrate metabolism in obese, hyperglycaemic mice appear to be secondary, in that they all return to normal after mild starvation.

There is also a range of alterations to lipid metabolism observed in genetically obese, hyperglycaemic mice. These include hypercholesterolaemia and excessive turnover in the plasma of triglyceride (Table 11.7: Salmon and Hems, 1973), free fatty acid, and glycerol (Table 11.7; Elliott *et al.*, 1974). A central process in these mice is the increased rate of conversion of plasma free fatty acid to hepatic triglyceride which is exported at an increased rate (Salmon and Hems, 1973) and enters fat and muscle (Rath *et al.*, 1974). These changes are not easily reversible by food deprivation, nor is their excessive lipogenesis (Hems *et al.*, 1975*b*).

Therefore, in seeking the inborn error in obese, diabetic mice, it is logical to consider an abnormality in lipid metabolism. The error could lie in the response of cells to catabolic hormones, as shown by experiments with vasopressin. Vasopressin can inhibit fatty acid synthesis in normal mouse liver (Ma and Hems, 1975) but in genetically obese mice this response is lacking even after severe food privation (Table 11.8; Hems and Ma, 1976). This abnormality in obese mice is one of the most irreversible yet to be observed. For a variety of

Table 11.8 Resistance to the inhibitory action of vasopressin on fatty acid synthesis in liver of genetically obese mice

| Mice | Vasopressin (mU/ml) | Number of perfusions | Fatty acid synthesis (μmole C_2 units/g in 2 hr) | | Glucose output (μmole/g min^{-1}) |
			Total	From [^{14}C]lactate	
Lean	Control	4	79	38	0·6
Lean	Vasopressin (4)	6	37	10	4·0
Diet-restricted obese	Control	7	46	19	0·6
Diet-restricted obese	Vasopressin (1)	3	45	18	2·1
Diet-restricted obese	Vasopressin (4)	3	40	19	3·6

Results are mean values from Hems and Ma (1976), and Ma and Hems (1975). Reproduced by permission of the Biochemical Society.

reasons discussed by Hems and Ma (1976), it appears warranted to regard this finding as representative of their inborn error. Thus, the lesion in obese mice may consist of an impairment within the cellular responses to extracellular effectors, which do not necessarily act through cyclic AMP. The action of vasopressin on liver, at least on glycogen breakdown, may involve extracellular Ca^{2+} (Stubbs *et al.*, 1976), so that the lesion in mice could involve cation transport systems. This conclusion has implications about cell reception processes in diabetes as well as in obesity, and should repay further investigation.

b. Insulin resistance, diabetes, and the liver

Genetically obese, hyperglycaemic rodents exhibit relative impairment of insulin actions in muscle and adipose tissue (Abraham and Beloff-Chain,

1971), and indeed provide an excellent model of the phenomenon of insulin resistance. The possibility arises that such insulin resistance can occur in liver in such diabetic animals. Indeed, the number of insulin receptors is diminished in the liver of obese mice (Soll *et al.*, 1975). However, it is unlikely that insulin resistance in the liver is of significance in obesity. Firstly, this concept implies that a clearcut direct insulin action has been demonstrated in normal liver, and then shown to be impaired in any so-called insulin-resistant state. No such studies have been reported because reproducible direct actions of insulin on hepatic metabolism are hard to obtain. Secondly, insulin resistance—hepatic or otherwise—would not be expected to lead to obesity, which is a state of overall excessive insulin action.

It is plausible that a degree of hepatic insulin resistance occurs in those diabetics with the non-obese, insulin-resistant form of the disease. For example, there might be failure of repression of enzymes of gluconeogenesis, (that is, failure of one of the more credible of the direct hepatic actions of insulin). However, such a sub-group of subjects has not been identified.

PROGNOSIS

If a degree of confusion has emerged from the preceding account of liver metabolism in diabetes, this may be partly attributable to the confusion of the subject, as well as to failure by the narrator! Some problems have been highlighted, such as (i) what does insulin do directly to the liver, (ii) how are inherent hepatic alterations brought about in the intact diabetic animal, (iii) what are the control processes of glycogen and glyceride metabolism, (iv) what is insulin resistance, and (v) how does insulin act on cells?

These topics should induce a high degree of occupancy, and occasional saturation, among biochemical endocrinologists at least for some time yet.

ACKNOWLEDGEMENTS

It affords me the deepest pleasure to pay tribute to Sir Ernst Chain, in his 70th year. He created the Department of Biochemistry at Imperial College virtually single-handed. By this achievement he provided the opportunity for many scientific novitiates to engage in one of the most pleasurable endeavours which man can enjoy—the unfettered pursuit of creativity. This is, of course, a largely delusional state, greatly vulnerable to extraneous threat. Sir Ernst posed no such threats, but on the contrary, allowed full rein to the imagination. I began to realize his qualities in this direction, from the earliest days of our acquaintance, when we agreed that diabetes might have little to do with glucose—or even insulin—and that control of enzymes in cells had little to do with enzymology!

My chance to carry out investigations, such as those described here, has also depended on the unfailing efforts of a group of magnificent colleagues. In particular, Drs. P. Whitton, G. Ma, and M. Salmon have shaped the tone and

234

endeavours of our laboratory. A special debt is owed to Terry Verrinder in our laboratory, many at Imperial College, and especially to David Green and David Spayne in the Animal Unit. If our experiments have been at all productive, this must reflect the influence of Sir Hans Krebs, who set a transcendental example at a time when I was perhaps even still receptive to it. Both Sir Ernst and Dr. Beloff-Chain helped so often at critical moments. For all this, no words could appropriately express my appreciation. Many happy returns indeed Sir Ernst; to the fray, on behalf of medical science.

REFERENCES

Abraham, R. R., and Beloff-Chain, A. (1971) *Diabetes*, **20**, 522.
Abraham, R. R., Dade, E., Elliott, J., and Hems, D. A. (1971) *Diabetes*, **20**, 535.
Alberts, A. W., Ferguson, K., Hennessy, S., and Vagelos, P. R. (1974) *J. Biol. Chem.*, **249**, 5241.
Alford F. P., Cook, P. S., and Reaven, G. M. (1975*a*) *Diabetologia*, **11**, 181.
Alford, F. P., Millia, M. E., Reaven, E. P., Shorenstein, R. G., and Reaven, G. M. (1975*b*) *Diabetologia*, **11**, 191.
Barling, P. M., and Beloff-Chain, A. (1973) *Horm. Metab. Res.*, **5**, 154.
Barnes, A. J., and Bloom, S. R. (1976) *Lancet*, *i*, 219.
Basso, L. V., and Havel, R. J. (1970) *J. Clin. Invest.*, **49**, 537.
Beloff-Chain, A., Bovet, D., Cantanzaro, R., Chain, E. B., Kohn, R., Masi, I., and Pocchiari, G. (1956*a*) *Sel. Sci. Pap., Ist. Super. Sanità*, **1**, 304.
Beloff-Chain, A., Catanzaro, R., Chain, E. B., Kohn, R., and Pocchiari, F. (1956*b*) *Sel. Sci. Pap. Ist. Super. Sanità*, **1**, 328.
Beloff-Chain, A., Catanzaro, R., Chain, E. B., Masi, I., and Pocchiari, F. (1956*c*) *Sel. Sci. Pap. Ist. Super. Sanità*, **1**, 293.
Beloff-Chain, A., Freund, N., and Rookledge, K. A. (1975) *Horm. Metab. Res.*, **7**, 374.
Birch, G. G., Lee, E. Y. C., and Hems, D. A. (1974) *Int. J. Biochem.*, **5**, 867.
Bloch, K., and Kramer, W. (1948) *J. Biol. Chem.*, **173**, 811.
Bray, G. A., and York, D. A. (1971) *Physiol. Rev.*, **51**, 598.
Chain, E. B., Beloff-Chain, A., and Pocchiari, F. (1956) *Sel. Sci. Pap., Ist. Super. Sanità*, **1**, 389.
Chernick, S. S., and Scow, R. O. (1959) *Am. J. Physiol.*, **196**, 125.
Chiasson, J. L., Liljenquist, J. E., Finger, F. E., and Lacy, W. W. (1976) *Diabetes*, **25**, 283.
Christensen, N. J. (1974) *Diabetes*, **23**, 1.
Christlieb, A. R., Assal, J. P., Katsilambros, N., Williams, G. H., Kozak, G. P., and Suzuki, T. (1975), *Diabetes*, **24**, 190.
Clark, D. G., Rognstad, R., and Katz, J., (1974) *J. Biol. Chem.*, **249**, 2028.
Claus, T. H., and Pilkis, S. J. (1976) *Biochim. Biophys. Acta*, **421**, 246.
Das, I., and Hems, D. A. (1974) *Horm. Metab. Res.*, **6**, 40.
de Dominicis, G. (1889) *Giorn. Intern. Sci. Med.*, p. 801.
Elliott, J., Dade, E., Salmon, D. M. W., and Hems, D. A. (1974) *Biochim. Biophys. Acta*, **343**, 307.
Elliott, J., Hems, D. A., and Beloff-Chain, A. (1971) *Biochem. J.*, **125**, 773.
Exton, J. H. (1971) *Metabolism*, **21**, 945.
Exton, J. H., Corbin, J. G., and Harper, S. C. (1972*a*) *J. Biol. Chem.*, **247**, 4996.

235

Exton, J. H., and Harper, S. C. (1975) *Adv. Cyclic Nucleotide Res.* **5**, 519.

Exton, J. H., Harper, S. C., Tucker, A. L., Flagg, J. L., and Park, C. R. (1973) *Biochim. Biophys. Acta*, **329**, 41.

Exton, J. H., Lewis, S. B., Ho, R. J., Robison, G. A., and Park, C. R. (1971*a*) *Ann. N.Y. Acad. Sci.*, **185**, 85.

Exton, J. H., Miller, T. B., Jr., Harper, S. C., and Park, C. R. (1976) *Am. J. Physiol.*, **230**, 163.

Exton, J. H., and Park, C. R. (1972) *Handbook of Physiology*, Section 7, Vol. 1, p. 437.

Exton, J. H., Robison, G. A., and Sutherland, E. W. (1972*b*) *Handbook of Physiology*, Section 7, Vol. 1, p. 425.

Exton, J. H., Robison, G. A. Sutherland, E. W., Park, C. R. (1971*b*) *J. Biol. Chem.*, **246**, 6166.

Fain, J. N. (1974) *M.T.P. Reviews, Biochemistry*, Series 1, Vol. 8, p. 1.

Fain, J. N., Tolbert, M. E. M., Pointer, R. H., Butcher, F. R., and Arnold, A. (1975) *Metabolism*, **24**, 395.

Felig, P. (1975) *Diabetes*, (Vallance-Owen, J., ed.), *Int. Rev. of Science*, M.T.P. Press, Butterworths, London, U.K., p. 93.

Felig, P., and Wahren, J. (1975) in *Contemporary Topics in the Study of Diabetes and Metabolic Endocrinology* (Shafrir, E., ed.), Academic Press, New York and London, p. 2.

Gellhorn, A., and Benjamin, W. (1966) *Adv. Enz. Regul.*, **4**, 19.

Glinsmann, W. H., Hern, E. P., and Lynch, A. (1969) *Am. J. Physiol.*, **216**, 698.

Glinsmann, W. H., and Mortimore, G. E. (1968) *Am. J. Physiol.*, **215**, 553.

Haft, D. E. (1967) *Am. J. Physiol.*, **213**, 219.

Haft, D. E. (1968) *Diabetes*, **17**, 244.

Hastings, A. B., Renold, A. E., and Teng, C. T. (1955) *Rec. Prog. Horm. Res.*, **11**, 381.

Heimberg, M., Wilcox, H. G., Dunn, G. D. Woodside, W. F., Breen, K. J., and Soler Argilaga, C. (1974) in *Regulation of Hepatic Metabolism*, (Lundquist, F., and Tygstrup, N., Pub.), Munksgaard, Copenhagen, p. 119.

Hems, D. A. (1975*a*) *Proc. Nutr. Soc.*, **34**, 225.

Hems, D. A. (1975*b*) *Enzyme*, **20**, 359.

Hems, D. A., and Brosnan, J. T. (1970) *Biochem. J.*, **120**, 105.

Hems, D. A., Harmon, C. S., and Whitton, P. D. (1975*a*) *FEBS Letters*, **58**, 167.

Hems, D. A., and Ma, G. Y. (1976) *Biochem. J.*, **160**, 23.

Hems, D. A., Rath, E. A., and Verrinder, T. R. (1975*b*) *Biochem. J.*, **150**, 167.

Hems, D. A., Rodrigues, L. M., and Whitton, P. D. (1976) *Biochem. J.*, **160**, 367.

Hems, D. A., and Whitton, P. D. (1973) *Biochem. J.*, **136**, 705.

Hems, D. A., Whitton, P. D., and Ma, G. Y. (1975*c*) *Biochim. Biophys. Acta*, **411**, 155.

Hems, D. A., Whitton, P. D., and Taylor, E. A. (1972) *Biochem. J.*, **129**, 529.

Hers, H. G., Stalmans, W., De Wulf, H., Laloux, M., and Hue, L. (1974) *Regulation of Hepatic Metabolism*, ed. Lundquist, F., and Tygstrup, N., Pub. Munksgaard, Copenhagen, p. 237.

Hue, L., Bontemps, F., and Hers, H. G. (1975) *Biochem. J.*, **152**, 105.

John, D. W., and Miller, E. E. (1969) *J. Biol. Chem.*, **244**, 6134.

Kirk, C. J., and Hems, D. A. (1974) *FEBS Letters*, **47**, 128.

Kirk, C. J., Verrinder, T. R., and Hems, D. A. (1976) *Biochem. J.*, **156**, 592.

Lardy, H. A., Zahlten, R. N., Stratman, F. W., and Cook, D. E. (1974). In *Regulation of Hepatic Metabolism*, ed. Lundquist, F., and Tygstrup, N., Pub. Munksgaard, Copenhagen, p. 19.

Long, C. N. H., Katzin, B., and Fry, E. G. (1940) *Endocrinology*, **26**, 309.

Loten, E. G., Assimacopolous-Jeannet, F., le Marchand, V., Singh, A., and Jeanrenaud, B., (1974) *Adv. Enz. Regul.*, **12**, 45.

Ma, G. Y., and Hems, D. A. (1975) *Biochem. J.*, **152**, 389.

McGarry, J. D., and Foster, D. W. (1972) *Metabolism*, **21**, 471.

236

McGarry, J., Robles-Valdes, C., and Foster, D. W. (1975) *Proc. Nat. Acad. Sci.*, *U.S.A.*, **72**, 4385.
McGarry, T. D., Wright, P. H., and Foster, D. W. (1974) *J. Clin. Invest.*, **55**, 1202.
Mackrell, D., and Sokal, J. E. (1969) *Diabetes*, **18**, 724.
Mahler, R., and Ashmore, J., (1962) *Endocrinology*, **71**, 673.
Maina, G., Kessler, R. J., and Green, D. E. (1975) *Biochem. Biophys. Res. Comm.*, **67**, 1567.
Meier, J., McGarry, J. D., Faloona, G. R., Unger, R. N., and Foster, D. W. (1972) *J. Lipid Res.*, **13**, 228.
Migliorini, R. H. (1972) *Acta Physiol.*, *Latin Amer.*, **23**, 642.
Migliorini, R. H., and Chaikoff, I. L. (1962) *Am. J. Physiol.*, **203**, 1019.
Mondon, C. E., and Burton, S. D. (1971) *Am. J. Physiol.*, **220**, 724.
Mondon, C. E., Dolkas, C. B., Olevsky, J. M., and Reaven, G. M. (1975) *Diabetes*, **24**, 225.
Nakajima, K., Matsutaka, H., and Ishikawa, E. (1970) *J. Biochem.*, *Tokyo*, **67**, 779.
Oelz, O., Froesch, E. R., Bunzli, H. F., Humbel, R. E., and Ritschard, W. F. (1972) *Handbook of Physiology*, Section 7, Vol. 1, p. 685.
Pain, V. M., and Garlick, P. J. (1974) *J. Biol. Chem.*, **249**, 4510.
Parrilla, R., Goodman, M. N., and Toews, C. J. (1974) *Diabetes*, **23**, 725.
Parrilla, R., Jiminez, I., and Ayuso-Parrilla, S. (1975) *Eur. J. Biochem.*, **56**, 375.
Penhos, J. C., Ezequiel, M., Lepp, A., and Ramey, E. R. (1975) *Diabetes*, **24**, 637.
Pilkis, S. J., Claus, T. H., Johnson, R. A., and Park, C. R. (1975) *J. Biol. Chem.*, **250**, 6328.
Pilkis, S. J., Exton, J. H., Johnson, R. A., and Park, C. R., (1974) *Biochim. Biophys. Acta*, **343**, 250.
Pilkis, S. J., and Park, C. R. (1974) *Ann. Rev. Pharmacol.*, **14**, 365.
Plas, C., and Nunez, J., (1976) *J. Biol. Chem.*, **251**, 1431.
Randle, P. J., Hales, C. N., Garland, P. B., and Newsholme, E. A. (1963) *Lancet*, *i*, 785.
Rath, E. A., Hems, D. A., and Beloff-Chain, A., (1974) *Diabetologia*, **10**, 261.
Reaven, E. P., and Reaven, G. M. (1974) *J. Clin. Invest.*, **54**, 1167.
Renold, A. E., Ashmore, J., and Hastings, A. B. (1956) *Vitam. Horm.*, **14**, 139.
Robertson, R. P., and Porte, D., Jr. (1973) *J. Clin. Invest.*, **52**, 870.
Salmon, D. M. W., Bowen, N. L., and Hems, D. A. (1974) *Biochem. J.*, **142**, 611.
Salmon, D. M. W., and Hems, D. A. (1973) *Biochem. J.*, **136**, 551.
Salmon, D. M. W., and Hems, D. A. (1974) *Biochem. Soc. Trans.*, **2**, 1011.
Salmon, D. M. W., and Hems, D. A. (1975) *Biochem. Soc. Trans.*, **3**, 510.
Salmon, D. M. W., and Hems, D. A. (1976) *Biochem. Soc. Trans.*, **4**, 659.
Scow, R. O. (1960) *Endocrinology*, **60**, 359.
Soll, A. H., Kahn, R., and Neville, D. M., Jr. (1975) *J. Biol. Chem.*, **250**, 4702.
Steiner, D. F. (1966) *Vitam. Horm.*, **24**, 1.
Stubbs, M., Kirk, C. J., and Hems, D. A. (1976) *FEBS Letters*, **69**, 199.
Sutherland, E. W., and Robison, A. (1969) *Diabetes*, **18**, 797.
Tan, A. W. H., and Nuttall, F. Q. (1976) *Biochim. Biophys. Acta*, **445**, 118.
Topping, D. L., and Mayes, P. A. (1972) *Biochem. J.*, **126**, 295.
Unger, R. H. (1971) *Diabetes*, **20**, 834.
Unger, R. H. (1976) *Diabetes*, **25**, 136.
Van Lan, V., Yamaguchi, N., Garcia, M. J., Ramey, E. R., and Penhos, J. C. (1974) *Endocrinology*, **94**, 671.
Volpe, J. J., and Vagelos, P. R. (1974) *Proc. Nat. Acad. Sci.*, *U.S.A.*, **71**, 889.
von Mering, J., and Minkowski, O. (1889) *Arch. exp. Path.*, **26**, 375.
Wagle, S. R., Ingebretsen, W. R., and Sampson, L., (1975) *Diabetologia*, **11**, 411.
Wagle, S. R., and Sampson, L. (1975) *Biochem. Biophys. Res. Comm.*, **64**, 72.
Weber, G., Trevisani, A., and Heinrich, C. (1974) *Adv. Enz. Regul.*, **12**, 11.
Whitton, P. D. and Hems, D. A. (1975*a*) *Horm. Metab. Res.*, **7**, 524.

Whitton, P. D., and Hems, D. A. (1975*b*) *Biochem. J.*, **150**, 153.
Whitton, P. D., and Hems, D. A. (1976*a*) *Biochem. J.*, **156**, 585.
Whitton, P. D., and Hems, D. A. (1976*b*) *Biochem. Pharmacol.*, **25**, 405.
Whitton, P. D., and Hems, D. A. (1977) *FEBS Letters*, **74**, 195.
Wilcox, H. G., Dishmon, G., and Heimberg, M. (1968) *J. Biol. Chem.*, **243**, 666.
Windmueller, H. G., and Spaeth, A. G. (1967) *Arch. Biochem. Biophys.*, **122**, 362.
Woodside, W. F., and Heimberg, M. (1976) *J. Biol. Chem.* **251**, 13.

12
Metabolic Approaches to Myocardial Infarction

K. R. L. Mansford

Beecham Pharmaceuticals Research Division, Betchworth, Surrey, U.K.

and

D. J. Hearse

Myocardial Metabolism Laboratory, The Rayne Institute, St. Thomas' Hospital, London, U.K.

INTRODUCTION

If the Western World were smitten by a new plague which affected approximately a million persons in the USA each year and which was responsible for 40 per cent of all deaths in men aged 45–54 years, there would be a public outcry for resources to be set aside, as a matter of urgency, for all possible means to stamp out this new scourge. Unfortunately, the new 'plague' is already in our midst in the form of ischaemic heart disease, and the alarming statistics reveal the immense toll in both human and economic terms brought about by this disease in modern society. The annual loss to the economy of the USA from heart disease has been calculated (by Felton and Cole) to be $4·2 billion. In recent years, publicity has been given to the problem and the middle-aged, obese, anxious, chain-smoking executive is urged to revolutionize his life style before the impending day of myocardial judgement. Until recently, the complete lack of success of attempts to halt the march of the disease has added considerable impetus to research aimed at understanding the biochemical processes affected by myocardial ischaemia and investigating possible approaches to myocardial protection.

Sir Ernst's interests in cardiac metabolism arose initially from his long fascination with the mode of action of insulin. Extensive studies using diaphragm muscle preparations were undertaken in the laboratories of Dr. Anne Beloff-Chain in Rome. Sir Ernst was irritated by the criticisms made of the results of these studies because of the 'unphysiological' nature of the diaphragm preparation with its cut edges and poor oxygenation of all but the outermost layers of cells. Fisher at Oxford had shown what could be achieved with a carefully controlled Langendorff perfused heart preparation, and Sir Ernst seized the opportunity provided by the opening of his new laboratories at

Imperial College to persuade one of the authors (K.R.L.M.) to embark upon a metabolic investigation of the influence of insulin on cardiac metabolism using perfused heart preparations.

The authors were most fortunate in having the opportunity of a very productive collaboration with Dr. Lionel Opie whose interests in bridging the gap between biochemical and clinical research found great support with Sir Ernst and led to studies involving anoxic and ischaemic heart preparations in attempts to mirror some of the facets of human ischaemic heart disease.

MYOCARDIAL OXYGEN DEPRIVATION AND TISSUE DAMAGE

An understanding of the natural history of myocardial ischaemia in biochemical, structural, and functional terms is a prerequisite for the rational investigation of the possibilities and limitations of myocardial cell protection. Current knowledge of myocardial ischaemia is derived from a multitude of studies using many different experimental models, and a wide variety of experimental animals. The resulting confusions of terminology and contradiction of results requires the clarification of a number of points.

a. Definitions

Oxygen deprivation

There are several ways by which oxygen deficiency can arise in the myocardium, resulting in anoxia, hypoxia, or ischaemia. A clear distinction between these conditions must always be made since each can have markedly differing metabolic and functional consequences. With hypoxia or anoxia, one is usually dealing with situations in which the coronary flow is normal (or possibly even increased) while tissue oxygen availability is decreased by reduction of the partial pressure of oxygen delivered to the tissue. Thus, although little (hypoxia) or no (anoxia) oxygen is being delivered to the tissues, the supply of substrates and the removal of toxic metabolites by the blood may be normal. In contrast, during myocardial ischaemia, which is the more frequently encountered clinical condition, the oxygen available to the tissue is reduced by the coronary flow to that tissue being restricted. Under these conditions the supply of substrates such as fatty acids and glucose, and the removal of metabolites, including lactate, H^+, and carbon dioxide, is limited similarly. Tissue ischaemia usually results from an absolute reduction in coronary flow rate. However, since ischaemia occurs as soon as the myocardial oxygen demand exceeds the oxygen supply, it can be induced under conditions of constant coronary flow by increasing the myocardial oxygen or energy demand.

Degree of ischaemia

The severity of ischaemia is determined by the extent to which the oxygen or energy demand of the tissue exceeds the supply. Complete tissue ischaemia rarely occurs since even following the complete occlusion of one or more coronary arteries the extensive capacity for collateralization of most mammalian hearts ensures significant coronary flow to the affected tissue. Under these conditions the tissue is not anoxic, and partial oxidation metabolism will contribute substantially to its survival.

Heterogeneity

Regional variations in coronary vasculature, differential reduction of blood supply and collateralization, the complex interdigitation of muscle fibres, and their varying work loads and energy demands render any area of ischaemia highly heterogeneous. Rapidly varying patterns of blood flow and work-load create a dynamic situation in which the ischaemic area can be seen as an ever changing 'patchy' complex in which areas of well-perfused tissue may be interspersed with, and be adjacent to, areas of severely ischaemic, damaged tissue. Despite the heterogeneity of any area it is often possible to define several zones of ischaemia. An area of severely reduced flow often represents the 'core' of the ischaemic tissue. It is this core which will most rapidly evolve through the process of myocardial infarction to an area of necrosis. Surrounding the core is a 'peripheral' area of tissue which although underperfused is less severely ischaemic. Cellular deterioration occurs at a much slower rate and the fate of this tissue may be determined by a number of complex factors. In many preparations, the core and periphery of the infarct are clearly defined by a sharply demarcated zone of cyanosis. Surrounding this area is the 'peri-infarct' zone; here the normally contracting tissue is well perfused—often hyperperfused. Distal to this area is an area which has been designated 'normal' myocardium.

Individual variation

The interpretation of any studies of myocardial ischaemia must be viewed in the light of known major species variations in susceptibility to tissue damage, response to various pharmacological interventions, and all the other variables imposed upon any model by such factors as sex, age, nutritional and hormonal status, the presence of disease processes, and so on.

Reversibility of damage

Immediately following the onset of myocardial ischaemia there occurs a number of metabolic, functional, electrophysiological, and structural changes. As has been so clearly defined by Jennings and his colleagues, and by a number of other workers, these changes are initially reversible such that if normal coronary flow is restored a complete functional recovery is possible. As the duration or intensity of ischaemia increases, tissue damage becomes more severe and recovery takes longer. However, beyond a certain point, the restoration of flow no longer consistently reverses injury, the cells then enter a phase of irreversible damage, and the tissue dies and becomes necrotic. A detailed understanding of the characteristics of reversible and irreversible damage, and the transition between these two states is crucial in order to provide effective myocardial protection. Clearly, irreversibly damaged tissue will not respond to protective interventions, but reversibly damaged regions represent an area of enormous potential for the reduction of ischaemia-induced tissue damage. Evolving from this field is a large number of terms such as 'blighted' (irreversibly damaged), 'jeopardized' or 'twilight' tissue (reversibly damaged), 'salvage' (reduction of tissue damage), and from the work of the laboratories of Braunwald, Shell, Sobel, Maroko, and many others has grown the concept of the 'reduction (and occasionally the extension) of infarct size'.

THE NATURE OF ISCHAEMIC DAMAGE

Myocardial ischaemia initiates a multitide of cellular changes; virtually every aspect of cellular metabolism, especially carbohydrate, fatty acid, and protein metabolism is affected by the lack of oxygen and impending energy deficit. Major electrophysiological and contractile changes occur, and there are also changes in cellular ultrastructure. The time of onset of these changes and the extent to which they may be reversed is dependent upon a number of factors such as the severity and duration of ischaemia and the nutritional status of the species under study. Figure 12.1 depicts a few of the many changes which are known to occur following the onset of myocardial ischaemia. It also attempts to ascribe an approximate sequence for their occurrence and suggests a possible point for the transition between reversible and irreversible damage in severely ischaemic cells. The figure is highly speculative as is the suggested timescale of events which should be taken as very approximate.

Immediately following the onset of ischaemia, there is a precipitous decline in contractile activity, probably associated with the disturbance of intracellular ionic shifts, in particular those for Ca^{2+}. Within 10 seconds, the myocardium becomes cyanotic and noticeably cooler. Electrocardiographic changes occur during the first minute or so, for example alterations in ST-segment evolve over the first few minutes during which time contraction virtually ceases. Dissolved oxygen is depleted within seconds and there is a striking reduction in oxidative metabolism, electron transport, and hence ATP production. Utilization of creatine phosphate and ATP stores is initiated, and sensitive metabolic controls stimulate glycolysis and glucose transport. Increased glycolytic flux and possible extracellular glucose depletion leads to the mobilization and utilization of intracellular glycogen stores, a process which is further stimulated by catecholamine release. Also during the early minutes of ischaemia, substrate

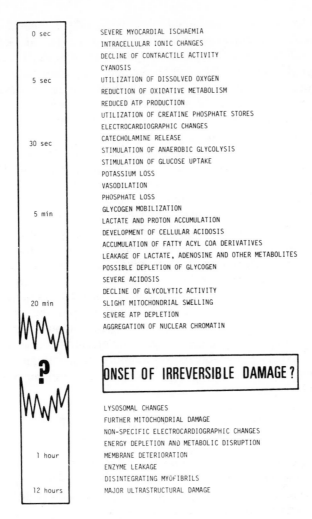

0 sec	SEVERE MYOCARDIAL ISCHAEMIA
	INTRACELLULAR IONIC CHANGES
	DECLINE OF CONTRACTILE ACTIVITY
	CYANOSIS
5 sec	UTILIZATION OF DISSOLVED OXYGEN
	REDUCTION OF OXIDATIVE METABOLISM
	REDUCED ATP PRODUCTION
	UTILIZATION OF CREATINE PHOSPHATE STORES
	ELECTROCARDIOGRAPHIC CHANGES
	CATECHOLAMINE RELEASE
30 sec	STIMULATION OF ANAEROBIC GLYCOLYSIS
	STIMULATION OF GLUCOSE UPTAKE
	POTASSIUM LOSS
	VASODILATION
	PHOSPHATE LOSS
5 min	GLYCOGEN MOBILIZATION
	LACTATE AND PROTON ACCUMULATION
	DEVELOPMENT OF CELLULAR ACIDOSIS
	ACCUMULATION OF FATTY ACYL COA DERIVATIVES
	LEAKAGE OF LACTATE, ADENOSINE AND OTHER METABOLITES
	POSSIBLE DEPLETION OF GLYCOGEN
	SEVERE ACIDOSIS
	DECLINE OF GLYCOLYTIC ACTIVITY
20 min	SLIGHT MITOCHONDRIAL SWELLING
	SEVERE ATP DEPLETION
	AGGREGATION OF NUCLEAR CHROMATIN

? ONSET OF IRREVERSIBLE DAMAGE ?

	LYSOSOMAL CHANGES
	FURTHER MITOCHONDRIAL DAMAGE
	NON-SPECIFIC ELECTROCARDIOGRAPHIC CHANGES
	ENERGY DEPLETION AND METABOLIC DISRUPTION
1 hour	MEMBRANE DETERIORATION
	ENZYME LEAKAGE
	DISINTEGRATING MYOFIBRILS
12 hours	MAJOR ULTRASTRUCTURAL DAMAGE

Figure 12.1 Some cellular changes known to occur following the onset of severe tissue ischaemia. The exact sequence of events, time course, and point of transition between reversible and irreversible damage should be viewed as highly speculative

uptake and utilization patterns may alter, especially those of free fatty acids which may accumulate intracellularly as their fatty acyl-CoA derivatives (which may interfere with the translocation of energy from residual mitochondrial ATP production). Membrane control deteriorates; during the first few minutes a loss of intracellular K^+, Mg^{2+}, and inorganic phosphate is observed, and there is a cellular uptake of Na^+. In an attempt to increase oxygen availability, a marked vasodilation and an increase in the efficiency of oxygen extraction from any limited coronary flow occur. As a result of increased glycolytic flux, reduced mitochondrial activity, and decreased metabolite removal, there is a cellular accumulation of lactate and H^+, and a consequent fall of intracellular pH. The rapid development of intracellular acidosis from accumulated H^+, and possibly carbon dioxide, may contribute to the early decline or subsequent failure of contractile activity. This failure has a conservative effect upon cellular ATP supplies. However even with this reduced requirement and the increased glycolytic ATP production, the demand exceeds the supply, and a further fall in cellular ATP levels is observed; a process which is soon accelerated by a lactate and acidosis-induced decline of the transiently activated glycolytic process. In addition, during the first 10–15 minutes, ultrastructural changes may begin to be evident; mitochondria may exhibit slight swelling and a cellular oedema may occur.

It is generally accepted that all the changes so far described, which probably occur during the first 20 or 30 minutes of severe ischaemia, are reversible. If, however, the ischaemia is maintained for longer periods, then the restoration of flow no longer consistently reverses injury and the cell enters a phase of irreversible damage. Considerable evidence now suggests that reperfusion may even extend the injury. Under these conditions a further swelling and malfunction of mitochondria, a loss of matrix density, and the appearance of intramitochondrial granules are observed. Major lysosomal alterations occur, non-specific electrocardiographic changes are detected, there is severe depletion of ATP, extensive metabolic disruption occurs, membranes deteriorate, and macromolecules such as cytoplasmic enzymes leak from the cell and can be detected in the blood.

THE CONCEPT OF THE PROTECTION OF THE ISCHAEMIC MYOCARDIUM

Since the size of an infarct is an important determinant of morbidity as well as mortality, streneous efforts have been made to devise ways of reducing the ultimate size of an evolving infarct (Table 12.1). Two basic phenomena would suggest that such an objective is at least feasible.

(*i*) Numerous potentially deleterious changes (described in the previous section) are known to occur in the ischaemic myocardium. Having identified and defined these changes it is highly probable that interventions can be designed to combat them.

(*ii*) The heterogeneity between adjacent areas with varying degrees of ischaemia, with their inherently different rates of tissue deterioration, means that at any time, as well as irreversibly damaged tissue, there may also be a significant amount of potentially salvageable tissue. This jeopardized myocardium may deteriorate very slowly and may remain in a state of fine balance between ultimate death or effective recovery for a long time, requiring only a very slight influence to determine its fate. Substantial amounts of tissue may possibly remain in this state for many hours thereby extending the time during which any intervention may be effective.

Table 12.1 Preservation of the ischaemic myocardium

(*i*) Reduce myocardial energy or oxygen demand
    Reduce contractility
    Reduce afterload
    Reduce heart size
    Reduce fatty acid utilization
    Reduce peripheral demand

(*ii*) Increase myocardial energy or oxygen supply
    Increase coronary flow
    Increase oxygen delivery
    Modify substrate utilization or metabolism

(*iii*) Miscellaneous approaches
    Osmotic control
    Steroids and membrane stabilization
    Cellular pH control

As Braunwald and colleagues, Scheidt and many other authors have revealed, there now exists a very large number of interventions suggested for the reduction of infarct size. These procedures vary widely and may be based on metabolic manipulation, or the use of various drugs or surgery. For the convenience of discussion these interventions can be considered to fall into one of the categories listed in Table 12.1.

a. Reduction of myocardial energy demand

Factors determining myocardial oxygen or energy demand include intraventricular tension, heart rate, stroke volume, inotropic state, and systolic ejection time. Any decrease in these or associated parameters should reduce oxygen demand and may help to restore the metabolic balance of the tissue.

The use of various β-blockers to reduce contractility, and hence oxygen demand, has been shown to be effective in a number of clinical and experimental studies. However, this procedure cannot be used in patients with congestive failure or shock. Myocardial oxygen requirements can also be reduced by reducing cardiac afterload. This can be achieved by the use of peripheral vasodilators, such as nitroprusside. Alternatively, the surgical technique of intra-aortic balloon counter pulsation may be used for this purpose. A third approach is reducing heart size with diuretics. In the failing heart, digitalis has also been used. Although digitalis increases oxygen consumption in the normal heart, in the failing heart the net effect is a reduction of heart size and a slowing of heart rate resulting in a decrease in wall tension and myocardial oxygen consumption. The P:O ratio, and hence the number of molecules of ATP produced per atom of oxygen consumed, is lower when fatty acids, as opposed to carbohydrates, are the substrates for myocardial energy production. The use of various measures to reduce plasma fatty acid levels, thus avoiding the relative energy wastage associated with fatty acid metabolism, has been reported in a number of studies and will be discussed in greater detail below. A final rather indirect approach which has been proposed is the use of hypothermia in order to reduce the peripheral demand.

b. Increase of myocardial energy supply

Perhaps the most obvious approach is to attempt to increase coronary flow. This has been achieved with considerable success using agents which specifically induce coronary vasodilation. It has also been suggested that coronary flow may be increased by surgical revascularization during the acute phase of myocardial infarction. Such an approach, however, although successful in patients with long-term ischaemic heart disease and angina, has attracted some criticism when applied to myocardial infarction. Criticism has arisen due to the increased risks associated with surgery in a seriously ill patient, the possibility that revascularization may occasionally extend infarcts, and the general lack of convincing evidence that the technique and the reperfusion of previously ischaemic tissue leads to any net tissue salvage. It has also been proposed that coronary flow may be increased using agents which increase coronary perfusion pressure such as noradrenaline. This procedure is of debatable value since the simultaneous increase in contractility and oxygen demand may negate the value of the increased perfusion pressure. Furthermore, it must be questioned whether any increased coronary flow may be confined to the normal areas of the myocardium. Other than use of specific coronary vasodilators, perhaps the greatest increase in coronary flow derives from the development of collateral circulation.

It may be possible to increase the myocardial energy supply without altering the coronary flow by increasing the amount of oxygen which is delivered to the tissue. The use of hyperbaric oxygen has attracted a great deal of attention. At two atmospheres pressure of pure oxygen it is possible to increase the oxygen-carrying capacity of the blood by almost 20 per cent. However, the technique is both difficult and expensive; also the possibility of oxygen toxicity effects should not be underestimated. An alternative lies in the development of haemoglobin substitutes with increased oxygen-carrying capacity. Some of these compounds are already available and they may assume some importance in the future. Again, it is possible theoretically to increase oxygen delivery by shifting haemoglobin–oxyhaemoglobin dissociation curves, but the clinical value of such an approach has not been tested.

A totally different approach to the problem of increasing the myocardial energy supply has been one of the major topics of cardiac biochemistry investigated at Imperial College by Sir Ernst Chain and his colleagues, Mansford, Opie, and Hearse. In common with many other laboratories throughout the world, and workers such as Neely, Morgan, Kubler, Brachfeld, Bing, Wollenberger and Oliver, the belief has been strongly held that myocardial energy availability might be increased either by modifying substrate utilization patterns through the provision or removal of certain substrates in the coronary blood, or by activating or inactivating metabolic pathways in order to optimize cellular energy production. Table 12.2 lists some of these methods which will be discussed in detail in the next section.

Table 12.2   Approaches to the preservation of the ischaemic myocardium

a. Glucose potassium insulin regime
b. Free fatty acids and anti-lipolytic agents
c. Dichloroacetate and pyruvate metabolism
d. Catecholamines and β-adrenergic blockade
e. Calcium and calcium antagonists
f. Oxygen supply and coronary flow
g. Extracellular ATP and creatine phosphate and adenine nucleotide conservation
h. Osmolality, diffusion, and permeability changes
i. Glycogen, pH, and anaerobic ATP—miscellaneous interventions

METABOLIC AND PHARMACOLOGICAL INTERVENTIONS

a. Glucose–insulin–potassium

The therapeutic use of glucose in heart disease has been propounded since the early part of the century. Büdingen produced a remarkable rationale in 1914 based on the role of glucose as a myocardial substrate. He also suggested the correlation between glycogen depletion and various forms of heart disease. The addition of insulin to the glucose therapy was a natural consequence of the studies carried out on the effects of the hormone on glucose uptake by cardiac muscle. Evans and colleagues made the important observation in 1933, using the heart–lung preparation, that during deprivation of oxygen the heart took up more glucose and there was production of lactate in contrast to the normal lactate uptake. The addition of K^+ to glucose–insulin therapy came in the 1950s following observations of increased coronary venous K^+ concentrations in blood leaving the ischaemic myocardium. Sayle, Bajusz, Raab and their collaborators stressed the possible role of the K^+ loss in promoting heart-cell necrosis. The full polarizing regime of glucose–insulin–K^+ (GIK) was actively promoted by Sodi-Pallares in 1962.

Large-scale clinical studies have been organized to confirm the findings of Sodi-Pallares, but with conflicting results. A multicentre trial organized by the Medical Research Council failed to show any improvements in patients with acute myocardial infarction treated with GIK. Opie has criticized this trial on several grounds: the doses of glucose, insulin, and K^+ used were low compared with those theoretically and experimentally desirable; not all patients with myocardial infarction need necessarily benefit from the GIK therapy; and those patients in whom deficient glucose utilization by the heart might be anticipated should be selected. This group would include those with a poor insulin secretion rate, with a diabetic tendency, or with a very high circulating free fatty acid level.

Recent developments have aroused new interest in the benefits of this combined therapy. Regan has shown that GIK reverses cumulative K^+ loss from the ischaemic myocardium and greatly reduces the incidence of ventricular tachycardia and fibrillation. Maroko and colleagues showed the effect of GIK in decreasing infarct size in dogs following experimental coronary artery occlusion. Opie has shown in baboons that GIK given within the first hour of coronary arterial ligation, improves levels of high-energy phosphate compounds in the infarcting myocardium. More recently, Opie has also demonstrated that GIK infused into dogs over six hours increases cardiac glycogen, raises ATP and creatine phosphate in the infarcted zone, and improves the K^+/Na^+ ratio (indicative of reduced necrosis) in the border zone.

Apart from these animal studies with experimental ischaemia, the work of Opie, Mansford, Chain and Hearse and many others using perfused rat hearts underlines the importance of anaerobic glycolysis in providing ATP, thus 'protecting' the myocardium from the metabolic consequences of oxygen deprivation. In the well-perfused myocardium, the beneficial effects of GIK have been readily demonstrated. In severely ischaemic tissue, there is evidence of the initial rapid acceleration of glycolysis being followed by inhibition of phosphofructokinase, probably as a result of accumulation of H^+. Similar results have been obtained in the whole heart model by Neely's group. However, as the depletion of glycogen continues even in central infarction zones, glycolytic flux must presumbably continue. Moreover, in the milder ischaemic tissue, glucose is accessible and glycolysis is probably both aerobic and anaerobic with insulin able to influence the former in favour of increased glycolytic flux. In acute myocardial infarction, Allison has reported insulin resistance and a circulating insulin level inappropriately low in relation to the elevated blood sugar. The possibility of insulin also having effects independent of glucose must be considered in view of reports of enhanced membrane polarization in skeletal muscle and of inhibition of lysosomal activity in hypoxic heart tissue. Recently, Russell and co-workers have claimed that GIK infusion in patients with acute myocardial infarction with symptoms of less than 12 hours duration results in a significant reduction of hospital mortality of 52 per cent.

A further argument on the possible mechanisms of action of GIK is the possible interaction with lipid metabolism. GIK given to patients with acute myocardial infarction reduces circulating free fatty acid possibly by inhibiting lipolysis. The increased glycolytic flux produces an increase in α-glycerophosphate which is then available for re-esterification of intracellular free fatty acids that accumulate in ischaemia. The desirability of reducing concentrations of free fatty acids is discussed in the next subsection.

These effects taken together suggest that it is time to reassess the use of GIK in myocardial infarction despite overenthusiasm of earlier workers and one negative trial organized by the Medical Research Council. More needs to be understood about the separate contributions of the components so that the best combination of protective agents can be predicted and then tested in carefully selected patients.

b. Free fatty acids

Concentrations of free fatty acids (FFA) in blood are elevated markedly in acute myocardial infarction. Increased catecholamine activity mediating lipolysis in adipose tissue is the probably cause of this. Plasma FFA may be elevated beyond the concentration at which they are carried by the two principal binding sites on albumin (a 2:1 molar ratio is exceeded when plasma FFA levels are greater than 1200 μEq/l). As the FFA:albumin ratio increases, fatty acids are bound progressively more weakly to albumin and their entry into the cell is enhanced. Oliver has postulated a direct arrhythmogenic action due to these elevated FFA cellular concentrations, whereas Opie using similar levels of FFA (but a higher level of serum albumin) was unable to provoke arrhythmias. The clinical situation is equally controversial. In four studies, patients with the highest circulating FFA concentrations were found to be more likely to have serious arrhythmias or other complications, but five other studies failed to confirm this association.

The evidence for the involvement of FFA in other metabolic effects relating to myocardial infarction is less controversial. High FFA levels reduce contractility of hypoxic rat papillary muscle and the isolated ischaemic rat heart. Myocardial enzyme release from rat hearts with coronary arterial ligation is several times greater with palmitate in the perfusate than with glucose or glucose plus insulin. There is also evidence that catecholamines can sensitize the heart to the effects of FFA. Thus FFA levels of approximately 1400 μEq/l during isoprenaline infusion were associated with higher ST-segment elevation than seen during triglyceride–heparin infusion in which concentrations of FFA exceeded 3000 μEq/l. The explanation for this sensitization could be in the recent observation by Mathur and Mokler that catecholamines increase myocardial FFA uptake. Alternatively, the proposed triglyceride–FFA cycle in heart may include a catecholamine-sensitive lipase which could yield elevated tissue FFA and glycerol. No convincing evidence has yet been presented however for increased amounts of FFA in ischaemic myocardium.

The possible effect of elevated FFA on mitochondrial metabolism, involving uncoupled respiration and increased oxygen uptake by the heart, is not yet adequately supported by experimental data. However, in the well-perfused rat heart, Challoner and Steinberg showed a 40 per cent increase in oxygen uptake when FFA was the sole substrate. Recently, Shug and Shrago have drawn attention to an additional mechanism for impaired ATP production. The intracellular FFA can readily be activated to long-chain esters (acyl-CoA). If acyl-CoA accumulates in ischaemia it inhibits the translocase mechanism by which mitochondria in the heart take up ADP and discharge ATP. This inhibition can be reversed by carnitine.

The crucial test of the hypothesis that FFA is 'toxic' to the heart is the ability of measures which reduce FFA to benefit the ischaemic myocardium. Kjekshus has found that pretreatment of animals with β-pyridylcarbinol, an antilipolytic agent, reduces ST-segment elevation after coronary artery ligation. Recently this observation has been followed up with similar results in man. Rowe and Oliver have provided preliminary evidence that antilipolytic therapy can reduce the incidence of ventricular tachycardia in patients provided that such therapy is started within five hours of the symptoms appearing.

c. Dichloroacetate and the control of glycolysis

The utilization of glucose by the heart involves the glycolytic sequence in which phosphofructokinase and pyruvate dehydrogenase are the key enzymes subject to inhibition by the oxidation of fatty acids and ketone bodies. The mechanisms of this inhibition may involve accumulation of citrate (for phosphofructokinase) and conversion to an inactive form or end-product inhibition by acetyl-CoA accumulation (for pyruvate dehydrogenase). 2-Bromo-fatty acid derivatives have been shown to inhibit palmitate oxidation via inactivation of carnitine acyltransferase. However, these derivatives also lead to interference with ATP synthesis and the cessation of muscular contraction, thus they are not suitable for clinical use.

An alternative approach has arisen from an observation that di-isopropyl-ammonium dichloroacetate raises the respiratory quotient in alloxan-diabetic rats, suggesting an increase in glucose oxidation. Randle and co-workers then showed that in perfused rat heart utilizing acetate, dichloroacetate directly increases pyruvate oxidation by activating pyruvate dehydrogenase from a phosporylated inactive form. Since this activation leads to a change in the proportion of glucose utilized by the heart and to a decrease in the utilization of FFA, it is of interest to see if dichloroacetate can benefit the infarcted myocardium. Recent evidence from Oliver's group indicates that this may be the case.

d. Catecholamines and β-blockers

Acute myocardial infarction is accompanied by acute release of catecholamines. The resulting urinary excretion of catecholamine and blood levels are very similar to those observed in severe emotional stress. The blood levels of both adrenaline and noradrenaline are thought to have an important influence on the regulation of circulating FFA concentration (see subsection b). Serious arrhythmias have also been linked with elevated urinary catecholamine excretion in acute myocardial infarction patients. Experimentally, catecholamine infusions can precipitate arrhythmias even four days after coronary arterial ligation. The metabolic response of the ischaemic area to catecholamines appears to be dose related; using very small subpressor doses, the loss of K^+ and inorganic phosphate is prevented and ST-segment elevation is decreased, while at higher doses however, these beneficial changes are reversed, and necrosis may be exacerbated.

In attempts to counteract the effects of catecholamines, the β-adrenergic antagonist propanolol has been given to dogs after coronary artery ligation. This results in decreased ST segment elevation and reduced tissue necrosis. When given intravenously to patients with recent acute myocardial infarction, propanolol (0·1 mg/kg) decreases metabolic damage as indicated by improved lactate extraction. Propanolol also decreases the affinity of haemoglobin for oxygen at low tensions which might result in a greater release of oxygen in hypoxic tissues. β-Blocking drugs are not equal in their effects on cardiac ischaemia or hypoxia. Nayler claims that in the hypoxic rabbit heart model, the ultrastructural changes, loss of creatine phosphokinase and rise in intracellular Ca^{2+} are not affected by d-propanolol (the potent β-blocking isomer). A dimethyl-quaternary analogue of propanolol (UM-272) is not, however, a β-blocker but like propanolol, it reduces the ST-segment elevation in dogs during ischaemia.

It is obviously beneficial to control the inotropic effect of excess catecholamines on an ischaemic myocardium in which oxygen delivery is reduced and mitochondrial function impaired. There are dangers however, associated with the use of β-blockade in patients in which left ventricular failure may complicate the situation. The inotropic and chronotropic effects of low concentrations of catecholamines may in fact be critically important in the early stages of acute myocardial infarction. Oliver has suggested that a specific β-blocker, which only prevents the activation of adipose tissue lipolysis by catecholamines, would be of considerable interest. Opie advocates the co-administration of an antilipolytic agent if low doses of catecholamines are used as inotropic agents in specific circumstances, such as cardiogenic shock. This treatment would hopefully control the FFA elevation and minimize the risk of arrhythmias and of ultimate functional deterioration of the myocardium.

e. Calcium and calcium antagonists

Ca^{2+} functions as a transmitter substance to transfer the excitation 'message' from the membrane surface of the cardiac fibre in order to initiate the intracellular contractile elements. During excitation, therefore, there is a rapid increase in the intracellular concentration of free Ca^{2+} which initiates the hydrolysis of ATP by the Ca^{2+}-dependent ATPase of the myofibrils so that the high energy of the phosphate bond is transformed into mechanical work. Thus, the mechanical activity of the excited myocardium can be completely abolished by removal of Ca^{2+}, without any major impairment of the excitatory process. Many substances produce an inotropic effect by either enhancing Ca^{2+} action or interfering with it. During the last 10 years more than 30 drugs with clear Ca^{2+}-antagonistic side effects have been described by Fleckenstein. These include β-blockers, antiarrhythmics, barbiturates, and local anesthetics. The most interesting development, however, has been the emergence of a group of extremely potent Ca^{2+} antagonists which can inhibit excitation–contraction coupling in a highly specific way which is currently thought to be *via* the blocking of special Ca^{2+} channels in the mammalian cardiac muscle fibre membranes. The simultaneous movement of Na^+ which is connected with the action potential is not affected by these specific Ca^{2+}-antagonists (verapamil, D600—a methoxy derivative of verapamil—and nifedipine). In contrast, local anaesthetics lack this Ca^{2+} specificity and may interfere more with Na^+ movements than with Ca^{2+} transfer into the myocardium, for example, prenylamine has partial specificity towards Ca^{2+} but also reduces the Na^+ inward current somewhat.

Since less ATP is consumed under the influence of Ca^{2+}-antagonists because of depression of ATPase activity, high-energy phosphates accumulate in the cardiac muscle. Cardiac oxygen requirements are reduced therefore because the consumption of ATP strictly determines the rates of glycolysis and respiration. Catecholamines, particularly isoprenaline have been shown to bring about excessive Ca^{2+} uptake and precipitous falls in the high-energy phosphate content of heart muscle. The Ca^{2+} antagonists have been shown to protect the heart against the effects of an overdose of catecholamines. In this connection, it is interesting that KCl and $MgCl_2$ when given orally are also capable of inhibiting the excessive Ca^{2+} influx brought about by isoprenaline, explaining the important results of Selye and Bajusz who discovered the beneficial influence of K^+ and Mg^{2+} salts in preventing experimental cardiac fibre necroses (see subsection a).

In man, the Ca^{2+} antagonists have important antiarrhythmic effects; for example verapamil has been shown to be an effective agent in reducing the ventricular rate in atrial fibrillation. In as far as the described metabolic effects of isoprenaline resemble some of the metabolic consequences of ischaemia—Ca^{2+} influx and loss of ATP—one could predict that Ca^{2+} antagonists might be beneficial to the ischaemic myocardium. Nayler has shown that verapamil reduces creatine phosphokinase release during hypoxic perfusion of rabbit hearts. Also, both verapamil and prenylamine have been claimed to be beneficial in cases of angina pectoris. In isolated preparations, however, many of the Ca^{2+} antagonists show a pronounced negative inotropic action on the myocardium. While this is moderated *in vivo* by other actions of these compounds, such as coronary and peripheral vasodilation, any interference with contractility in the early stages of acute myocardial infarction should be viewed with concern. Not all antiarrhythmic drugs can be considered beneficial to the ischaemic heart. Bretylium tosylate—advocated by Sanma as an antifibrillation agent—has been shown by Braunwald to increase the severity and extent of myocardial injury following acute coronary occlusion.

Procaine and lignocaine do not show the same specific Ca^{2+} antagonistic activity as verapamil and nifedipine, but they do prevent arrhythmias, stabilize cell membranes to conserve tissue K^+, and decrease infarct size in coronary ligatured heart preparations (see also later experimental use of procaine).

f. Coronary flow and oxygen supply

As discussed earlier in this review, the extent of the infarcted zone can be determined by the size of the imbalance between energy supply and energy demand. Thus, drug interventions which reduce oxygen consumption, such as propranolol, practolol, nitroglycerine, and anti-lipolytics all reduce ischaemic injury following coronary-artery occlusion. Conversely, isoprenaline, bretylium, glucagon, and tachycardia increase the oxygen requirement and exacerbate myocardial injury.

An alternative approach is to attempt to increase the oxygen supply by (*i*) increasing arterial pressure, which may influence the perfusion pressure of the coronary arteries, and consequently increase the collateral flow to the ischaemic myocardium; (*ii*) increasing the concentration of oxygen in the inspired gas mixture; or (*iii*) redistribution of blood flow by altering total systemic and/or coronary vascular resistance.

Each of these approaches has been attempted. Elevation of coronary perfusion pressure using methoxamine, neosynephrine, or noradrenaline has been claimed to show some beneficial effects under carefully controlled conditions, including co-administration with nitroglycerine. The combination of nitroglycerine and phenylephrine is claimed by Epstein to benefit acute myocardial infarction patients as judged by a diminution in ST-segment elevation.

The use of enriched oxygen mixtures to elevate the arterial pO_2 has been described by Maroko in experimental coronary ligation. Also, the possibility has been raised that the oxygen effects may be additive to those of pharmacological and biochemical interventions.

The alteration of coronary flow is a two-edged sword. Minoxidil, which reduces total systemic and coronary vascular resistance, can lead to the so-called 'steal' phenomenon in which, despite a several-fold increase in blood supply to the non-ischaemic myocardium, the regional blood flow to both the peripheral and central ischaemic zones declines. This can bring about an increase in ischaemic injury. On the other hand, nitroglycerine alone can redistribute the flow in the ischaemic area more favourably. Nitroprusside has also been used in this connection, but is claimed by Epstein to differ from nitroglycerine in being a more potent dilator of coronary and systemic arterioles, whereas nitroglycerine is more effective in decreasing coronary collateral flow resistance. In patients with heart failure, nitroprusside appears to improve the haemodynamics, whereas in experimental dogs without heart failure, nitroprusside decreases collateral flow and increases injury in coronary artery occlusion.

Nifedipine, like nitroglycerine, has a relaxant effect on spiral strip preparations of the large epicardial coronary artery of the pig, whereas dipyridamole, carbochromen, and theophylline appear only to dilate the small coronary resistance vessels. However, the action of dipyridamole, carbochromen, and hexobendine may be *via* their effects on potentiation of the vasodilator effects of adenosine, the concentration of which rises during ischaemia. Unlike nitroglycerine, prenylamine and nifedipine do not appear to act significantly to dilate veins, thus with concomitant arterial dilatation it is possible for the nifedipine group of coronary dilators to increase venous return and hence increase right atrial pressure.

g. Exogenous high-energy phosphates and preservation of nucleotides

Isolated reports dating from the mid 1950s have suggested that exogenous ATP can improve contractility in hypodynamic hearts, although there is apparently no effect when the ATP is administered during an anaerobic phase. ATP added to the coronary circulation of perfused guinea-pig hearts is broken down to ADP, AMP, and finally to adenosine. Consequently, the ATPase and the 5'-nucleotidase are apparently leached out of the cardiac muscle by the perfusing fluid. Adenosine produced can be taken up into cardiac muscle by facilitated diffusion and can subsequently be phosphorylated and enter the ATP pool (or pools). There is also some evidence of a rise in cyclic AMP leading to increased myocardial glycolysis. Parratt and Marshall showed that the anoxia-induced decrease in myocardial contractility is less marked in the presence of 0.118 mM ATP. Similar effects have been seen with creatine phosphate, albeit at much higher concentrations (at which ATP produces a negative inotropic effect). Since creatine alone is ineffective and NaH_2PO_4 potentiates the decrease in contractility, Parratt and Marshall were forced to conclude that exogenous high-energy phosphate bonds could influence cellular events. Wollenberger showed that loss of glycogen and creatine phosphate from the isolated hypothermic dog heart could be minimized by direct injection of ATP into the coronary arteries. Using ATP labelled with both ^{14}C and ^{32}P Wollenberger concluded that at a pH of five or less and under hypothermic conditions, ATP could penetrate the cells, probably as ADP and AMP, and influence regulatory cell processes. The importance of the pH lies in the sensitivity of the Lohmann reaction

$$ATP + creatine \rightleftharpoons ADP + creatine\ phosphate$$

with the equilibrium being strongly displaced to ATP and creatine formation at pH values of less then seven. An alternative approach, is the use of xanthine oxidase inhibitors, such as allopurinol, to prevent the breakdown of nucleosides and purine bases to uric acid. De Wall and his colleagues showed that allopurinol reverses or prevents ST-segment elevation and exhibits prolonged antiarrhythmic effects in animals with acute myocardial infarction. Part of the effect observed may have been due to the coronary dilation effect of adenosine. This is consistent with the recent results of Furuse *et al.* who showed that administration of allopurinol produces a significant increase in blood flow in unobstructed coronary arteries, but in ischaemic myocardium this drug diminishes myocardial pO_2, thereby aggravating myocardial hypoxia by the steal phenomenon. Kubler has reported interesting results with dipyridamol, which inhibits the degradation of adenine nucleotides by as much as 80 per cent. Dipyridamol also functions as a coronary vasodilator, but has been claimed by several authors to be ineffective in patients with coronary heart disease. The clinical world appears to be equally divided over the activity or inactivity of coronary vasodilators, and over the significance of the steal phenomenon as it affects coronary circulation to the critical ischaemic area.

h. Interventions involving osmolarity, diffusion and/or permeability changes

As Willerson, Leaf, Brachfeld, and others have stressed, osmotic factors may be very important because ischaemic tissue rapidly becomes oedematous, and cellular and subcellular swelling occurs rapidly leading to myocardial damage. In addition to the effect of cell swelling on the firmness of the ventricular wall and on myocardial membrane tensions, the effect on capillary endothelial cells can be critical. Such swelling may cause the trapping of blood elements thereby further reducing blood flow, resulting in a secondary ischaemia which may potentiate the initial damage.

The use of hypertonic mannitol in dogs to improve ventricular function, to increase both total and collateral coronary blood flow, and to reduce ST-segment elevation during experimental acute myocardial ischaemia is well-documented. Mannitol also prevents mitochondrial swelling in hypoxic and ischaemic myocardial cells, and reduces the cellular swelling seen during hypoxia in the isolated Langendorff rat heart.

Hyaluronidase increases diffusion through the extracellular space thereby facilitating delivery of substrates to ischaemic cells. Maroko and Braunwald have shown that, in experimental coronary artery occlusion, hyaluronidase decreases myocardial ischaemic injury substantially. It produces a dramatic reduction in ST-segment elevation; a sparing effect on myocardial creatine phosphokinase activity has also been observed. Encouraging preliminary clinical results with hyaluronidase in acute infarction patients have also been reported recently.

Following coronary artery occlusion, necrosis which can be observed after 20 minutes, proceeds to develop for many hours. During this period several factors may contribute to the increase in capillary permeability, intestinal oedema, leukotaxis, phagocytosis, and cell membrane disruption which follow the initial anoxic damage.

The use of hydrocortisone to prevent lysosomal leakage and to stabilize other cell membranes has been shown in dogs to limit myocardial ischaemic injury. However, patients given methylprednisolone seven hours after the onset of symptoms showed deleterious changes indicative of an increased infarct size and an increased incidence of arrhythmias. Steroids undoubtedly can be shown to have an effect upon cell membranes; there is a number of studies in which enzyme leakage has been reduced, and lysosomal latency and sedimentability have been improved. However, this highlights the importance of determining whether these steroids (or any other potential protective agent under investigation) have any effect upon cell viability. It should be noted that the reduction of major enzyme release or the maintenance of lysosomal latency, which may possibly be associated with the irreversible damage, may not necessarily be indicative of tissue salvage.

A related approach, based on attempts to limit the inflammatory reactions following myocardial ischaemic cell damage, has led to the study of cobra venom factor. This enzymically cleaves C_3 to prevent the effects of the complement system which can result in release of leukotactic factors leading to an increase in capillary permeability and intestinal oedema. Similarly, the effects on experimental infarct size of aprotinin, an inhibitor of the kallikrein system, have been studied since the kallikrein system may enhance leukotactic activity, capillary permeability, interstitial oedema, and proteolytic activity. Both cobra venom factor and aprotinin show beneficial effects in the dog preparation with an occluded coronary artery. However, no report of successful clinical application of these two agents has appeared to date.

i. Miscellaneous metabolic interventions

It is known that glycogen stores afford some protection to the ischaemic myocardium. Scheuer *et al.* have shown that a significant elevation of cardiac glycogen can improve mechanical resistance to anoxia. However, under normal conditions myocardial glycogen reserves are small and can be rapidly exhausted. While methods do exist for increasing these stores, in order to be effective it would be necessary that this stimulation be carried out in the as yet unidentifiable 'pre-infarction' state. Even then it would appear that the additional protection afforded would be of very limited duration.

It is generally believed that there is no ATP production in mitochondria in the absence of oxygen. However, a number of workers have described experiments in which hearts were anoxically perfused with high concentrations of certain citric acid cycle intermediates, for example fumarate, malate, and oxaloacetate. It was reported that anoxic beating and post-anoxic recovery were enhanced. A pathway has also been described which would allow for mitochondrial ATP production under these anerobic conditions. At the present time, however, it would appear that this approach is of little quantitative importance.

The control of cellular pH offers an interesting approach to the protection of the ischaemic myocardium. As Scheuer has concincingly shown in the hypoxic rat heart, either a respiratory alkalosis of pH 7·8 induced by a lowered pCO_2, or a similar metabolic alkalosis induced by bicarbonate is able to confer considerable protection upon ventricular function and post-hypoxic recovery. This approach, together with the role of pH in cell damage, undoubtedly warrants further investigation.

MYOCARDIAL PROTECTION DURING OPEN HEART SURGERY WITH ISCHAEMIC ARREST: A POLYPARAMETRIC APPROACH

In the preceding section, a number of interventions has been described. In most instances this has been aimed at the amelioriation of a single aspect of ischaemic damage. However, since myocardial ischaemia initiates a multitude of biochemical changes and since these changes are not necessarily related, it would seem unlikely that they could be combated with a single intervention—however efficacious that intervention might be. For this reason, studies at Imperial College on myocardial protection have been orientated to a more broadly based study. In this 'polyparametric' approach to the maintenance of cell welfare, Hearse, Chain and their collegues have evaluated a variety of potentially protective interventions, each aimed at a different aspect of cell damage. Approaches considered included interventions which affect trans-membrane and cellular ionic balance, metabolic activity, energy production, electrophysiological activity, metabolic rate, cell swelling and pH, and metabolite degradation. Stimulated by discussions with, and the work of, Braimbridge and his surgical colleagues at St. Thomas' Hospital, it was decided to direct these studies away from the classical regional ischaemia which occurs in chronic heart disease or acute myocardial infarction to the transient but very severe global ischaemia which is often induced in man during open-heart surgey.

Open-heart surgery with cardiopulmonary bypass requires a still and relaxed heart. Cardiac arrest, otherwise known as cardioplegia, in diastole can be induced by a number of procedures which may or may not require coronary perfusion. While few workers would question the metabolic and morphological advantages of maintaining coronary perfusion throughout the period of arrest, the simplicity and practical advantages of non-perfusion methods has resulted in the widespread use of ischaemic arrest. Since many surgeons, by necessity or choice, utilize ischaemic arrest (induced by aortic cross clamping), often for longer than an hour, and since during this time extensive myocardial damage may occur, it seemed to be of considerable importance to devise and evaluate an effective procedure for myocardial protection under these conditions.

For a number of years, several workers, notably Bretschneider, Kirsch and their colleagues, have advocated the infusion of various solutions into the coronary vessels just prior to the induction of ischaemia. it was suggested that following aortic cross clamping, these solutions are trapped, for a time at least, in the vascular bed and may afford an element of protection to the ischaemic tissue. It seemed that this would be an ideal situation for a polyparametric approach to myocardial protection. The isolated perfused working rat heart preparation appeared to provide an ideal testing ground.

a. Experimental model

Although many differences exist between the isolated perfused rat heart and the human heart *in situ*, there have been many studies in which the former

258

preparation has yielded results of direct relevance to the human heart. The
metabolic patterns of the rat heart preparation are similar to those of the
human heart, especially when allowance is made for the higher heart rate,
cardiac output, and oxygen consumption of the former.

The model, devised by Neely and colleagues, which has been extensively
described in the literature, is essentially a left-heart preparation in which
oxygenated perfusate enters the cannulated left atrium at a pressure of 20 cm
H_2O. Fluid is then passed to the left ventricle, where it is spontaneously ejected
via the aortic cannula against a hydrostatic pressure of 100 cm H_2O. Coronary
flow exits from the right heart, and if required can be pooled and recirculated
with the aortic outflow. If provided with sufficient oxygen and substrate, this
preparation will work effectively for many hours.

Cardiac bypass may be simulated by clamping both the atrial and aortic
cannulae. Under these conditions a globally ischaemic preparation is pro-

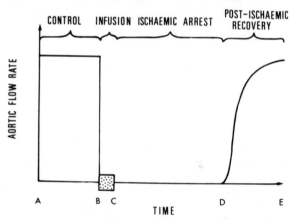

Figure 12.2 Experimental time course. Hearts are
mounted on the apparatus at time A. Between times A
and B (pre-ischaemic control period) hearts are allowed
to work aerobically with an adequate supply of substrate
(glucose, 10 mM) for 20 minutes in Krebs bicarbonate
buffer. During this period control values for aortic flow
rate (illustrated), heart rate, coronary flow rate, and
aortic pressure are obtained. At time B the heart is
bypassed, the aorta is clamped and aortic flow falls to
zero. Between B and C, (2 minutes) various protective
solutions are infused into the coronary bed via the root
of the aorta. At time C the infusion is terminated and the
heart is maintained at 37°C, or at any desired degree of
hypothermia, for a fixed period of ischaemia. At time D
atrial perfusion is resumed and the heart is allowed to
recover. Recovery is monitored between D and E, and is
expressed as a percentage of the pre-ischaemic control
value.

duced. Coronary infusion of cardioplegic or protective solutions may be accomplished *via* the root of the aorta with the aid of a suitable side arm on the aortic cannula.

b. Experimental time course

The time course is expressed diagrammatically in Figure 12.2. The percentage recovery obtained by this procedure can be related to the duration and severity of ischaemia and the nature of the protective infusate introduced prior to ischaemia.

c. Protective action of various infusates

Initially, and in order to provide a comparative baseline, hearts were infused *via* the root of the aorta with a substrate-free infusion medium containing no protective agents. The hearts were then subjected to ischaemia for 30 minutes at 37°C. The results (Table 12.3) reveal that upon reperfusion the hearts failed to recover greater than 3 per cent of their control aortic flow.

Table 12.3 The effect of various coronary infusates upon recovery of hearts from 30 minutes of ischaemia

Infusate composition	Recovery of aortic flow (per cent)
Buffer	3.0 ± 1.2
Buffer + 16 mM K^+ (chloride)	29.9 ± 8.0
Buffer + 16 mM K^+ (aspartate)	28.1 ± 7.6
Buffer + 16 mM K^+ (citrate)	11.1 ± 5.4
Buffer + 16 mM K^+ (chloride) + 16 mM Mg^{2+}	68.1 ± 5.7
Buffer + 7.4 mM procaine	26.6 ± 10.4
Buffer + 16 mM K^+ + 16 mM Mg^{2+} + 10 mM glucose	66.5 ± 8.1
Buffer + 16 mM K^+ + 16 mM Mg^{2+} + 10 mM glucose + insulin (0.01 I.U./ml)	65.8 ± 3.1
Buffer + 16 mM K^+ + 16 mM Mg^{2+} + 10 mM ATP	86.8 ± 0.9
Buffer + 16 mM K^+ + 16 mM Mg^{2+} + 10 mM ATP + 10 mM CP + 7.4 mM procaine	93.1 ± 1.0
Buffer + 16 mM K^+ + 16 mM Mg^{2+} + 10 mM ATP + 10 mM CP + 7.4 mM procaine + hypothermia (30°C)	97.4 ± 0.7

Number of experiments in each group = 6.
CP = creatine phosphate.

Myocardial ischaemia initiates a number of deleterious changes in cellular ionic balance, for example the loss of intracellular K^+. In the first series of experiments, it was investigated whether alteration of the ionic composition of the extracellular fluid is able to protect the ischaemic myocardium. Hearts were therefore subjected to a pre-ischaemic infusion for two minutes with a variety of solutions containing elevated concentrations of K^+, Mg^{2+}, citrate, and/or aspartate. All of these ions have been suggested to afford protection to the ischaemic myocardium. The results (Table 12.3) revealed that the infusion of potassium chloride(16 mM) improved the post-ischaemic recovery from 3 per cent to almost 30 per cent. If the potassium chloride was replaced by potassium aspartate the recovery did not vary, but if potassium chloride was replaced by potassium citrate the recovery was approximately 11 per cent. If the concentration of magnesium chloride, in addition to that of potassium chloride, was increased to 16 mM, then the recovery was dramatically improved to almost 70 per cent.

These results illustrate the marked protective action of K^+ and also of Mg^{2+}, and show that their effects are additive. This protection is probably due to their ability to reverse unfavourable ionic losses and to induce rapid cardiac arrest, thus conserving the limited supplies of energy available during ischaemia for cellular maintenance and protection. Contrary to the suggestions of Bretschneider and Kirsch, the inclusion of aspartate does not significantly improve protection. The inclusion of citrate, which may have a potential damaging effect through its ability to chelate Ca^{2+} and inhibit energy production, reduces significantly the protection afforded by K^+.

Procaine has been suggested as an effective cardioplegic agent and may possibly also act as a protective agent through its rapid induction of arrest and prevention of ischaemic beating. The ability of residual procaine to combat any rhythmic disturbances during recovery may add to its potential value. The results in Table 12.3 reveal that if hearts are infused with a solution containing 7·4 mM procaine protection can be improved from 3 per cent to almost 27 per cent.

In addition to protecting the ionic and electrical aspects of the ischaemic cell, a number of studies have been directed towards the metabolic activity of the cell, particularly in relation to energy production. It is clearly of interest to investigate whether glucose in combination with insulin and K^+ is able to protect the ischaemic heart. Initially hearts were infused with a solution containing 16 mM K^+ and Mg^{2+} with or without glucose and insulin. The results (Table 12.3) reveal that the inclusion of glucose (10 mM) results in a reduction of recovery from $68·1 \pm 5·7$ per cent to $66·5 \pm 8·1$ per cent. The additional inclusion of insulin (0·01 I.U./ml) results in a further fall to $65·8 \pm 3·1$ per cent. While this fall is not statistically significant, the inclusion of glucose and insulin clearly does not improve recovery in this particular situation, and therefore these compounds were not included in subsequent infusates.

The protective properties of extracellular high-energy phosphates were investigated. In a series of studies, ATP (10 mM) was included in the high Mg^{2+}, high K^+ infusate. This increased the recovery to $86·8 \pm 0·9$ per cent (Table 12.3). In further studies, the protective properties of creatine phosphate and procaine were evaluated. The results are positive and indicate that the protective actions of both of these compounds are additive to those of Mg^{2+},

K^+, and ATP. In this way, hearts which would normally recover to only 3 per cent of original values after 30 minutes of normothermic ischaemia can be made to recover to $93 \cdot 1 \pm 1 \cdot 0$ per cent simply by the inclusion of ATP (10 mM), creatine phosphate (10 mM), procaine (7·4 mM), Mg^{2+} (16 mM), and K^+ (16 mM) in the infusate. This recovery can be further improved by including an element of moderate hypothermia, thus maintaining the myocardium at 30°C for the duration of ischaemia permitted a recovery of almost 100 per cent.

The striking protective effects of hypothermia and the relationship between protection and degree of hypothermia were illustrated in a series of studies in which isolated working rat hearts were infused with a protective solution containing K^+, Mg^{2+}, ATP, creatine phosphate and procaine. Various degrees of hypothermia (4–37°C) were maintained for 60 minutes. The hearts were then allowed to recover at 37°C; the results are shown in Figure 12.3. As the temperature of the myocardium during ischaemia falls from 37°C to 4°C there is a progressive increase in recovery from 0 per cent to 96 per cent.

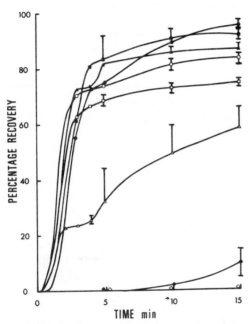

Figure 12.3 Degree of hypothermia against recovery of aortic flow. Hearts were perfused prior to ischaemia with a solution containing 12 mM K^+, 16 mM Mg^{2+}, 10 mM ATP, 10 mM creatinine phosphate, and 1·0 mM procaine. The hearts were subjected to ischaemia for 60 minutes at various degrees of hypothermia (●), 4°C; (■), 12°C; (▲), 20°C; (○), 25°C; (□), 28°C; (△), 30°C; (◆), 33°C; (◇), 37°C. Each point represents the mean for six hearts and the bars represent the S.E.M.

The results of these studies illustrate several points. Firstly, that tissue damage during severe whole-heart ischaemia, such as occurs during open-heart surgery, can be extremely detrimental to the heart, but by the use of appropriate interventions this damage can be substantially reduced. Secondly, the most effective protection can only be achieved by simultaneously combating the several unrelated deleterious changes which occur during ischaemia. In this way, the infusion of an appropriate multicomponent solution into the heart prior to ischaemia can permit hearts, which would otherwise be rendered almost completely non-functional, to recover almost 100 per cent of their capability. Thirdly, from these and other studies which the authors have undertaken, it is suggested that effective protection during ischaemic cardiac arrest can be resolved into two components: the rapid induction of complete arrest, and the amelioration of various deleterious ischaemia-induced changes.

With reference to the rapid induction of cardiac arrest, although immediately following the onset of myocardial ischaemia there is a reduction of contractile activity, some contraction continues for several minutes and may recur later. Cardioplegic agents, such as K^+ and procaine, induce and maintain immediate cardiac arrest, thereby conserving vital cellular energy supplies for the maintenance of morphological and biochemical integrity, and subsequent functional recovery.

The second component of effective protection relies on the ability, in theory at least, of certain compounds to combat one or more of the deleterious changes which occur as a result of tissue ischaemia. K^+ and Mg^{2+} may exert their protective effect by reducing intracellular ionic losses. Procaine, like K^+, in addition to inducing rapid cardiac arrest, may exert a protective action by reducing the incidence of dysrhythmias during the recovery period. The effects of intracellular ATP and creatine phosphate are of particular interest. As described earlier, it is commonly held that cell membranes are impermeable to high-energy phosphates, but there have been several reports in the literature suggesting that ATP is in fact able to cross the muscle cell membrane. Whether the extracellular high-energy phosphates enter the cell or whether they act on the cell membrane is unknown, but their protective effect is striking and, most significantly, is additive to that of K^+, Mg^{2+}, and procaine.

Finally, topical hypothermia for the duration of ischaemia, through its ability to reduce metabolic rate, energy consumption, and degradative processes can be a powerful adjunct to the protective action of various infusates. The greater the degree of hypothermia the greater the protection.

These results are, of course, limited to observation in the rat heart, but in collaborative studies with the cardiac surgeons at St. Thomas' Hospital it has been possible to apply the findings obtained in the isolated rat heart at Imperial College to human hearts during surgery. Preliminary results using carefully formulated infusates would suggest that the human myocardium responds very well to this form of metabolic protection.

In conclusion, it is now possible to gain considerable encouragement from a variety of recent studies in patients with ischaemic heart disease. The knowledge gained from fundamental observations of the control of metabolism in isolated rat heart preparations may be of clinical significance in minimizing the morbidity and mortality of this modern 'plague'. Sir Ernst must obtain great satisfaction from seeing how in this field, like so may others with which he has been associated, the precept 'biological observation first biochemical explanation second' has proven to be a rewarding strategy.

BIBLIOGRAPHY

Bing, R. J. (1965) *Physiol. Rev.*, **45**, 171.

Brachfeld, N. (1974) *Bull. N.Y. Acad. Med.*, **50**, 261.

Bretschneider, H. J. (1964) *Ver. Dsch. Ges. Kneislanfforsch*, **30**, 11.

Chain, E. B., Mansford, K. R. L., and Opie, L. H. (1969) *Biochem. J.*, **115**, 537.

Hearse, D. J., Stewart, D. A., and Braimbridge, M. V. (1975) *Circul. Res.*, **36**, 481.

Hearse, D. J., Stewart, D. A., and Braimbridge, M. V. (1976) *Circulation*, **54**, 193.

Hearse, D. J., Stewart, D. A., and Chain, E. B. (1974) *Circul. Res.*, **35**, 448.

Jennings, R. B., and Ganote, C. E. (1974) *Circul. Res.*, **34**, Suppl. 3, 156.

Kirsch, U., Rodewald, G., and Kalmar, P. (1972) *J. Thorac. Cardiovas. Surg.*, **63**, 121.

Kjekshus, J. K. (1976) *Acta Med. Scand.*, **199**, Suppl. 587, 35.

Kones, R. J. (1975) *N.Y. State J. Med.*, **75**, 1463.

Kubler, W., and Spieckermann, P. G. (1970) *J. Mol. Cell. Cardiol.*, **1**, 351.

Leaf, A. (1973) *Circulation*, **48**, 455.

Maroko, P. R., and Braunwald, E. (1976) *Circulation*, **53**, Suppl. I, 162.

Maroko, P. R., Kjekshus, J. K., Sobel, B. E., Watanabe, T., Covell, J. W., Ross, J., and Braunwald, E. (1971) *Circulation*, **43**, 67.

McAllister, A., Allison, S. P., and Randle, P. J. (1973) *Biochem. J.*, **134**, 1067.

Mjøs, O. D., Kjekshus, J. K., and Lekven, J. (1974) *J. Clin. Invest.*, **53**, 1290.

Neely, J. R., Liebermeister, H., Battersby, E. J., and Morgan, H. E. (1967) *Am. J. Physiol.*, **212**, 804.

Neely, J. R., Rovetto, M. J., Whitner, J. T., and Morgan, H. E. (1973) *Am. J. Physiol.*, **225**, 651.

Oliver, M. F. (1974) *Adv. Cardiol.*, **12**, 84.

Opie, L. H. (1968) *Am. Heart, J.*, **76**, 665.

Opie, L. H. (1969*a*) *Am. Heart J.*, **77**, 120.

Opie, L. H. (1969*b*) *Am. Heart J.*, **77**, 383.

Opie, L. H. (1975) *Am. J. Cardiol.*, **36**, 938.

Opie, L. H., Mansford, K. R. L., and Owen, P. (1971) *Biochem. J.*, **124**, 475.

Opie, L. H., and Mansford, K. R. L. (1971) *Eur. J. Clin. Invest.*, **1**, 295.

Scheuer, J., and Stezoski, S. W. (1972) *J. Mol. Cell. Cardiol.*, **4**, 599.

Shell, W. E., and Sobel, B. E. (1974) *N. Eng. J. Med.*, **291**, 481.

Sobel, B. E. (1975) *Adv. Cardiol.*, **15**, 86.

Sodi-Pallares, D. (1969) *Ann. N.Y. Acad. Sci.*, **156**, 603.

Willerson, J. T., Watson, J. T., Hutton, I., Fixler, D. E., Curry, G. C., and Templeton, G. H. (1975) *J. Clin. Invest.*, **55**, 892.

Wollenberger, A., and Krause, E. (1968) *Am. J. Cardiol.*, **22**, 349.

DISCUSSION

Dr. A. Dixon

One is reminded of Sydney Ringer's experiments. Dr. Hearse, did you try Ca^{2+}?

Dr. D. Hearse

Yes, if calcium is removed from the heart it immediately stops beating. Thus, at first sight calcium depletion would appear an excellent way to arrest a heart during surgery. However, as we and others have shown, such an action is extremely dangerous since upon re-admission of calcium tremendous cellular damage is observed. In this so called 'calcium paradox' the sudden influx of calcium ions to the cell, especially to the mitochondria, causes immense ultrastructural damage and irreversibly injures the cell to such an extent that it is no longer able to beat. This damage can be extremely rapid, occurring within 30 seconds of the re-admission of calcium and after as short a period as 3 minutes calcium-free perfusion.

The alteration of the extracellular concentration of various ions, particularly calcium, magnesium, potassium, and sodium, is currently being used as an effective means for arresting the heart during cardiac surgery. However, as we now realize with calcium and as cardiac surgeons found 20 years ago with high concentrations of potassium, these alterations must be carefully controlled and fully understood or the consequences may be disastrous.

13
Metabolism and Transmitter Function of Amino Acids in the Nervous System

H. F. Bradford

Department of Biochemistry,
Imperial College of Science and Technology, London, U.K.

NEUROCHEMISTRY AT IMPERIAL COLLEGE

It was the long-standing interest of Sir Ernst, Anne Beloff-Chain, and their colleagues in defining the link between overall patterns of glucose and energy metabolism in the different tissues and their special functions which led to the establishment of a neurochemistry group within the Medical Research Council Metabolic Reactions Research Unit at Imperial College (Chain 1965). Since certain amino acids feature as strongly in the mainstream energy metabolism of the nervous system as they do in other tissues they have naturally formed a central part of any consideration of brain metabolism in relation to brain function. It was during studies aimed in this direction that the Chains demonstrated the relatively rapid formation of γ-aminobutyrate (GABA) from glucose in brain (Beloff-Chain *et al.*, 1955). This compound was previously well known in micro-organisms but not in animal tissues. Although it is now known that the kidney produces small amounts of GABA (Whelan *et al.*, 1969) it remains a substance characteristic of nervous rather than other tissues and is present in substantial quantities (250 nmole/g tissue). In spite of this, it was not until 1950 that GABA was first detected in the vertebrate neural system (Roberts and Fraenkel, 1951).

The interest in the role of amino acids in brain function has continued to be a main theme in neurochemistry at Imperial College. The need to establish fast, sensitive, and automatic methods for their assay which are capable of coping with large numbers of samples was met by Dr. Alan Thomas and has resulted in the development during the period 1967–73 of a new kind of amino acid autoanalyser, which is now available commercially as the Rank–Hilger Chromaspek. This instrument currently completes one cycle of analysis and regeneration in 60 minutes, and can measure fluorometrically in the 1–50 pmole range using 100 μl of sample. In addition, it carries on-line data processing and radioactivity counting facilities. The high speed and sensitivity of this autoanalyser has greatly facilitated the progress of the author's research

266

on both *in vitro* and *in vivo* release, and metabolism of amino acids in the nervous system. The instrumentation and electronics group, headed by Dr. Thomas from 1967, has been a strong feature of the Biochemistry Department since its inception in 1964.

AMINO ACIDS IN MAINSTREAM METABOLISM

The ready formation of alanine, aspartate, glutamate, glutamine, and GABA by transamination or decarboxylation of products from glycolytic or citric acid cycle activity has focused interest in these amino acids in the brain. The high levels of glutamate in the brain compared with other organs such as liver, and the occurrence of GABA, initiated speculation on the special roles these compounds might have. The high levels of glutamate appear to be linked to the similarly high levels of 2-oxoglutarate found in brain. This, in turn, may be understood in terms of the kinetics of the oxidation systems, since the K_m value for oxidation of pyruvate is one-tenth that for 2-oxoglutarate, whereas in

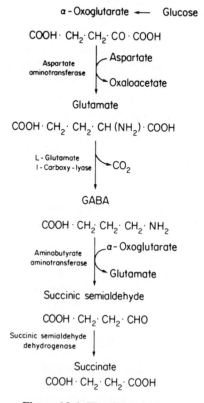

Figure 13.1 The GABA-shunt pathway

the liver mitochondrial oxidation system these values are of equivalent magnitude (Balazs *et al.*, 1964). The so-called GABA-shunt pathway is a special modification, or epicycle, of the citric acid cycle in brain and kidney, and its activity is 100-fold greater in brain tissue. The shunt pathway is unfavourable in energy terms since diverting the flow from the main cycle at 2-oxoglutarate and returning it at succinate (Figure 13.1) leaves out the formation of ATP from succincyl-CoA. Thus, the GABA shunt in brain must have selective value in evolutionary terms and this is most likely resident in the properties of GABA itself. It is, for instance, not only an extremely good brain mitochondrial substrate through its linkage to the citric acid cycle, but also a potent inhibitory agent and almost certainly functions as a major inhibitory synaptic transmitter. Glutamate and aspartate (Lee *et al.*, 1974) are also good mitochondrial substrates and no doubt provide immediate stores of ketoacid in times of short-term need by the citric acid cycle when restricted availability of glucose or pyruvate threatens rates of mitochondrial oxidation. These amino acids, in contrast to GABA, are, of course, actively involved in protein and peptide synthesis in the brain as well as in several other biosynthetic pathways.

AMINO ACIDS IN NEUROTRANSMISSION

The probable involvement of several of these simple, universally essential compounds as chemical mediators at the majority of synapses in the nervous system has been the most radical development in amino acid neurochemistry of the past 15–20 years. It was the Japanese neurochemist Hayashi who first proposed that glutamate and GABA merited serious consideration as neurotransmitters. This suggestion was based on these amino acids' extensive and potent actions when applied to the brain *in vivo* (Hayashi, 1954).

On common sense grounds, this suggestion did not seem very likely since neurotransmitters would seem best fitted for their task when they are rather specialized molecules, not themselves involved in other major metabolic activities in the neurone and present only in small quantities in the localized regions of the nerve terminal. These appeared, after all, to be the characteristics of acetylcholine and noradrenaline, although it is now clear that the catecholamines are widely distributed throughout their neurones in low concentration (Falk *et al.*, 1962). Amino acids, however, are present in most neural tissue cells at overall concentrations several orders of magnitude greater than those of acetylcholine or the catecholamines, and, because of their high potency, these are levels far in excess of those required for neurotransmission. The case for the participation of glutamate, GABA, and glycine in neurotransmission in both invertebrate and vertebrate nervous systems is now extremely persuasive (see Curtis and Johnston, 1974), and there is a vast literature on their neuropharmacological potency (Curtis and Watkins, 1965). The other amino acids currently strongly indicated as neurotransmitters are aspartate, and taurine.

The criteria used to establish the participation of a substance as the chemical transmitter at a defined synapse include the following.

(*i*) It should be both present and enzymically synthesized in the presynaptic neurones.

(*ii*) It should be released from the presynaptic neurone by a quantitized and Ca^{2+}-dependent mechanism.

(*iii*) Mechanisms for its rapid inactivation should exist in or close to the synapse.

(*iv*) When applied to the post-synaptic neurone, in the region of the synapse, it should mimic the electrical effects of the natural transmitter observed during neurotransmission.

(*v*) Pharmacological agents which interact with the synaptically released transmitter should interact with the suspected transmitter in an identical manner.

In practical terms criteria *iv* and *v* are fundamental, and have often been the initial observations providing the focus of interest. Positive results for these two criteria tend to lay the foundation for a strong case, but it is left to neurochemistry for confirmation through application of the remaining criteria.

a. Neurochemical evidence

Studies on release

A central problem when studying release of substances which are in a freely-soluble state in the cytoplasm is the possibility of artefactual release by cell damage. This is to some extent overcome by (*i*) requiring that the release is Ca^{2+}-dependent if it is to be attributed to synaptic activity, (*ii*) searching for a common releasing action of several treatments known to initiate synaptic activity, and (*iii*) demonstrating a selectivity in the release of the soluble compounds. For instance, both electrical pulses and K^+-induced depolarization should ideally cause release of the amino acid transmitter candidate from the preparation employed.

A second problem arises because of the high concentration and ubiquity of the amino acids in all the cellular compartments of nervous tissue. This is in contrast to the low concentrations and neuronal localization of acetylcholine and catecholamines, and consequently greatly diminishes the certainty with which one can ascribe the source of the released amino acids to synaptic regions of whole tissue preparations. However, useful indications of a transmitter role for glycine (Hopkin and Neal, 1971), glutamate, GABA (Katz *et al.*, 1969), and taurine (Kaczmarek and Davison, 1972) have come from studies of their release from cerebral cortex or spinal cord slices. Also, the isolated retina (Starr and Voaden, 1972; Pasantes-Morales *et al.*, 1972) and hemisected spinal cord (Roberts and Mitchell, 1972) have provided relatively intact preparations which may be stimulated directly by light or *via* the spinal nerve roots. This has allowed correlation between stimulation of the neural system by physiological routes, and the extent and identity of the transmitters involved.

The pyriform cortex slice provides a similar opportunity. When carefully prepared from the olfactory cortex on the underside of the brain, this preparation includes the lateral olfactory tract (LOT) as a white band of fibres running over its surface and synapsing with the superficial neurones of the prepyriform cortex. When appropriately incubated and maintained, stimulation of the LOT results in the generation of presynaptic action potentials and post-synaptic excitatory potentials. It has recently been demonstrated that this synaptic activation is paralleled by the specific release of glutamate into the incubation medium (Bradford and Richards, 1976; Figure 13.2). Although some 18 other

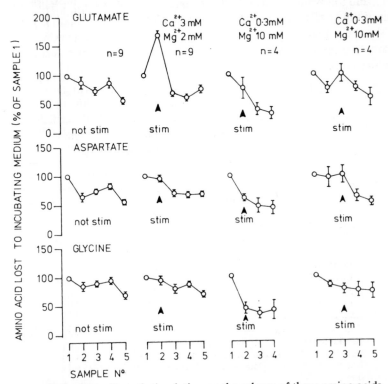

Figure 13.2 The effect of stimulation on the release of three amino acids from slices of olfactory cortex. Each column shows the time course of the release of amino acids from a particular group of slices. The first column shows the time course of release of amino acids into normal medium containing 3 mM Ca^{2+}. 2 mM Mg^{2+} in the absence of stimulation. In the experiments shown in the remaining three columns, stimulation was given during the second or third incubation period as indicated by the arrows. Note that the release of glutamate to normal medium increased during stimulation (column 2), but when Ca^{2+} was reduced and Mg^{2+} increased the stimulus-induced release was suppressed (column 3), or much reduced (column 4). All values are expressed as per cent $\pm$ S.E.M. of the amount of amino acid released in the first period following recovery. The number of slices in each group is given at the head of each column. Data from Bradford and Richards (1976)

amino acids have been measured, only glutamate has been detected in increased amounts in the incubation medium following stimulation and this augmented release requires the presence of Ca^{2+} (Table 13.1). Glutamate release due to LOT stimulation following preloading of the slices with radioactive glutamate has been reported by Yamamoto and Matsui (1976), although they did not test the specificity of the effect. As elsewhere in the cerebral cortex, cells in the prepyriform cortex are excited by ionophoretically applied glutamate (Richards et al., 1975). Furthermore, the pyriform cortex contains relatively more glutamate than other areas of cortex (Johnson and Aprison, 1971), and following removal of the ipsilateral olfactory bulb, which causes the fibres of the LOT to degenerate, these high glutamate levels fall (Harvey et al., 1975). These pieces of evidence taken together with the specific release of glutamate support the notion that glutamate is an excitatory transmitter in the olfactory cortex.

Table 13.1 Potassium stimulation of synaptosome beds: effect of calcium on release of amino acids

| | Supernatant amino acid content (nmole/100 mg protein) | | |
| | Control | Stimulated | |
		$+Ca^{2+}$	$-Ca^{2+}+EGTA$
Aspartate	146	333	103
Glutamine	211	294	118
Serine	530	660	328
Glutamate	249	635	259
Glycine	310	359	281
Alanine	410	535	244
GABA	47	133	45

Cortical synaptosome beds incubated in Krebs bicarbonate medium at 37°C. 10 minute exposure to 56 mM EGTA after 30 minutes preincubation. EGTA included at 0·5 mM as indicated. Values are mean of 6 experiments, S.E.M. ± 10 per cent. Adapted from de Belleroche and Bradford (1972), with permission.

A somewhat simpler system which has become widely used for transmitter release studies is the synaptosome preparation whose major cytoplasmic component is the isolated, apparently intact and metabolically active nerve terminal. These preparations are necessarily enriched with the biochemical agents and morphological structures directly mediating synaptic transmission. In some ways the use of synaptosomes overcomes the limitations imposed by the more intact and complex preparations, particularly with regard to specifying the origin of released amino acid. However, gains in simplicity are necessarily losses in complexity; the absence of the post-synaptic cell, the axon, and the surrounding glial cells may also mean the absence of important influences modulating the metabolism and release of amino acids. The candidature of the synaptosome preparation, which is metabolically viable and capable of responding to quite different categories of depolarizing stimuli with enhanced glucose and energy metabolism, appropriate ion-flux changes, and Ca^{2+}-dependent transmitter release, has been thoroughly reviewed elsewhere (Bradford 1975; de Belleroche and Bradford, 1973). A disadvantage of this system, which it shares with cortex slices and other more intact preparations, is its heterogeneity in terms of the range of transmitter represented. Terminals from cholinergic and catecholaminergic neurones may be present together with those from neurones employing amino acid transmitters, and on stimulation a range of these compounds are released from the different terminals. The selective release of glutamate, aspartate, and GABA from cortical synaptosomes is seen in Figure 13.3. These amino acids together with glycine are also released from spinal cord preparations. These results correlate with the observed potencies of the physiological actions of the compounds in the two regions. Thus, applied aspartate and glutamate are excitatory agents while GABA is an inhibitory agent in both regions. Glycine, however, shows high potency as an inhibitory agent only in the spinal cord. Ca^{2+} is necessary for the release (Table 13.1), which may be induced by both electrical pulses or high K^+ concentrations. These depolarizing treatments cause a parallel augmentation of metabolism which is reflected by increased respiratory and glycolytic rates, responses which are characteristic of healthy and viable tissue preparations and opposite in kind to those expected if the tissues had sustained damage due to these treatments. This, and similar evidence from synaptosomes (Redburn and Cotman, 1974; Raiteri et al., 1975; Ryan and Roskoski, 1975), together with that from the more complex tissue preparations, strongly indicates that mechanisms exist for the Ca^{2+}-coupled secretions of physiologically active amino acids at nerve terminals.

Transport and inactivation

The finding that both high (K_m 10 μM) and low (K_m 1 mM) affinity inward transport systems exist for those tissue amino acids showing potent excitatory or inhibitory properties (Logan and Snyder, 1972) adds an additional feature distinguishing these compounds, since other amino acids are transported only by low-affinity mechanisms. It therefore seems very likely that this is a high-affinity inactivating system which rapidly removes small amounts of amino acid transmitter from the synaptic cleft and other regions of the extracellular space, where contact with receptors is possible, to cell cytoplasm. It is now clear that these high-affinity systems provide the primary mechanisms for inactivating most known transmitters (Iversen, 1974); acetylcholine hydrolysis remains the only example of enzymic inactivation. In addition, these transport systems are now known to be equally enriched in glial cells and neurones (Figure 13.4) (Iversen et al., 1973; Iversen and Kelly, 1975) and the presence of low-affinity uptake in nervous tissue has become a positive index of the likely transmitter role of compounds under scrutiny in this respect.

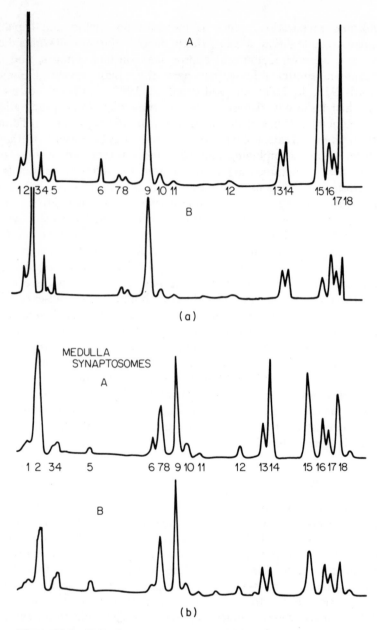

Figure 13.3 Selective release of amino acids from synaptosomes of (a) cerebral cortex and (b) spinal cord. Amino acid chromatograms are from incubation media of: A, electrically stimulated; and B, control samples. Amino acids are: 1, arginine; 2, ammonia; 3, lysine; 4, tryptophan; 5, histidine; 6, GABA; 7, phenylalanine; 8, tyrosine; 9, norleucine; 10, leucine; 11, isoleucine; 12, valine; 13, alanine; 14, glycine; 15, glutamate; 16, serine; 17, glutamine; and 18, aspartate.

From Bradford (1970)

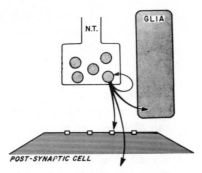

Figure 13.4 The possible role of tissue uptake systems in limiting the availability of transmitter at post-synaptic receptor sites. Fate of transmitter following release from nerve terminal (N.T.). From Iversen (1974)

b. Compartmentation and the transmitter role of amino acids

One striking and important finding has been that each neurone appears to possess only that high-affinity transport system appropriate to the amino acid that it releases. Glial cells, in contrast, possess a wide spectrum of systems. This has been inferred both from studies employing electron microscopic autoradiography and from density-gradient separation of mixed synaptosome populations. Iversen and Bloom (1972) showed that only fixed proportions of nerve endings present in brain homogenates could take up radiolabelled GABA or glycine. Matus and Dennison (1971), and Hokfelt and Ljungdahl (1971) demonstrated the same effect for glycine in spinal cord slices, where the entry was largely into terminals carrying 'flattened' vesicles and long thought to be associated exclusively with inhibitory endings. In peripheral sensory ganglia, the uptake is mainly into glial cells, but of course here the bipolar neurones do not possess a dendritic tree receiving impinging synaptic contacts (Bowery and Brown, 1972; Schon and Kelly, 1974*a,b*), and it seems clear that these ganglion glial cells can release GABA (Minchin and Iversen, 1974). In isolated retina, glial cells (Müller cells) preferentially absorb radioactive GABA (Neal and Iversen, 1972; Marshall and Voaden, 1974) together with certain of the neurones (amacrine cells).

A contrasting autoradiographic picture is seen from slices of substantia nigra which are rich in GABA. Here, half the nerve terminals become labelled and this amount is substantially reduced when the incoming fibres are cut (Hattori *et al.*, 1973; Storm-Mathieson, 1972). In parallel, there is a reduction in glutamate decarboxylase activity, the enzyme involved in the synthesis of GABA and found concentrated in nerve terminals. The glial cells of this preparation are much less active in accumulating exogenous GABA. Following injection of labelled GABA *in vivo*, autoradiographic studies tend regularly to produce pictures in which both glial and neuronal labelling appears to occur (Iversen and Kelly, 1975). However, the neuronal uptake still appears to take place principally at the expected sites. Thus, the inhibitory basket and stellate cells of the molecular layer of the cerebellum, and stellate neurones of the cerebral cortex showed very marked affinity for [³H]GABA injected *in vivo* (Hokfelt and Ljungdahl, 1972). In this case, [³H]glycine accumulated in large amounts in inhibitory interneurones of the spinal cord (Ljungdahl and Hokfelt, 1973). It seems clear that both glial cells and neurones possess sensitive, rapid, transmitter-uptake mechanisms designed to ensure the lowest concentration of transmitters in the extracellular space where they might make accidental contact with their receptor. A means of distinguishing between glial and neuronal uptake for GABA has recently become available through the finding that the analogue diaminobutyric acid (DABA) is much more effective than β-alanine in blocking neuronal uptake, and *vice versa*, for glial cells (see Iversen and Kelly, 1975).

The second line of evidence for specific neuronal uptake of amino acids comes from the finding that following incubation of brain slices with mixtures of transmitter amino acids labelled with different radioactive isotopes these radioisotopes clearly separate during density-gradient centrifugation of the nerve-terminal subfractions (Snyder *et al.*, 1973). Although this technique is not in any sense preparative, it does clearly indicate the existence of neuronal subpopulations capable of accumulating specific transmitters when these amino acids are presented exogenously, and presumably, therefore, capable of preferentially reabsorbing their own transmitter following its release *in situ*.

The presence of a special compartmentation in brain amino acid metabolism was highlighted by Berl and colleagues (see Berl and Clarke, 1961) who demonstrated the existence of a localized system within the tissue, which rapidly converted glutamate to glutamine. This apparently small compartment also converted preferentially to glutamine compounds such as acetate, bicarbonate, leucine, and C_{1-2} compounds, which give rise directly to acetyl-CoA, and so rapidly enter the Krebs cycle. This was in preference to glucose, lactate, and compounds entering the Krebs cycle *via* glycolysis (Berl and Clarke, 1969). These observations indicate the existence of two acetyl-CoA pools linked to two separate Krebs cycles. The considerable evidence on this curious phenomenon has now been digested and the emerging picture is one in which the glial cells constitute the small compartment and produce glutamine at a rapid rate while GABA is produced in neurones and subsequently metabolized *via* succinic semialdehyde in the glia. Autoradiographic studies with isolated sensory ganglia strikingly support these conclusions, [¹⁴C]glucose being preferentially absorbed and metabolized by sensory neurones largely into glutamate, while [¹⁴C]acetate is taken up almost exclusively by glia where it is converted principally to glutamine and GABA. The featuring of GABA production in glial cells rather than in neurones is a property of these peripheral ganglia and is unlikely to occur centrally (Minchin and Beart, 1975; Figure 13.5). The high levels of glutamine in cerebrospinal fluid 0·5 mM, and

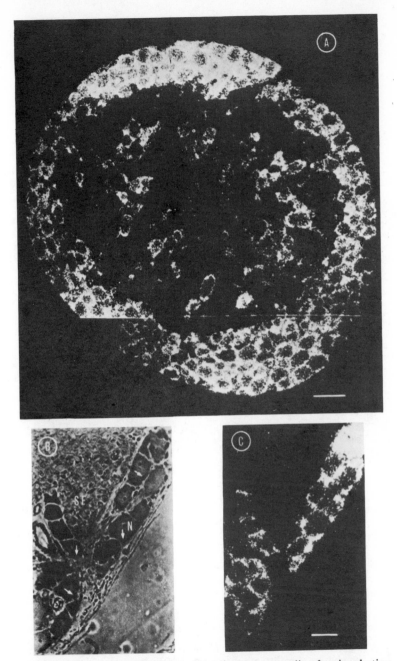

Figure 13.5(a)   Autoradiography of dorsal root ganglia after incubation for 90 minutes with [^{14}C]acetate. A, Dark-field autoradiography showing photomontage of a section through a whole ganglion. Radioactivity is preferentially localized in the satellite glial cells surrounding the large neuronal cell bodies. The sensory fibres in the interior of the ganglion are unlabelled. Exposure time, 11 days; calibration bar, 100 µm. B and C, Phase-contrast and corresponding dark-field autoradiograph of dorsal root ganglion. Silver grains are predominantly located over satellite glial cells (arrows), whereas the neurones (N) and sensory fibres (SF) show little labelling. Exposure time, 5 days; calibration bar, 50 µm. From Minchin and Beart (1975)

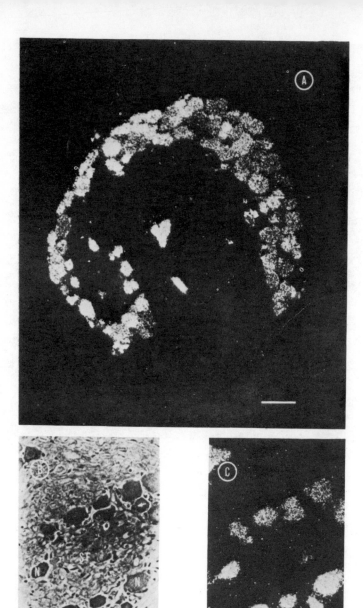

Figure 13.5(b) Autoradiography of dorsal root ganglia after incubation for 90 minutes with [^{14}C] glucose. A, dark-field autoradiograph showing photomontage of a section through a whole ganglion. Radioactivity is localized to a greater extent over neuronal cell bodies than over the satellite glial cells. The sensory fibres in the interior of the ganglion are unlabelled. Exposure time, 24 days: Calibration bar, 100 μm. B and C, Phase-contrast and corresponding dark-field autoradiograph of the dorsal root ganglion. Silver grains are localized to a lesser extent over the satellite glial cells (arrows) than over the neuronal cell bodies (N). The sensory fibres (SF) are devoid of label. Exposure time, 24 days; calibration bar, 50 μm

presumably also in extracellular space, are therefore likely to receive a large contribution from glial cell metabolism of compounds, such as GABA and glutamate, taken up by high-affinity systems from the extracellular space and emanating originally largely from neurones.

To complete the cycle it is necessary that neurones absorb the extracellular glutamine and reconvert it to glutamate. Evidence of a localization of glutaminase in neurones, or at least at the nerve endings, was provided by Salganicoff and De Robertis (1965) and has been confirmed subsequently (Bradford and Ward, 1976). In support of a non-glial localization the author has not been able to detect the enzyme in C6-glioma preparations (Bradford *et al.*, unpublished observations). In addition, [^{14}C]glutamine when present in cerebrospinal fluid at levels of 0·5 mM in the presence of excess glucose (10 mM), is readily incorporated into the amino acid pools (particularly glutamate and aspartate) of isolated nerve endings and labels these pools to about 50 per cent of the glutamine-specific radioactivity (Bradford and Ward, 1975; Table 13.2). In addition, glutamine under these conditions is able to

Table 13.2 Incorporation of [U-^{14}C]glutamine into the amino acids of synaptosomes

	Specific radioactivities of amino acids (μCi/μmole)		
	0 min	30 min	60 min
Aspartate	0	0·140 ± 0·020 (4)	0·251 ± 0·018 (4)
Glutamate	0	0·274 ± 0·009 (4)	0·301 ± 0·035 (4)
GABA	0	0·087 ± 0·006 (4)	0·131 ± 0·016 (4)

Synaptosome beds were incubated at 37°C in Krebs bicarbonate medium, containing glucose (10 mM) and glutamine (0·50 mM, 0·32 μCi/ml). The specific radioactivity of the added glutamine was 6·22 μCi/μmole. Values are mean ± S.E.M. for the number of samples in parentheses. From Bradford and Ward (1975), with permission.

maintain the pool sizes of synaptosomal amino acids which glucose alone does not (Bradford *et al.*, 1975). Taken together this information suggests that glutamine is an important immediate source of carbon, and probably nitrogen, for nerve endings *in situ* and possibly also for the whole neurone, although at present this glutamine would be seen as deriving originally from glucose metabolized by brain and not from the bloodstream.

The scheme presented in Figure 13.6 represents the likely flux of glutamate between glial cells and nerve endings. The entry to nerve terminals would be greatly assisted by its low concentration in these structures which do not appear either to possess glutamine synthetase or to form glutamine from glucose or glutamate (Salganicoff and De Robertis, 1965; Bradford and Thomas, 1969). The strong inhibition of glutaminase by glutamate at concentrations in the range normally found in synaptosomes (2–5 mM) indicates a feedback

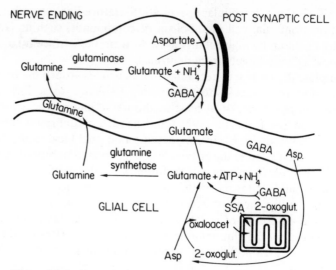

Figure 13.6 Proposed cycle of release, uptake, and metabolism of amino acids between neurones and glial cells

mechanism controlling the rate of glutamine hydrolysis (Figure 13.7). NH_4^+ is an effective inhibitor at lower concentrations (0.5–1.0 mM) (Bradford and Ward, 1975; Quastel, 1976), but these conditions are unlikely to be attained except in disease such as hepatic encephalopathy, in which NH_4^+ inhibition of

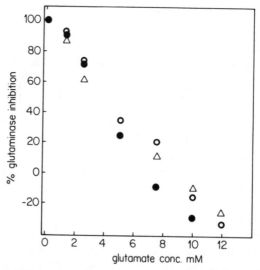

Figure 13.7 Inhibition of synaptosomal glutaminase by glutamate. Glutaminase was measured by following NH_4^+ release spectrophotometrically in a system containing 50 mM borate buffer, 5 mM potassium phosphate, and 0.5 mM glutamine. 100 per cent activity represents 8–10 μmole glutamine hydrolysed/100 mg protein hr^{-1}.
From Bradford & Ward unpublished results

279

glutaminase resulting in restricted availability of glutamate could underlie the aetiology of the encephalopathy and coma characteristic of the condition. It is not yet clear whether the glutamate produced from glutamine in nerve endings is generated in a special pool serving metabolism, or transmitter release, or both, but answers to these questions are currently being sought.

REFERENCES

Balazs, R., Maygar, K., and Richter, D. (1964) in *Comparative Neurochemistry*, (Richter, D., ed.), Pergamon Press, London, p. 225.
Beloff-Chain, A., Catanzaro, R., Chain, E. B., Masi, I., and Pocchiari, F. (1955) *Proc. Roy. Soc. Series B.*, **144**, 221.
Berl, S., and Clarke, D. D. (1969) in *Handbook of Neurochemistry*, Vol. 2, (Lajtha, A., ed.), Plenum Press, New York, p. 447.
Bowery, N. G., and Brown, D. A. (1972) *Nature, New Biol.*, **238**, 89.
Bradford, H. F. (1975) in *Handbook of Psychopharmacology*, Vol. 1, (Iversen, L. L., Iversen, S. D., and Snyder, S. H., eds.), Plenum Press, New York, pp. 191–251.
Bradford, H. F., Jones, D. G., Ward, H. K., and Booher, J. (1975) *Brain Res.*, **90**, 245.
Bradford, H. F., and Richards, C. D. (1976) *Brain Res.*, **105**, 168.
Bradford, H. F., and Thomas, A. J. (1969) *J. Neurochem.*, **16**, 1495.
Bradford, H. F., and Ward, H. K. (1975) *Biochem. Soc. Trans.*, **3**, 1223.
Bradford, H. F., and Ward, H. K. (1976) *Brain Res.*, **110**, 115.
Chain, E. B. (1965) in *Biochemical Research: Landmarks and Perspectives*, Inaugural Lecture, Imperial College, London.
Curtis, D. R., and Johnston, G. A. R. (1974) *Rev. Physiol.*, **69**, 98.
Curtis, D. R., and Watkins, J. C. (1965) *Pharmacol. Rev.*, **17**, 347.
de Belleroche, J. S., and Bradford, H. F. (1972) *J. Neurochem.*, **19**, 585.
de Belleroche, J. S., and Bradford, H. F. (1973) *Prog. Neurobiol.* **1**, 277.
Falk, B., Hillarp, N. A., Thiene, G., and Torp, G. (1962) *J. Histochem. Cytochem.*, **10**, 348.
Harvey, J. A., Schofield, C. N., Graham, L. T., and Aprison, M. H. (1975) *J. Neurochem.*, **24**, 445.
Hattori, T., McGeer, P. L., Fibiger, H. C., and McGeer, E. G. (1973) *Brain Res.*, **54**, 103.
Hayashi, T. (1954) *Keio. J. Med.*, **3**, 183.
Hokfelt, T., and Ljungdahl, A. (1971) *Prog. Brain Res.*, **34**, 88.
Hokfelt, T., and Ljungdahl, A. (1972) *Adv. Biochem. Psychopharmacol.* **6**, 1.
Hopkins, J., and Neal, M. J. (1971) *Brit. J. Pharmacol.*, **42**, 215.
Iversen, L. L. (1974) in *The Neurosciences 3rd Study Programme*, (Schmitt, F., and Worden, F. G., eds.), MIT Press, Cambridge, Mass., pp. 905–915.
Iversen, L. L., Bloom, F. E. (1972) *Brain Res.*, **41**, 131.
Iversen, L. L., Kelly, J. S., Minchin, M., Schon, F., and Snodgrass, S. R. (1973) *Brain Res.*, **62**, 567.
Iversen, L. L., and Kelly, J. S. (1975) *Biochem. Pharmacol.*, **24**, 933.
Johnson, J. L., and Aprison, M. H. (1971) *Brain Res.*, **26**, 141.
Katz, R. I., Chase, T. N., and Kopin, I. J. (1969) *J. Neurochem.*, **16**, 961.
Kaczmarek, L. K., and Davison, A. N. (1972) *J. Neurochem.*, **19**, 2355.
Lee, L. W., Liao, C.-L., and Yatsu, F. M. (1974) *J. Neurochem.*, **23**, 721.
Logan, W., and Snyder, S. H. (1972) *Brain Res.*, **42**, 423.
Ljungdahl, A., and Hokfelt, T. (1973) *Histochemie*, **33**, 277.
Marshall, J., and Voaden, M. J. (1974) *Biochem. Soc. Trans.*, **2**, 268.
Matus, A. I., and Dennison, M. E. (1971) *J. Neurocytol.* **1**, 27.

280

Minchin, M. C. W., and Beart, P. M. (1975) *Brain Res.* **83**, 437.
Minchin, M. C. W., and Iversen, L. L. (1974) *J. Neurochem.*, **23**, 533.
Neal, M. J., and Iversen, L. L. (1972) *Nature (London)*, **235**, 217.
Pasantes-Morales, H., Urban, P. F., Klethi, J., and Mandel, P. (1972) *Brain Res.*, **51**, 345.
Quastel, J. D. (1976) *Proceedings of Am. Soc. Neurochem.*, April 1976.
Raiteri, M., Federico, R., Coletti, A., and Levi, G. (1975) *J. Neurochem.*, **24**, 1243.
Redburn, D. A., and Cotman, C. W. (1974) *Brain Res.*, **73**, 550.
Richards, C. D., Russell, W. J., and Smaje, J. C. (1975) *J. Physiol.*, **248**, 121.
Roberts, E., and Fraenkel, S. (1951) *J. Biol. Chem.*, **188**, 789.
Roberts, P. J., and Mitchell, J. F. (1972) *J. Neurochem.*, **19**, 2473.
Ryman, L. D., and Roskoski, R. (1975) *Nature (London)*, **258**, 254.
Salganicoff, L., and De Robertis, E. (1965) *Neurochemistry*, **12**, 287.
Schon, E., and Kelly, J. S. (1974a) *Brain Res.*, **66**, 275.
Schon, F., and Kelly, J. S. (1974b) *Brain Res.*, **66**, 289.
Snyder, S. H., Young, A. B., Bennett, J. P., and Mulder, A. H. (1973) *Fed. Proc.*, **32**, 2039.
Starr, M. S., and Voaden, M. J. (1972) *Vision Res.*, **12**, 1261.
Storm-Mathieson, J. (1972) *Brain Res.*, **40**, 215.
Whelan, D. T., Scriber, C. R., and Mohyuddin, F. (1969) *Nature (London)*, **224**, 916.
Yamamoto, C., and Matsui, S. (1976) *J. Neurochem.*, **26**, 487.

DISCUSSION

Dr. R. Chaplain

On evaluating the role of amino acids in the brain one should also consider their intraneuronal actions. We have shown that glutamate injected intracellularly into isolated molluscan neurones induces the same effects on membrane depolarization and rhythmic discharge patterns. This seems even more interesting as these isolated neurones which discharge autonomously are completely free of any synaptic and ephaphtic inputs. Glutamate serves in these neurones as an activating modifier of the pyruvate kinase as well as the phosphofructokinase through its released ammonia moiety, together with a likely role as gluconeogenic substrate, with utile substrate cycles at the levels of fructose 6-phosphate and pyruvate controlling through their local fluctuations in ATP and H^+ the neuronal membrane activity. Our work in this field is described in two papers—Brain Res., (1975) **101**, 141; *ibid* (1975) **106**, 307.

14
Hypothalamic Hormones and Mechanisms of Neuroendocrine Integration

J. A. Edwardson and G. W. Bennett

Department of Biochemistry,
Imperial College of Science and Technology, London, U.K.

INTRODUCTION

Current advances in understanding the hypothalamic hormones and other cerebral peptides appear to weld many previously unrelated aspects of endocrine and neural integration within a new and far-reaching conceptual framework. The ability of certain hypothalamic neurones to elaborate biologically active peptides was believed, until recently, to reflect a specialization related wholly to the control of the pituitary gland. This idea provided the stimulus for our work on the biochemical and cellular aspects of hypothalamic neurosecretion. These investigations were greatly encouraged by Sir Ernst Chain who confidently predicted that such studies would yield both new mechanisms in neuroendocrine control and the recognition of novel active substances. The extent to which these shrewd forecasts have been fulfilled within a few years provides the substance of this contribution. However, the implications of recent work on the hypothalamic hormones extend far beyond the field of hypothalamo-pituitary relationships.

In summary, it appears that the biosynthesis and release of small peptide messengers are widespread attributes of neural tissues, rather than a specialized function of some hypothalamic neurones. Cerebral peptides, including the so-called hypothalamic hormones, are distributed extensively throughout the central nervous system, and, in some cases, outside of it, especially in the gastrointestinal tract. Furthermore, these peptides have complex, multiple actions ranging from their tropic effects on the pituitary gland and other endocrine organs to roles in the central nervous system involving synaptic function and behaviour. The list of cerebral peptides is large and rapidly growing; together they comprise a new group of biologically active substances. Many fundamental questions in regard to their biosynthesis, transport, storage, release, and mechanisms of action remain to be explored and the exploitation of these peptides, or their synthetic analogues, has only just begun.

In this chapter, a brief review of the emerging field of cerebral peptides, particularly in relation to the physiology of integration, will be presented and then the authors' recent findings on the importance of the neurosecretory nerve ending will be discussed in detail. The use of isolated nerve endings and other procedures *in vitro* has proved valuable in elucidating the mechanisms of action of neurotransmitters and steroid hormones which control the secretion of hypothalamic hormones. Evidence will be presented that such techniques may prove equally useful in the study of the wider significance of cerebral peptides and their synaptic functions.

HYPOTHALAMIC HORMONES AND THE CENTRAL NERVOUS SYSTEM

Hypothalamic hormones are among the first chemical messengers to be released in response to changes in the external or internal environment. Factors such as cold, hunger, stress, or sexual stimuli bring about their secretion during adaptive responses which frequently involve a behavioural component. For many years a few percipient investigators have argued that the hypothalamic and related peptide hormones could perhaps reinforce, or even elicit, the appropriate pattern of behaviour by direct action on the brain. Evidence to support this reasoning has accumulated slowly and, until recently, most neurophysiologists have shown little interest in the idea. There were grounds for this reluctance; certainly the peptide hormones do not produce such drastic effects on behaviour as the thyroid hormones or gonadal steroids. Also, it was difficult to see how peptides could cross the blood–brain barrier to act on the neural substrates which regulate adaptive behaviour. Despite these and other objections, there is now little doubt that peptide hormones do influence the central nervous system and it is significant that the hormones for which such actions have been described are produced mainly by the hypothalamus or the pituitary—two key centres in the integration of endocrine responses and behaviour.

Hypothalamic hormones are released from the endings of neurosecretory nerves which terminate on portal veins in the median eminence; these blood vessels provide a direct humoral route for their access to the pituitary. At least seven different hormones are produced by the anterior and intermediate lobes of the pituitary gland and each is under the extensive control of one or more 'releasing' or 'release-inhibiting' peptide hormones, secreted from the hypothalamus in minute amounts. The hypothalamic hormones have proved enormously difficult to isolate and characterize. An epic race to determine their structure was begun in the early 1960s and the first major breakthrough came in 1969 when the groups of Guillemin and of Schally announced independently that the factor which releases pituitary thyroid-stimulating hormone is a tripeptide with the somewhat unusual structure of pyro-Glu-His–ProNH$_2$

(Bowers *et al.*, 1970; Burgus *et al.*, 1970). This substance was named thyrotrophin-releasing hormone (TRH).

Within a few years the structures of several related hormones had been eludicated (Figure 14.1); these include the decapeptide luteinizing hormone-releasing hormone (LH–RH) (Matsuo *et al.*, 1971; Burgus *et al.*, 1972) which releases the pituitary gonadotrophins and also a slightly larger molecule, somatostatin, which inhibits the secretion of growth hormone (Brazeau *et al.*,

(a) pyro-Glu–His–ProNH$_2$
(b) pyro-Glu–His–Trp–Ser–Tyr–Gly–Leu–Arg–Pro–GlyNH$_2$
(c) Ala–Gly–Cys–Lys–Asn–Phe–Phe–Trp–Lys–Thr–Phe–Thre–Ser–Cys
(d) Cys–Tyr–Ile–Gln–Asn–Cys–Pro–Leu–GlyNH$_2$
(e) Cys–Tyr–Phe–Gln–Asn–Cys–Pro–Arg–GlyNH$_2$
(f) Pro–Leu–GlyNH$_2$
(g) Cys–Tyr–Ile–Gln–Asn
(h) Tyr–Gly–Gly–Phe–Met
(i) Tyr–Gly–Gly–Phe–Leu

Figure 14.1 The structure of some peptides from the mammalian hypothalamus: (a) thyrotrophin-releasing hormone; (b) gonadotrophin-releasing hormone; (c) somatostatin; (d) oxytocin; (e) argine-vasopressin; (f) MSH release-inhibiting hormone; (g) MSH-releasing hormone; (h) methionine enkephalin; and (i) leucine-enkephalin

1973). Besides these three well-established hypophysiotropic hormones, it is claimed (Celis *et al.*, 1971; Nair *et al.*, 1971) that a hypothalamic peptide with the structure Pro–Leu–GlyNH$_2$ has an inhibitory effect on the release of MSH from the intermediate lobe of the pituitary. This factor has been designated MIF (MSH release-inhibiting factor) and is, in fact, the C-terminal tripeptide of oxytocin, another hormone produced by the hypothalamus and transported to the neural lobe of the pituitary gland from which it is released directly into the systemic circulation. Relatively small peptides such as TRH, LH–RH, somatostatin, and MIF have been synthesized in the laboratory without difficulty. It was when these substances became available in large amounts for biological and clinical studies that evidence for behavioural effects began to emerge.

No attempt shall be made in this review to unravel the delicate question of the priority of discoveries in this field, although such matters have received inordinate attention from many of the investigators involved. A spate of reports on the direct actions of hypothalamic hormones on the central nervous system appeared during 1971–72 (for a review, see Kastin *et al.*, 1975) and it is clear that this explosion was spurred on by the belief that their widespread use in the clinical treatment of nervous disorders was imminent. This optimism proved to be premature; nevertheless, such studies have opened one of the most fruitful avenues of current research in neurobiology.

Some of the earliest findings were made by Prange at the University of North Carolina, in collaboration with Plotnikoff and others at Abbott Laboratories,

Chicago. Prange and his colleagues had long been interested in the interactions between thyroid hormones and drugs used to treat depression, and were thus prompted to examine the effects of TRH in a test used to screen novel compounds for potential antidepressant properties. The test involved mice treated with pargyline, a monoamine oxidase inhibitor, and L-dopa. By simultaneously preventing the breakdown and increasing the synthesis of dopamine in the brain, this combination brings about the stimulation of dopaminergic systems and produces a characteristic pattern of hair erection, salivation, marked irritability, jumping, squeaking, and fighting. It was shown that TRH, in common with some established antidepressants, is highly effective in potentiating the behavioural responses observed in this test (Plotnikoff *et al.*, 1972). Furthermore, by using hypophysectomized and thyroidectomized animals, they demonstrated that neither pituitary nor thyroid secretions are necessary for TRH to be active, the results suggesting a direct action of TRH on the nervous system (Plotnikoff *et al.*, 1974).

Clinical trials at various centres indicated that TRH produces a rapid but transient improvement in depression. Such trials, however, are notoriously difficult to control and evaluate, and more detailed studies eventually concluded that TRH is of little or no value as an antidepressant (Ehrensing *et al.*, 1974), although the peptide may hold promise as a diagnostic tool for distinguishing between different types of depression.

Despite the uncertainty regarding its clinical efficacy, there is little doubt that TRH can interact with aminergic systems, believed by many to have a role in the control of mood. Just as L-dopa is the precursor for catecholamines, the amino acid tryptophan is the precursor for 5-hydroxytryptamine or serotonin. This neurotransmitter, also a monoamine, has been implicated in the control of pituitary secretion, sexual behaviour, agression, and sleep. Green and Grahame-Smith (1974) used a combination of tryptophan and a monoamine oxidase inhibitor to elevate brain serotonin and showed that TRH dramatically potentiates the syndrome of increased locomotor activity which follows such treatment. TRH has been shown to modify the effects of various pharmacological agents, and there are reports that this peptide mitigates the severity of symptoms produced by strychnine (Brown and Vale, 1975), barbiturates (Prange *et al.*, 1974), and ethanol (Breese *et al.*, 1974).

Micro-iontophoretic application of TRH, LH–RH, and somatostatin to single neurones has been shown to depress both spontaneous and glutamate-induced firing of nerve cells in the hypothalamus, cerebral cortex, cerebellum, and other regions (Renaud *et al.*, 1975). Rapid responses were recorded and the reduced frequency of discharge was associated with an increase in spike amplitude which indicates hyperolarization of the nerve cell membrane. Similar electrophysiological effects of hypothalamic hormones have been reported from other laboratories.

Not only are the hypothalamic hormones active at neural centres outside the hypothalamus, but also there is now abundant data to show that they are present in other brain regions. A number of studies using radioimmunoassay and immunohistochemistry reports these peptides to have distinctive distributions in both fibres and terminals throughout the central nervous system, including the spinal cord and, in the case of somatostatin, even in the gut and pancreas (Jackson and Reichlin, 1974; Brownstein *et al.*, 1975; Hokfelt *et al.*, 1975*a,b*). The wide distribution of nerve cells containing the so-called 'hypothalamic' hormones raises two crucial questions. Firstly, what is the physiological significance of these peptidergic systems and how do they relate to the behavioural effects which have been observed? Secondly, what are the cellular and biochemical mechanisms involved in the interaction of these peptidergic neurones with other parts of the central nervous system.? Answers to these questions are at best fragmentary, but there are signs that the pieces are beginning to fall together in a most cohesive way.

In the case of TRH, an elegant study by Wei *et al.* (1975) has given an insight into the possible functions of this hormone in extra-hypothalamic systems. This group noted a report by Prange *et al.* (1974) that the systemic administration of TRH to pentobarbital-anaesthetized rats caused, among other symptoms, lacrimation, paw tremor, and a peculiar shaking movement of the head and trunk—behaviour characteristic of morphine withdrawal. Using intracerebral micro-injections of TRH, they plotted the areas where the hormone produced tremor and intense shivering. Massive responses were obtained in localized mesodiencephalic and medullary regions, areas considered important in the physiological control of shivering. Furthermore, they claimed that this response to intracerebral TRH exhibits a high degree of chemical specificity—various substances including neurotransmitters, drugs, and toxic agents do not produce this behaviour. They suggested that the intense muscular activity and peripheral vasoconstriction, which was also observed, represent the activation of heat gain systems by TRH.

If their interpretation is correct, TRH is the chemical mediator of both behavioural and hormonal mechanisms which enable the body to adapt to cold. The behavioural component would be of chief importance during the acute phase of cold adaptation, before the thyroid hormones can increase metabolic heat production and provide for long-term acclimatization.

A role as mediator of both behavioural and hormonal changes during reproduction has similarly been proposed for LH–RH. Studies in the Department of Physiology at the University of Texas Health Science Center indicate that LH–RH can facilitate sexual receptivity in the ovariectomized rat (for a review, see Moss *et al.*, 1975). Priming with oestrogen is necessary before the response can be elicited, but the behavioural effects are specific—TRH, FSH, or LH does not induce mating behaviour in similarly treated females. Also, LH–RH exerts a stimulatory effect on the sexual behaviour of male rats, as suggested by the shortened time to ejaculation. The neural centres which produce LH–RH and regulate sexual behaviour overlap in the medial preoptic region of the hypothalamus. LH–RH may function not only in triggering the release of gonadotrophins from the pituitary gland but also in activating sexual behaviour by stimulating the mating centre.

It therefore seems sensible to consider each hypothalamic hormone and ask which behavioural responses are appropriate to the situation in which it is released. Unfortunately, there is still a large amount of ignorance about many aspects of hypothalamopituitary function. MIF is more potent than TRH in the dopa-potentiation test mentioned previously, and it is also highly active in an animal model of Parkinson's disease. However, the physiological role of MSH secretion in mammals is not understood at present and no clue to the significance of the actions of MIF in these neuropharmacological tests is available.

What general conclusions can be drawn from the variety of data so far obtained? It seems likely that discrete systems of peptidergic neurones may arise in the hypothalamus and project throughout the nervous system. Electrophysiological and histochemical studies show that at least some neurosecretory neurones are bipolar with axons projecting both to the vascular link with the pituitary and to synapses in other centres of the brain (Dyer, 1975). Detailed anatomical studies are required to determine the nature of these neural connections, but Herbert (1975) has recently speculated that peptidergic neurons may increase the specificity of the monoaminergic systems which also project into many centres and which are implicated in the control of different kinds of behaviour. Interactions between peptidergic and other synapses in a particular region could confer selectivity on a system otherwise difficult to define in functional terms.

In addition to the hypothalamic hormones, there is a number of other cerebral peptides with distinct actions or neural functions and behaviour. For many years workers have considered that the morphine receptor in brain must also react with an endogenous substance with opiate-like activity. A systematic search for the endogenous agonist was successfully concluded in a collaborative study between the groups of Hughes and Kosterlitz at Aberdeen and of Morris in the Department of Biochemistry, Imperial College, who isolated and characterized two pentapeptides (Figure 14.1) which are highly active on the morphine receptor (Hughes et al., 1975). These peptides were named enkephalins, and Morris recognized that methionine-enkephalin was identical to the 61–65 portion of pituitary β-lipotrophic hormone (LPH). He correctly predicted the existence of other larger peptide fragments of LPH in brain, and Guillemin's group subsequently reported the characterization of such molecules, the endorphines (Guillemin et al., 1976), one of which comprises the whole 61–91 C-terminal region of LPH and is, in molar terms, approximately 200 times more potent than morphine (Bradbury et al., 1976).

Other peptides which have been shown to be widespread in brain and spinal cord include substance P, neurotensin, αMSH, and various gut peptides, discussion of which is outside the scope of this brief review. Together with the neurohypophysial hormones and the as yet uncharacterized hypothalamic factors regulating the secretion of prolactin, ACTH, and other pituitary hormones, these peptides constitute a large and rapidly growing group of important substances which must be considered as candidates for the role of extracellular messengers in different brain regions.

RELEASE OF HYPOTHALAMIC HORMONES FROM ISOLATED NEUROSECRETORY NERVE ENDINGS

The biochemical and cellular interactions between peptidergic neurones and other elements in the central nervous system are poorly understood. However, some progress has been made towards elucidating these relations in the hypophysiotropic hypothalamus, the region which exercises immediate control over pituitary function and where the most extensive integrations of neural and humoral signals are achieved. The properties of isolated nerve endings (synaptosomes) prepared from the hypothalamus have been exploited to study the effects of neurotransmitters and steroid hormones on the release of hypothalamic hormones. Synaptosomes have been widely used to study the metabolic and morphological features of presynaptic organization (for a review, see de Belleroche and Bradford, 1973). The usefulness of this preparation derives from the fact that, during the homogenization of brain tissue, a high proportion of the nerve endings pinch off where the axon expands into the terminal, with rapid and effective resealing of the neurolemma at the point of rupture. Cytosol, mitochondria, secretory granules, and the other structural inclusions of the nerve ending are thus retained within the synaptosomes, which can be isolated from homogenates of brain by the differential and density-gradient centrifugation procedures as shown in Figure 14.2.

We have shown by bioassay and radioimmunoassay that synaptosomes isolated from the hypothalamus contain both neurohypophysial and hypothalamic hormones (Edwardson et al., 1972; Edwardson and Bennett, 1974; Bennett and Edwardson, 1975; Bennett et al., 1975). In fact, a considerable proportion of the hypothalamic content of these hormones is recoverable from the synaptosome-containing fractions. Figure 14.3 shows the distribution of immunoreactive TRH and LH–RH when a homogenate of rat hypothalami was separated on a continuous sucrose density gradient.

When the synaptosomal fraction is removed from the density gradient and resuspended in Krebs bicarbonate buffer containing glucose, a steady basal release of hypothalamic hormones is observed. This can be abruptly increased by the application of depolarizing stimuli, such as electrical field stimulation or the addition of specific neurotransmitters. Furthermore, the response is dependent upon the presence of free Ca^{2+} in the incubation medium. The effect of Ca^{2+} on the release of hypothalamic corticotrophin-releasing hormone (CRH) is shown in Table 14.1. In these experiments, CRH activity was measured by bioassay. Similar results have been obtained in studies on the release of immunoreactive LH–RH from sheep hypothalamic synaptosomes where, in the presence of 1 mM Ca^{2+}, the mean basal release is increased from 154 to 1372 pg LH–RH/hypothalamic equivalent by electrical field stimulation. Absence of Ca^{2+} from the incubation medium slightly decreases the basal release of LH–RH to 120 pg/hypothalamic equivalent and markedly reduces the response to electrical stimulation to 214 pg/hypothalamic equivalent.

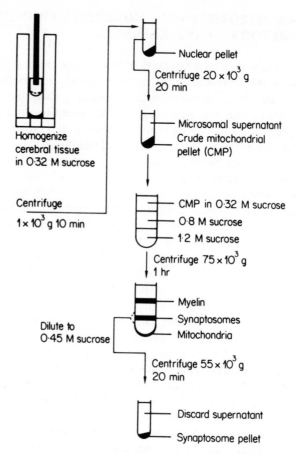

Figure 14.2 Stages in the preparation of synapto-somes from cerebral tissue. Diagram kindly supplied by Dr. J. S. de Belleroche

There is negligible loss of soluble cytoplasmic markers, such as lactic dehydrogenase, in response to electrical field stimulation or other depolarizing stimuli, thus indicating that it is not an artefactual breakdown of the membrane which brings about the release of the hypothalamic hormones. This fact, coupled with the Ca^{2+} dependence of the release mechanism, suggests that the secretion of hypothalamic hormones from synaptosomes *in vitro* may provide a valuable model for the study of humoral influences which directly affect the secretory processes of the neurosecretory nerve ending *in vivo*.

This model is important because of the extraordinary complexity of organi-zation of the hypothalamus as an endocrine organ. In most other endocrine tissues, there is a relatively simple vascular or neural supply which allows convenient study of the immediate stimuli bringing about the discharge of hormone. The wealth of neural, glial, and vascular connections in the

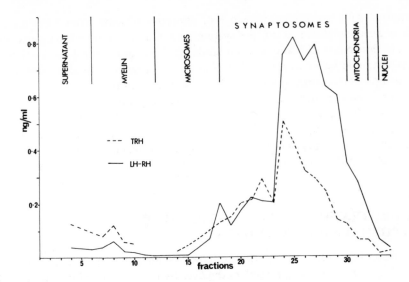

Figure 14.3 Subcellular distribution of immunoreactive LH–RH and TRH from rat hypothalami. A 10 per cent homogenate of six female rat hypothalami was prepared in 0·32 M sucrose and layered on to linear sucrose gradients (0·32–1·5 M). The gradients were centrifuged for 90 minutes at 130 000 g and 34 fractions collected from the pierced centrifuge tubes. The fractions were extracted with 0·1 N HCl and the LH–RH and TRH content (ng/ml) were measured by radioimmunoassay

Table 14.1 Effect of calcium on the release of CRH from sheep and rat hypothalamic synaptosomes

Species	Incubation medium (Krebs bicarbonate buffer)	Number of expts.	ACTH released (ng/ml)		Stimulation (per cent)
			Unstimulated	Electrically stimulated	
Sheep	Containing 0·75 mM Ca^{2+}	7	29·3 ± 5·0	55·6 ± 8·5*	97
Sheep	Without Ca^{2+}	5	23·4 ± 2·0	25·0 ± 1·7	10
Sheep	Without Ca^{2+} + 1 mM EGTA	5	26·2 ± 3·0	25·1 ± 2·8	0
Rat	Containing 0·75 mM Ca^{2+}	5	28·1 ± 4·3	45·9 ± 8·5*	61
Rat	Without Ca^{2+}	5	36·9 ± 4·9	37·6 ± 5·3	2

Values were determined by radioimmunoassay and represent ACTH released from paired, halved, rat adenohypophyses during a 45 minute incubation at 37°C in 1 ml synaptosome supernatant (means ± S.E.M.). Where Ca^{2+} was omitted from the synaptosome incubation medium, CaCl$_2$ (1 mmole/l) was added to the pituitary incubation medium to eliminate any inhibition of ACTH release due to reduced levels of Ca^{2+}.

As shown by the Wilcoxon test, there is a significant different (*$p < 0·05$) between the electrically stimulated and control preparations. EGTA, ethylene glycol-bis (β-amino ethylether)-N,N^1-tetraacetic acid. Data, with permission, from Bennett and Edwardson (1975).

hypothalamus and the convergence of afferent pathways from other parts of the central nervous system, the systemic circulation, and cerebrospinal fluid create enormous difficulties when studying the rapid control mechanisms in hypothalamic neurosecretion. It has been particularly difficult to distinguish between mechanisms involving the dendritic inputs or perikarya of the neurosecretory neurones, and those which may operate at the level of the nerve terminal. Work with synaptosomes has suggested that the neurosecretory nerve endings of the hypothalamic median eminence may have a great deal of functional autonomy and may provide an important locus of action for both neurotransmitters and steroid hormones in neuroendocrine integration.

NEUROTRANSMITTERS AND THE RELEASE OF HYPOTHALAMIC HORMONES

Afferent stimuli converge on the hypophysiotropic hypothalamus through diverse, multi-synaptic, neural pathways. Synaptic relay along these tracts involves many different chemical mediators including acetylcholine, monoamines, and the amino acid neurotransmitters. Much attention has focused on the identity of the neurotransmitters which are involved in synaptic contacts with the neurosecretory neurone itself. These have been identified to a considerable extent for the innervation of the CRH-producing neurone, at least as far as the dendritic and somal inputs are concerned (for a review, see Jones *et al.*, 1976). However, considerable amounts of different neurotransmitters are present in the external zone of the hypothalamic median eminence, where the neurosecretory nerve endings are in close proximity to the hypophysial portal vessel plexus, and a number of workers (for example Ganong, 1974) have proposed that there may be direct axo–axonic connections in this region which afford rapid neural modulation of the last stage in the final common pathway of neuroendocrine integration. Morphological and physiological evidence for such connections is poor, and synaptosomes have provided the most convincing demonstration for a functional connection between neurosecretory terminals and other nerve endings in the median eminence.

The first demonstration of such interactions came with the report that acetycholine (ACh), at concentrations as low as 10^{-11} M, stimulated release of CRH from hypothalamic synaptosomes (Edwardson and Bennett, 1974). This response to ACh was greater than the effects produced by electrical field stimulation. The action of ACh was suppressed in the presence of the muscarinic blocker atropine, unlike the action of ACh on CRH release at higher neural levels, which is mediated through nicotinic receptors (Jones *et al.*, 1976). Also, dopamine at 10^{-8} M blocked both the responses to ACh or electrical field stimulation. It was concluded from these data that receptors for neurotransmitters are present on the neurosecretory nerve terminal and that the release of hypothalamic hormones may be regulated partly through some kind of synaptic

interactions between cholinergic, dopaminergic, and CRH-containing terminals. Subsequently, the effects of a wide range of neurotransmitters at levels of
from 10^{-8} to 10^{-12} M on release of TRH and LH–RH from hypothalamic
synaptosomes were tested. The specificity of the responses obtained in these
studies is shown in Table 14.2.

Table 14.2 Effect of neurotransmitters on the release of
hypothalamic hormones from synaptosomes prepared from
the sheep median eminence

Neurotransmitter	CRH	TRH	LH–RH
Acetylcholine	+	0	0
Adrenaline	?	0	0
Noradrenaline	0	0	0
Dopamine	−	+	+
Serotonin	0	−	0

Significant stimulation (+) or inhibition (−) of hormone release with
doses of neurotransmitter of 10^{-8} M or smaller. 0, absence of effect.

In some experiments, sheep hypothalami were dissected into three fragments: the median eminence (approximately 70 mg wet weight); a more dorsal
periventricular region (300 mg); and the remaining tissue (300 mg). Synaptosomes were prepared separately and the responses to electrical stimulation and
dopamine were tested (Bennett *et al.*, 1975). Figure 14.4 shows the effects of
these procedures on release of LH–RH from the suspensions of nerve endings.
While synaptosomes from all three regions responded to electrical stimulation,
release of LH–RH by dopamine was obtained only using nerve endings from
the median eminence. The results suggest a functional differentiation of LH–
RH-containing nerve endings. Those from the median eminence, which presumably have a hypophysiotropic role, are responsive to the monoamine,
whereas those which project into other regions and which may be involved in
the regulation of sexual behaviour (see Introduction) do not respond to
dopamine. Similar results were obtained with TRH; dopamine stimulated
TRH release from median eminence and cerebral cortex synaptosomes, but
not from nerve endings prepared from other hypothalamic regions or from the
brain stem. Together these data suggest that the neurotransmitters present in
the hypothalamic median eminence may modulate specifically the release of
hypothalamic hormones, thus regulating pituitary function. Recently, Kizer *et
al.* (1976) have developed novel microdissection procedures to study the
regional distribution of releasing hormones, acetylcholine, and monoamines in
the bovine median eminence. The significant overlapping of discrete regions
rich in peptide hormones and the neurotransmitters lends strong support to the
idea of such interactions at the neurosecretory nerve terminal. In the absence
of good ultrastructural evidence for direct axo–axonic synapses in the median
eminence—although this has been carefully looked for—it is proposed that

292

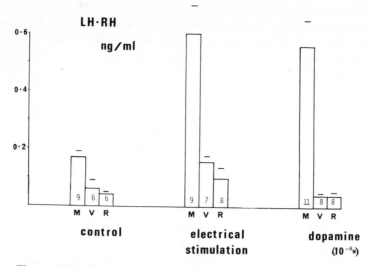

Figure 14.4 Release of immunoreactive LH–RH from synaptosomes prepared from dissected regions of the hypothalamus of
anoestrous sheep: effect of electrical field stimulation and incubation
with dopamine (10^{-8} M). Histograms represent ng of LH–RH (mean
and S.E.M.) released to 1 ml of Krebs bicarbonate medium during a
30-minute incubation at 37°C: M, median eminence synaptosomes;
V, synaptosomes from the periventricular hypothalamus; R, synaptosomes from the remainder of the hypothalamus. Number of experiments is shown at the base of each histogram.

neurotransmitters released in the median eminence may rapidly diffuse to
receptors on the peptidergic terminals. Such 'non-synaptic' connections occur
elsewhere; the complexity of local interactions between several neuronal cell
types has been recently recognized as a fundamental feature of brain tissue
(Schmitt *et al.*, 1976).

MECHANISMS IN HYPOTHALAMIC FEEDBACK REGULATION
BY STEROID HORMONES

Secretion of pituitary gonadotrophins and corticotrophin is under complex
multiple control which involves feedback regulation by the gonadal and
adrenal steroids. In the case of ACTH, this feedback is largely inhibitory. Both
soluble and nuclear corticosteroid-binding receptors are widely distributed
throughout the brain (Grosser *et al.*, 1971; McEwen *et al.*, 1970, 1972),
although the hypothalamus is supposedly deficient in this respect. It has been
shown that the release of CRH from hypothalamic synaptosomes can be
prevented by pretreatment *in vivo* with corticosteroids or by physiological
concentrations added *in vitro* (Edwardson and Bennett, 1974). Table 14.3
shows that the electrically induced release of CRH from sheep hypothalamic

Table 14.3 Effect of corticosteroids on the release of CRH produced by electrical stimulation of sheep hypothalamic synaptosomes

Hormone	Dose (nmol/l)	Number of expts.	ACTH released (ng/ml)		Increase (per cent)
			Control	Stimulated	
None	—	10	28·5 ± 4·0	59·3 ± 7·5*	108
Corticosterone	750	6	31·3 ± 4·2	36·3 ± 5·9	16
Cortisol	600	5	49·2 ± 13·3	48·4 ± 13·1	0
Cortisol	60	6	62·3 ± 8·2	62·9 ± 12·0	10
Cortisol	6	5	49·1 ± 4·8	65·4 ± 8·1	33
11-Deoxycorticosterone	800	6	34·7 ± 4·0	58·9 ± 8·7*	70
11-Deoxycortisol	850	5	43·4 ± 7·5	88·2 ± 18·0*	101
Progesterone	950	3	42·1 ± 6·4	68·2 ± 13·1	62
Oestradiol-17β	1100	3	37·6 ± 6·2	57·0 ± 8·5	52
Deoxycortisol	850 ⎫	3	21·3 ± 4·3	42·2 ± 6·0	99
+ Cortisol (for last 25 min)	600 ⎭				
Cortisol (assay control)	600	4	25·2 ± 4·1	45·6 ± 6·3*	81
Corticosterone (assay control)	750	5	29·2 ± 6·1	55·5 ± 9·2*	90

Steroids were present during the 35 minutes incubation of nerve endings and electrical stimulation was for the last 25 minutes. Values shown were determined by radioimmunoassay and represent ACTH released from paired halves of rat adenohypophyses during a 45 minute incubation in 1 ml synaptosome supernatant (mean ± S.E.M.). As shown by the Wilcoxon test there is a significant difference ($*p < 0.05$) between the electrically stimulated and control unstimulated preparations except where cortisol or corticosterone were present during incubation of synaptosomes. Assay controls had the steroid added to the stimulated preparation after incubation of the synaptosomes. Data from Edwardson and Bennett (1974), with permission.

synaptosomes can be blocked by 6 nM cortisol added directly to a suspension of the nerve endings. This concentration of steroid is lower than the increase in free plasma cortisol which occurs during stress in the sheep. There is considerable specificity for this effect; progesterone at 0·95 μM and oestradiol-17β at 1·1 μM produce a smaller inhibition of CRH release than 6 nM cortisol. Also, preincubation with 600 nM deoxycortisol, which by itself has no direct effect on CRH release, completely abolishes the blockade which is produced by 600 nM cortisol.

Cortisol blocks the response to electrical depolarization and also the acetylcholine-induced release of CRH from synaptosomes. Both of these effects can be obtained using 10 nM dibutyryl cyclic AMP and it has been proposed that this cyclic nucleotide may be involved in the feedback inhibition of CRH release by corticosteroids, at least at the neurosecretory nerve terminal (Edwardson and Bennett, 1975). Clearly, these effects in isolated nerve endings cannot be exerted *via* the classical mechanisms involving a cytoplasmic receptor, translocations to the cell nucleus, and changes in RNA and protein synthesis. The authors' attention was caught by the impressive arguments of Goldberg (1975) who has suggested that glucocorticoids act, not by raising the intracellular concentration of cyclic AMP, but by sensitizing the cell to existing levels of this nucleotide. An attempt has been made to test this hypothesis and preliminary experiments indicate that preincubation with low levels of corticosteroid does potentiate the inhibitory effect of a threshold dose of dibutyryl cyclic AMP on the release of CRH from synaptosome suspensions (Edwardson and Bennett, 1975). Potentiation was not observed when the cyclic nucleotide was added before the steroid, lending support to Goldberg's hypothesis. It is difficult to eliminate entirely the possibility of effects on the pituitary gland in the bioassay for CRH but similar findings have been observed in experiments on the actions of gonadal steroids on the release of LH–RH from synaptosomes.

Hypothalamic synaptosomes from anoestrous sheep (May–November) released approximately 100 pg immunoreactive LH–RH/hypothalamic equivalent when incubated for 30 minutes in Krebs bicarbonate buffer. 17β-Oestradiol or progesterone (10^{-8} M) added *in vitro* reduced this secretion by half and the effect was additive when both steroids were applied. The inhibition of LH–RH release was mimicked by incubation with dibutyryl cyclic AMP, but not with cyclic GMP which caused a slight increase in release of LH–RH (Bennett and Edwardson, 1977). These findings are consistent with earlier work on the effects of corticosteroids on CRH release from isolated nerve endings and provide the first evidence that the hypothalamic feedback regulation of gonadotrophin secretion may involve the mediation of cyclic nucleotides. McKelvy (1975) has recently isolated a specific cyclic AMP-dependent protein kinase from bovine pituitary-stalk median eminence tissue. In addition, there is considerable evidence (for a review, see Singhal and Sutherland, 1975) for the involvement of cyclic AMP in many of the effects of gonadal steroids on the reproductive tract and accessory sex organs.

When synaptosomes were isolated from sheep killed during the seasonal polyoestrous period a six-fold increase in release of LH–RH to the medium was observed, compared with preparations from anoestrous animals. Preincubation with progesterone and 17-β oestradiol at doses of 10^{-10} M, which alone had no effect on LH–RH release, produced a marked potentiation of the effects of dibutyryl cyclic AMP and inhibition of release. Again, potentiation was not observed when the nucleotide and steroid were added in the reverse order.

Experiments with hypothalamic synaptosomes prepared from female rats at different stages of the oestrous cycle reveal a cyclic pattern of LH–RH release and corresponding variations in the responsiveness of this secretion to the inhibitory effects of gonadal steroids and cyclic nucleotides (Bennett and Edwardson, 1977). Synaptosomes prepared at oestrus released approximately half the amount of LH–RH which was obtained with preparations from pro-oestrous or met/dioestrous rats. This could reflect a depletion of LH–RH at the time of the LH surge. Inhibition of LH–RH release in response to gonadal steroids was most marked with synaptosomes from pro-oestrous rats, suggesting that the nerve endings of the median eminence are most sensitive to steroid feedback during the critical preovulatory stage of the cycle. During pro-oestrus there is also an increased sensitivity to the actions of cyclic AMP and cyclic GMP.

In these studies on the effects of gonadal steroids on LH–RH release from rat and sheep nerve endings, no effect on TRH secretion was observed. The findings show that the feedback inhibition of pituitary secretion produced by both adrenal and gonadal steroids is at least partly mediated by specific receptors at the neurosecretory nerve terminal and that there may be a general mechanism of action involving a rapid increase in the sensitivity of the nerve ending to cyclic nucleotides. The nature of the mechanisms involved in this feedback inhibition is unknown but may well involve the monoamines which have also been shown to be active at the nerve terminals. The hypothalamus can concentrate oestrogens in specific catecholaminergic neurones (Grant and Stumpf, 1973) and can rapidly synthesize catecholoestrogens, whereas the pituitary and cerebral cortex do not (Fishman and Norton, 1975). Catecholoestrogens compete with the catecholamines for the enzyme catechol-o-methyl transferase (COMT) which may thereby control amine levels and in turn regulate secretion of the hypothalamic hormones (Breuer and Koster, 1975).

SYNAPTIC INTERACTIONS BETWEEN HYPOTHALAMIC HORMONES AND NEUROTRANSMITTERS IN SPINAL CORD, BRAIN STEM, AND CEREBRAL CORTEX

In the introduction some of the behavioural, electrophysiological, and neuropharmacological effects of the so-called hypothalamic hormones have been described which suggest that these peptides may play an as yet unspecified role in the process of neurotransmission, especially in relation to the monoaminergic systems of the brain. However, aminergic terminals represent only a minute fraction of the synaptic population and it is reasonable to suppose that peptidergic projections could interact with neurones containing ACh, the putative amino acid neurotransmitters, or even other peptide species. An attempt has been made to explore such interactions using isolated nerve endings prepared from various extrahypothalamic regions of rat and sheep brain.

Elsewhere in this volume, Bradford has described how synaptosomes exhibit a preferential release of the amino acid neurotransmitters in response to depolarizing stimuli. The authors have investigated the effects of TRH, LH–RH, somatostatin, and some other cerebral peptides on the K^+-induced release of amino acids from sheep brain-stem synaptosomes, using the sensitive chromatographic procedure described by Bradford *et al.* (1973). Figure 14.5

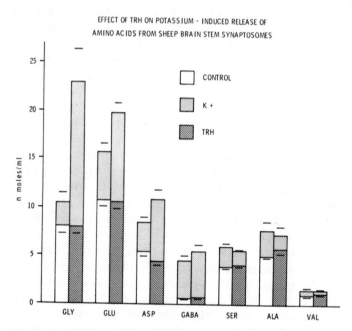

EFFECT OF TRH ON POTASSIUM - INDUCED RELEASE OF
AMINO ACIDS FROM SHEEP BRAIN STEM SYNAPTOSOMES

Figure 14.5 Effect of TRH on potassium-induced release of amino acids from sheep brain stem synaptosomes. Histograms represent nmoles of amino acid (S.E.M. of 5 experiments) released to 1 ml of Krebs bicarbonate medium containing 10 mM glucose from synaptosomes incubated at 37°C for 30 minutes. Basal and K^+-induced (60 mM/l) release is shown in both control medium and medium containing TRH (30 nM/l). Although no effect on basal release was observed, TRH enhanced the K^+-induced release of glycine, and glutamic and aspartic acids but not other amino acids

shows that TRH $(10^{-8} M)$ added to the synaptosome suspension caused a 6-fold increase in the K^+-induced release of glycine and to a lesser extent increased the release of glutamic acid, aspartic acid, and GABA. In the absence of increased K^+ levels, the basal release of these and other amino acids was unaffected by TRH. Somatostatin and LH–RH were without effect under all conditions tested. An enhanced release of amino acid neurotransmitters was similarly observed with synaptosomes prepared from rat cerebral cortex.

Conversely, the effects of various amino acids and hypothalamic hormones on the release of TRH from synaptosomes was tested. The most marked effects were obtained with glycine (10^{-4} M) and somatostatin (10^{-8} M), which caused a two-to-three-fold increase in the release of immunoreactive TRH from brain stem synaptosomes. Neither of these stimuli caused release of TRH from cerebral cortex synaptosomes which, as has been mentioned previously, are sensitive to dopamine in this respect. Together these findings are consistent with a more widespread synaptic function for the hypothalamic hormones than has previously been recognized; synaptosomes represent only the presynaptic component of the synaptic complex and these observations indicate the existence of monoamine–peptide, amino acid–peptide, and even peptide–peptide interactions.

CONCLUSIONS: EXPLOITATION OF HYPOTHALAMIC HORMONES AND RELATED PEPTIDES

Hypothalamic hormones have a variety of actions apart from their hypophysiotropic effects on the anterior pituitary gland. Until now, it is this latter function which has been exploited both clinically and in veterinary practice. The manipulation of endocrinological states by hypothalamic peptides or their synthetic analogues will continue to be important, but the experimental evidence presented here points to significant new realms of exploitation. The neurosecretory nerve terminal is now recognized as much more than an evolutionary specialization of the hypothalamus; it is an ubiquitous form of synaptic body which may be essential to the behavioural and neurophysiological correlates of neuroendocrine integration.

The biosynthesis, storage, secretion, and mechanisms of action of cerebral peptides are processes in which the primary lesion of major mental disorders could reside. As such candidates, peptidergic systems satisfy at least four important criteria: they have been shown in animal models to be important in behavioural control; they are functionally related to monoaminergic systems—already implicated in the affective disorders and schizophrenia; they are structurally or biochemically organized in ways which could provide selective impairment of mental function; and they are susceptible to modification by environmental influences such as stress or dietary factors. The further exploration of hypothalamic hormones and other cerebral peptides in psychiatric and neurological disorders will undoubtedly lead to the development of more active derivatives with enormous potential in the treatment of diseases of the nervous system.

298

ACKNOWLEDGEMENTS

The Medical Research Council provided financial support for the authors' experimental work described in this chapter. We are grateful to Mrs. J. Pennington for expert technical assistance, and to Dr. S. L. Jeffcoate, Miss D. Holland, and Miss N. White for their collaboration in the measurement of hypothalamic hormones. Above all, on this special occasion, we thank Professor Sir Ernst Chain for his enthusiastic encouragement, advice, and practical support.

REFERENCES

Bennett, G. W., and Edwardson, J. A. (1975) *J. Endocrinol.*, **65**, 33.
Bennett, G. W., and Edwardson, J. A. (1977) in *Hypothalamic Hormones: Proceedings of the Second European Colloquium on Hypothalamic Hormones*, (Gupta, D., and Voelter, W., eds.), Verlag Chemie, Weinheim and New York, in press.
Bennett, G. W., Edwardson, J. A., Holland, D., Jeffcoate, S. L., and White, N. (1975) *Nature (London)*, **257**, 323.
Bowers, C. Y., Schally, A. V., Enzmann, F., Boler, J., and Folkers, K. (1970) *Endocrinology*, **86**, 1143.
Bradbury, A. F., Smyth, D. G., Snell, C. R., Birdsall, N. J. M., and Hulme, E. C. (1976) *Nature (London)*, **260**, 793.
Bradford, H. F., Bennett, G. W., and Thomas, A. J. (1973) *J. Neurochem.*, **21**, 495.
Brazeau, P., Vale, W., Burgus, R., Ling, N., Butcher, M., Rivier, J., and Guillemin, R. (1973) *Science, N.Y.*, **179**, 77.
Breese, G. R., Cott, J. M., Cooper, B. R., Prange, A. J., and Lipton, M. A. (1974) *Life Sci.*, **14**, 1053.
Breuer, H., and Koster, G. (1975) in *Advances in Biosciences 15: Schering Workshop on Central Actions of Estrogenic Hormones* (Raspe, G., ed.), Pergamon Press, Oxford, pp. 287–299.
Brown, M., and Vale, W. (1975) *Endocrinology*, **96**, 1333.
Brownstein, M., Arimura, A., Sato, H., Schally, A. V., and Kizer, J. S. (1975) *Endocrinology*, **96**, 1456.
Burgus, R., Butcher, M., Amoss, N., Ling, M., Monahan, J., Rivier, R., Bellows, R., Blackwell, R., Vale, W., and Guillemin, R. (1972) *Proc. Nat. Acad. Sci., U.S.A.*, **69**, 278.
Burgus, R., Dunn, T. F., Desiderio, D., Ward, D. N., Vale, W., and Guillemin, R. (1970) *Nature (London)*, **226**, 321.
Celis, M. E., Taleisnik, S., and Walter, R. (1971) *Proc. Nat. Acad. Sci., U.S.A.*, **68**, 1428.
de Belleroche, J. S., and Bradford, H. F. (1973) in *Progress in Neurobiology*, (Kerkut, G. A., and Phillis, J. W., eds.), Pergamon Press, Oxford, pp. 275–298.
Dyer, R. G. (1975) in *Hypothalamic Hormones*, (Motta, M., Crosignani, P. G., and Martini, L., eds.), Academic Press, New York and London, pp. 169–182.
Edwardson, J. A., and Bennett, G. W. (1974) *Nature (London)*, **251**, 425.
Edwardson, J. A., and Bennett, G. W. (1975) *Biochem. Soc. Trans.*, **3**, 1138.
Edwardson, J. A., Bennett, G. W., and Bradford, H. F. (1972) *Nature (London)*, **240**, 554.
Ehrensing, R. H., Kastin, A. J., Schalch, D. S., Friesen, H., Vargas, R., and Schally, A. V. (1974) *Am. J. Psychiat.*, **131**, 714.
Fishman, J., and Norton, B. (1975) in *Advances in Biosciences 15: Schering Workshop on Central Actions of Estrogenic Hormones* (Raspe, G., ed.), Pergamon Press, Oxford, pp. 123–129.

Ganong, W. F. (1974) in *The Neurosciences Third Study Program* (Schmitt, F. O., and Worden, F. G., eds.), M.I.T. Press, Cambridge, Mass., pp. 549–563.

Goldberg, M. L. (1975) *Med. Hypotheses*, **1**, 6.

Grant, L. D., and Stumpf, W. E. (1973) *J. Histochem. Cytochem.*, **21**, 404.

Green, A. R., and Grahame-Smith, D. G. (1974) *Nature (London)*, **251**, 252.

Grosser, B. I., Stevens, W., Bruenger, F. W., and Reed, D. J. (1971) *J. Neurochem.*, **18**, 1725.

Guillemin, R., Ling, N., and Burgus, R. (1976) *C.R. Acad. Sci. (Paris)*, **282**, 1.

Herbert, J. (1975) *Lancet*, Vol. 2, 991.

Hokfelt, T., Fuxe, K., Johannson, O., Jeffcoate, S. L., and White, N. (1975a) *Neurosci. Letters*, **1**, 133.

Hokfelt, T., Fuxe, K., Johansson, O., Jeffcoate, S. L., and White, N. (1975b) *Eur. J. Pharmacol.*, **34**, 389.

Hughes, J., Smith, T. W., Kosterlitz, H. W., Fothergill, L. A., Morgan, B. A., and Morris, H. R. (1975) *Nature (London)*, **258**, 577.

Jackson, I. M. D., and Reichlin, S. (1974) *Endocrinology*, **95**, 854.

Jones, M. T., Hillhouse, E., and Burden, J. (1976) in *Frontiers in Endocrinology* (Martini, L., and Ganong, W. F., eds.), Raven Press, New York, pp. 195–226.

Kastin, A. J., Plotnikoff, N. P., Hall, R., and Schally, A. V. (1975) in *Hypothalamic Hormones* (Motta, M., Crosignani, P. G., and Martini, L., eds.), Academic Press, New York and London, pp. 261–268.

Kizer, J. S., Palkovits, M., Tappas, M., Kebabian, J., and Brownstein, M. J. (1976) *Endocrinology*, **98**, 685.

Matsuo, H., Arimura, A., Nair, R. M. G., and Schally A. V. (1971) *Biochem. Biophys. Res. Comm.*, **45**, 822.

McEwen, B. S., Weiss, J. M., and Schwartz, L. S. (1970) *Brain Res.*, **17**, 471.

McEwen, B. S., Magnus, C., and Wallach, G. (1972) *Endocrinology*, **90**, 217.

McKelvy, J. F. (1975) *Biochem. Biophys. Res. Comm.*, **65**, 54.

Moss, R. L., Dudley, C. A., Foreman, M. M., and McCann, S. M. (1975) in *Hypothalamic Hormones* (Motta, M., Crosignani, P. G., and Martini, L., eds.), Academic Press, New York and London, pp. 269–278.

Nair, R. M. G., Kastin, A. J., and Schally, A. V. (1971) *Biochem. Biophys. Res. Comm.*, **43**, 1376.

Plotnikoff, N. P., Prange, A. J., Breese, G. R., Anderson, M. S., and Wilson, I. C. (1972) *Science, N.Y.*, **178**, 417.

Plotnikoff, N. P., Prange, A. J., Breese, G. R., Anderson, M. S., and Wilson, I. C. (1974) in *The Thyroid Axis, Drugs, and Behaviour* (Prange, A. J., ed.), Raven Press, New York, pp. 103–113.

Prange, A. J., Breese, G. R., Cott, J. M., Martin, B. R., Cooper, B. R., Wilson, I. C., and Plotnikoff, N. P. (1974) *Life Sci.*, **14**, 447.

Renaud, L. P., Martin, J. B., and Brazeau, P. (1975) *Nature (London)*, **255**, 233.

Schmitt, F. O., Parvati, D., and Smith, B. H. (1976) *Science, N.Y.*, **193**, 114.

Singhal, R. L., and Sutherland, D. J. B. (1975) in *Molecular Mechanisms of Gonadal Hormone Action*, Vol. 1 (Thomas, J. A., and Singhal, R. L., eds.), H. M. and M. Medical and Scientific Publishers, Aylesbury, pp. 225–282.

Wei, E., Sigel, S., Loh, H., and Way, E. L. (1975) *Nature (London)*, **253**, 739.

Closing Remarks

Sir Hans Krebs

Radcliffe Infirmary, Oxford, U.K.

The contributions of Sir Ernst's associates assembled in this book bring home the wide range of his interests, his resourcefulness, his originality of approach, his ability to inspire young people, and especially, his ability to establish links between pure and applied research, and between industry and medical science. The reference to 'exploration and exploitation' in the title of this book is therefore most appropriate.

There is one coherent thread in Sir Ernst's achievements. All his work has been 'real biochemistry', beginning with the formulation of a question concerning the living organism and then applying the techniques of chemistry to the solution of the biological problem. Several people, who are labelled 'biochemists', concern themselves not directly with biological problems, but merely with molecular mechanisms in materials derived from biological sources; this has been emphasized by Sir Ernst himself on several occasions. Molecular mechanisms are, of course, important, providing an essential deepening of biochemical knowledge, but by themselves they are chemistry rather than biochemistry. It is the job of the true biochemist to approach the exploration of the mysteries of life by asking a biological question. The study of the mysteries of chemistry is not the final objective of a biochemist. Thus, it is implied that one must start with whole organisms, or organs, or cells, or perhaps even an organelle—the smallest integrated units characteristic of biological systems.

In recent years, Sir Ernst has expressed concern about the neglect of these areas of biochemistry in Britain, and the predominance of the purely molecular non-living aspects of the science. This book illustrates the liveliness and present scope still of 'real biochemistry'—'Chainian' biochemistry. Its importance lies in particular in its great potential for exploiting the fundamental subject for the innumerable problems of 'applied' biochemistry—medicine, agriculture, and microbiology.

Several contributors have referred to Sir Ernst's personality and his inspiring influence. Dr. Christian Anfinsen—perhaps with his tongue in his cheek—has also referred to his shy and retiring trait. But it really does exist. Sir Ernst remarked to me that all the celebrations for the Symposium were planned behind his back; he did not know much about them and therefore had no chance to stop them. Otherwise, he might have tried to prevent what he called 'this fuss about myself'.

My many personal encounters with Sir Ernst began in 1934 when we were at Cambridge. He had come from University College Hospital Medical School, having met with some difficulties in the laboratory of Sir Charles Harington. We discussed these difficulties. Sir Ernst held the view, in no uncertain terms, that one could not really work properly in Harington's laboratory. Considering that Harington synthesized thyroxine and established its structure, I thought it was not quite appropriate for a youngster of 28 to criticize an accomplished biochemist as to what constituted proper working facilities. I thought as refugees we ought to be grateful for any facilities. Neither Harington nor I, at that time, really appreciated what was in Sir Ernst's mind. It was to Harington's great credit that years later he told Sir Ernst he had been right in criticizing the facilities. It would certainly have been impossible to develop penicillin in Harington's laboratory. In Cambridge, people soon began to appreciate Sir Ernst's infectious enthusiasm and his ebullience. We learned to appreciate his personality, his straightforwardness, and his high moral standards. Soon we also saw his originality and his capacity for hard work.

After Sir Ernst had been in Cambridge for about a year, it was Hopkins who told Florey that Sir Ernst was exactly the man he needed, when Florey was searching for a young biochemist. We all know the outcome of that!

Of necessity, there has been no mention in this volume of Sir Ernst's second area of accomplishment—music. Ernst studied the piano and conducting in Berlin at the same time as being a research biochemist. He could well have chosen music as a career, and I wonder whether he thought on lines similar to those of Jacques Monod, who was not only a top biochemist, but also an expert cellist. When asked about his choice of careers Monod said that only a small number of professional musicians may find their careers deeply gratifying, that is, only those few who reach the standard of concert performers. The rest have to teach pupils who are not always enthusiastic, or have to play the second fiddle. In science, Monod said, even second-rate people find their work gratifying. Not being sure of his potential as a musician, he chose science as a career. Perhaps Sir Ernst had a similar kind of view and a similar kind of humility. Those who know Sir Ernst well, realize that he is humble about himself, but not about his ideas, for which he fights with vigour, verve, enthusiasm, and powerful articulation, and also with great moral courage.

The birthday celebration from which this book originated was planned by Sir Ernst's companion of the last 28 years, Anne. Anne has been a decisive support since their marriage in 1948. During the first 15 years in this country, Sir Ernst appeared to be a hard-boiled bachelor, absorbed completely by his science, his music, and a number of very warm friendships. I recall vividly Sir Rudolph Peters telling me in 1948 that he had a great surprise for us: Ernst was due to marry Anne Beloff. Soon afterwards we heard all sorts of tales about this. The Oxford gossip—and there is never any shortage of gossip in Oxford—was that Sir Ernst had accepted an invitation to go to Rome and that he needed some help in setting up a new research department in the Istituto Superiore di Sanità. Anne, at the same time, had to be liberated from Somerville College where she lived and tutored in biochemistry. So it was a matter of mutual convenience to get together and marry. The gossip predicted that it would last a year. After 28 years we can calculate that the error so far is 2800 per cent!

As a family man, as a biochemist and an amateur musician, Sir Ernst has proved a brilliant success, as illustrated by the First Class Honours degree gained by Benny Chain in Cambridge a few days before the birthday celebration. Both Sir Ernst and Lady Chain can be equally proud. Success in family life is a more severe test of character and personality than anything else. Brilliance in this area is not so much a matter of intellectual powers but a matter of warmth, kindness, and understanding, which are required to a high degree when two highly individualistic personalities join together in marriage.

The fruits of scientific research usually mature very slowly. It must be a source of great satisfaction to Sir Ernst that in the long run his efforts in many different fields of biochemistry have yielded a rich harvest in the practical fields, as well as in the purely academic ones. Many contributors to the Symposium have expressed the personal affection which they feel for Sir Ernst. One hopes that if Sir Ernst had reservations about 'all the fuss' as he called it, he will now accept this Symposium as an appropriate birthday present.

An Epilogue

A. Baird Hastings

Department of Neurosciences,
University of California, San Diego, California, U.S.A.

Fond as I am of England and my many friends there, it seemed rather ridiculous to travel 6000 miles from La Jolla, California just to preside at a session of a symposium on Biologically Active Substances. But 'one good turn deserves another' and Anne had come to Ann Arbor, Michigan for my 70th birthday symposium, so the least I could do was to accept her invitation to attend Sir Ernst's.

Although Anne requested that there should be no remarks about Ernst, I am overriding her request, to the extent of one figure on which is plotted his life and work. Actually, it is the readout from a ABH computer 1066, which was

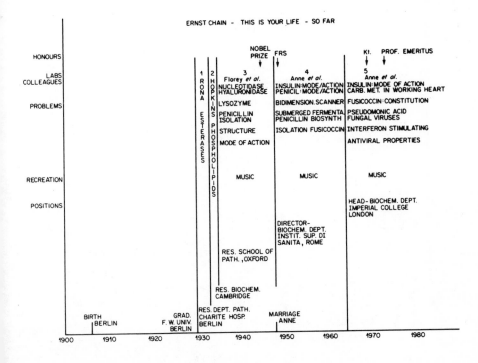

programmed for CHAIN reactions. These reactions began in 1906 and took place in five different laboratories.

After a latent period of 24 years from birth through education as a chemist, the readout takes off, beginning with three years working with Rona, in Berlin, then two years with Hopkins at Cambridge, followed by 13 years with Florey at Oxford during which Sir Ernst, with ingenuity, hard work, and intuition, made penicillin—the first practical member of a new antibiotic industry. Then came 13 years in Rome where Sir Ernst's genius extended beyond the chemical laboratory to plant-scale operations. Meanwhile, he shared the Nobel Prize in 1945, married Anne Beloff in 1948, and became a Fellow of the Royal Society in 1949. In 1964, he returned to England, where he and Anne, and their colleagues have pursued their studies on carbohydrate metabolism, hormones, antibiotics, and viruses in the Biochemistry Department of Imperial College. Ernst was knighted in 1969 and retired and made Professor Emeritus in 1973.

Were it possible for my computer to read music, I am sure that this readout would be interspersed with excerpts from Mozart, Handel, Beethoven, and Bach. Since my computer was programmed for only three-score years and ten, my readout stops in 1976—but knowing Anne as I do, I am sure that Sir Ernst will not.

I confidently predict many more productive years for this exergonic team, known affectionately to us all as the Ernst and Anne Bimolecular CHAIN REACTION.

Index